£25.00

WITHDRAWN-UNL

LIGHTWEIGHT CONCRETE
THIRD EDITION

Lightweight Concrete

Third Edition

ANDREW SHORT
and
WILLIAM KINNIBURGH

Formerly, Building Research Establishment,
Garston, Watford, U.K.

APPLIED SCIENCE PUBLISHERS LTD
LONDON

APPLIED SCIENCE PUBLISHERS LTD
RIPPLE ROAD, BARKING, ESSEX, ENGLAND

First edition 1963
Second edition 1968
Third edition 1978

ISBN: 0 85334 734 4

WITH 72 TABLES AND 204 ILLUSTRATIONS

© APPLIED SCIENCE PUBLISHERS LTD 1978

Printed in Great Britain by Galliard (Printers) Ltd, Great Yarmouth

Preface to the Third Edition

Structural lightweight concrete, whether made from lightweight aggregate or in the form of aerated concrete, is now an accepted form of construction, which means that it can compete both technically and economically with other established methods and materials of construction.

It is believed that the earlier editions of this book contributed significantly to widening the knowledge and understanding of lightweight concrete and thus to its increased use for structural and non-structural purposes in many parts of the world. With this increased use of lightweight concrete over a period of time, it was inevitable that practical difficulties should arise in some instances, as indeed has been the case with every other building material and method of construction throughout the history of building. The problems met with have usually come about from insufficient care and foresight in design and construction, and were thus the kinds of fault which it has been one of the purposes of this book to remedy. However, when careful design has been combined with adequate care in construction, lightweight concretes, both aggregate and aerated, have fulfilled their expectations.

The authors note with satisfaction that structural codes of practice throughout the world now almost invariably include references to the use of lightweight aggregate concretes and often of structural aerated concrete. In particular the *CEB–FIP Model Code for Concrete*, published by the Euro–International Committee for Concrete (CEB) (1978), which will form a basis for the progressive harmonisation of technical codification in this field throughout the world, together with the ACI 318–1978 *Building Code for Concrete*, published by the American Concrete Institute, represent a considerable step forward towards a full acceptance of lightweight aggregate concretes for structural purposes. The authors also welcome the publication by CEB of their *Manual for Lightweight Aggregate Concrete*, which contains a massive collection of detailed information on this subject.

For the present, third edition of *Lightweight Concrete*, the general lay-out adopted for the two previous editions has been retained, in the main. The contents have, however, been materially expanded and improved by bringing them up to date, by including an explanation of the CEB Limit State Design methods as applied to lightweight concrete, and treating in the text some new developments in practice and theory, relating both to materials properties and structural application.

A number of new illustrations of interest have been added and the text expanded to deal with additional subjects such as the use of lightweight concrete in developing countries, precast concrete, and other matters.

An enlarged up-to-date selection of references and a bibliography will enable the reader to pursue the study of lightweight concrete in greater depth through the now extensive literature.

An effort has been made to provide a reference volume which is helpful in its content, and easy to use in practice, and it is hoped that this edition of *Lightweight Concrete* may prove to be no less useful than its predecessors.

Acknowledgements

The authors are indebted to their many friends and colleagues at the Building Research Establishment, Garston, Watford, for valuable advice, criticism and assistance in preparing this Third Edition of *Lightweight Concrete*. In particular they wish to thank Mr D. C. Teychenné, B.Sc.(Eng.), who contributed the whole of the revised Chapter 3, 'Mix Design', and improved the substance and appearance of the book as a whole by including results obtained by him in the course of his researches.

They are grateful to many other authors, designers, research workers and engineers in the United Kingdom, and indeed throughout the world, for the opportunity of referring to and discussing their work. The authors are most sensible of the generosity of the many professional friends and associates in the various branches of the lightweight concrete industry in the United Kingdom and abroad who gave freely of their great experience and knowledge. Their help and advice has greatly contributed to the accuracy and practical usefulness of this book.

They also owe particular thanks to their colleagues Mr Bernard Howell for checking much of the manuscript and illustrations for accuracy and to Mrs Diane E. Uezzell and Mrs Shirley Riordan for preparing the typescript, and not least to all three for their patience and kind encouragement.

Finally, acknowledgement is due also to the organisations and individual research workers and engineers listed below who kindly supplied the following illustrations:

Ove Arup and Partners: FIGS. 16.23, 16.27.
Beecham Laboratories: FIG. 16.11.
Besser Co: FIG. 24.4.
J. Bobrowski and Partners: FIG. 16.21.
The Controller, Her Majesty's Stationery Office and the Building Research Establishment of the Department of the Environment: FIGS. 1.1, 1.2, 3.1–3.4, 4.1, 4.2, 5.1–5.4, 6.1–6.3, 6.5, 7.1, 8.1–8.3, 8.9, 8.11–8.13, 10.1–10.11, 10.14, 11.1–11.4, 12.1, 12.2, 13.1–13.5, 14.1–14.4, 15.1, 15.2, 17.5, 18.1–18.4, 19.1–19.3, 24.1–24.4, 24.7–24.12, 25.1.
Butterley Co. Ltd: FIGS. 8.5, 8.7, 16.11.
Euro–International Committee for Concrete (CEB), *Manual for Lightweight Concrete*: FIG. 12.6.
Celcon Ltd: FIGS. 17.6, 22.23.

Central Electricity Research Laboratory: FIG. 8.10.
Dyckerhoff & Widmann AG (Werkfoto) Germany: FIGS. 16.5, 16.6, 16.8, 16.13, 16.14, 16.22.
Foamed Slag Producers Federation Ltd: FIGS. 11.5, 16.1.
W & C French Ltd: FIGS. 8.6, 8.8, 16.28, 16.30, 16.32.
Gascon Co: FIG. 17.10.
Mr H. Hart, Neuwied, Germany: FIG. 16.4.
Hebel Gasbetonwerk, Germany: FIGS. 21.14, 22.6, 22.21, 22.22, 22.24.
Hemel Hempstead Lightweight Concrete Co. Ltd: FIG. 4.3.
Internationella Ytong AB, Sweden: FIGS. 1.5, 21.13, 21.20, 21.21.
Johnson Gas Appliances, USA: FIGS. 4.4, 4.5.
Joint Fire Research Organisation: FIG. 6.4.
Lee Magnum Co: FIG. 24.3.
Lytag Ltd: FIGS. 16.4, 16.9, 16.15, 16.16, 16.20, 16.21, 16.27, 16.31, 25.4.
Sir Robert MacAlpine and Sons Ltd: FIGS. 16.11, 16.12.
Portland Cement Association, Chicago, USA: FIGS. 10.12, 10.13, 16.20–16.22.
Dr A. G. Schneider-Arnoldi, Arbeitskreis Schüttbeton EV, Krefeld, Germany: FIGS. 16.29, 25.5, 25.6.
Société d'Éxploitation des Laitiers, Paris, France: FIG. 16.3.
Siporex Ltd and Durox Building Units Ltd: FIGS. 17.1, 17.2, 21.2–21.4, 21.19, 22.3, 22.5, 22.8, 22.10, 22.14, 22.15, 22.25, 22.27, 22.28.
Sogene S.A. Roma, Italy: FIGS. 16.24–16.26.
Stanton Ironworks Ltd: FIG. 8.4.
Thermalite Ltd: FIGS. 4.6, 17.3, 17.4, 21.15, 21.16, 22.4.
Welding Industries Ltd: FIGS. 24.5, 24.6.
Sir E. Owen Williams: FIGS. 1.4, 16.10.
George Wimpey and Co. Ltd: FIGS. 7.2–7.9.
Siporex Internationella AB Sweden: FIGS. 20.1, 21.1, 21.5, 21.18, 22.29.

Contents

Preface to the Third Edition v

Acknowledgements vii

1 INTRODUCTION 1

2 CHEMICAL ASPECTS OF LIGHTWEIGHT CONCRETE 15
    Introduction 15
    Types and Nature of Cements 16
    Setting of Cement 17
    Carbonation 18
    Sulphate Resistance 20
    Admixtures 21

3 MIX DESIGN 24
    General 24
    No-fines Concrete 29
    Partially Compacted Lightweight Aggregate Concrete . . 31
    Structural Lightweight Aggregate Concrete 32
    Aerated Concrete 39

4 CURING OF CONCRETE 42
    Fundamentals 42
    Experimental Work 44
    Practical Curing Methods 48

5 DRYING SHRINKAGE AND CRACKING 55
    Nature of Shrinkage Movements and Stresses 55
    Block Walls 58

6 FUNCTIONAL PROPERTIES OF LIGHTWEIGHT CONCRETE . . . 64
    Thermal Insulation 64
    Thermal Conductivity Values and their Measurement . . 68
    Acoustic Properties 72
    Fire Protection 78
    Durability 81
    Water Absorption 88
    Rain Penetration 88

7 NO-FINES CONCRETE 91
   General 91
   History and Development 92
   Strength 93
   Drying Shrinkage 96
   Thermal Conductivity 97
   Moisture Penetration 98
   Making No-fines Concrete 99
   Design 102
   Testing No-fines Concrete 104

8 LIGHTWEIGHT AGGREGATE AND LOADBEARING LIGHTWEIGHT
  AGGREGATE CONCRETE 107
   Introduction 107
   Furnace Clinker 109
   Foamed Blast-Furnace Slag 113
   Expanded Clay and Expanded Shale Aggregate . . . 118
   Expanded Slate 123
   Sintered Pulverised-Fuel Ash 126
   Raw Pulverised-Fuel Ash 130
   Furnace Bottom Ash 130
   Pumice and Scoria 131
   Diatomite 132
   Organic Aggregates 133
   Screeds 135

9 LIGHTWEIGHT AGGREGATE CONCRETE CONSTRUCTION . . . 139
   General 139
   Regulation of the Admission and Use of Structural Lightweight
     Aggregates and Concretes 141
   Lightweight Aggregates Suitable for Structural Reinforced
     Concrete 144
   Research on Reinforced Lightweight Concrete 145

10 THE PROPERTIES OF STRUCTURAL LIGHTWEIGHT AGGREGATE
  CONCRETE 150
   Density and Compressive Strength 150
   Tensile Strength and Modulus of Rupture 153
   Modulus of Deformation 158
   Effect of the Water/Cement Ratio 161
   Effect of the Admixture of Sand 163
   Creep 165
   Shrinkage 170

11 PROTECTION AGAINST DETERIORATION OF LIGHTWEIGHT AGGREGATE
  CONCRETE 173
   General 173
   Corrosion of Embedded Reinforcement 174

Resistance of Reinforced Lightweight Concrete Structures against
Deterioration 182

12 BOND STRENGTH OF REINFORCED LIGHTWEIGHT AGGREGATE
CONCRETE 189
General 189
Bond Tests 191
Plain Round Bars 195
Deformed Bars 199
Codes of Practice 203

13 SHEAR RESISTANCE OF LIGHTWEIGHT AGGREGATE CONCRETE
FLEXURAL MEMBERS 205
General 205
Tests on Lightweight Concrete Beams 208

14 DESIGN CONSIDERATIONS FOR STRUCTURAL LIGHTWEIGHT
AGGREGATE CONCRETE 213
General 213
Concrete Mixes 216
Methods of Design 220
Shear 232
Permissible Stresses in the Concrete 238
Permissible Steel Stresses 243
Stiffness and Cracking 246
Transverse Reinforcement 250
Prestressed Concrete 251

15 INSULATION-GRADE AGGREGATE CONCRETES 257
Exfoliated Vermiculite 257
Expanded Perlite 259

16 LIGHTWEIGHT AGGREGATE CONCRETE IN PRACTICE . . . 261
Walls 262
Precast Panels 263
Bridges 267
Composite Members 269
Ships 271
Multi-Storey Buildings 271
Other Buildings 276
Cast-*in-situ* Wall Construction 279
Other Uses 283
Screeds 289

17 AERATED CONCRETE—MANUFACTURE AND PROPERTIES . . . 291
General 291
Manufacture 294
Properties 301
Gascon 307

18 PROTECTION OF AERATED CONCRETE AGAINST DETERIORATION . 310
    Corrosion of Steel Embedded in Aerated Concrete . . . 310
    Methods of Preventing Corrosion 312
    Prevention of the Deterioration of Aerated Concrete . . 318

19 BOND STRENGTH IN REINFORCED AERATED CONCRETE . . . 322
    General 322
    Effect of the Diameter and Position of the Embedded Bars and
        their Embedment Length 323
    Effects of Autoclaving, of the Compressive Strength and of the
        Saturation of the Concrete with Water 326
    Effect of Bituminous Coating 327
    Effect of Cement–Casein–Rubber Coating 328
    Effect of Using Deformed Bars 328
    Effect of End Anchorages 329
    Effect of Welded Crossbars 329

20 DESIGN CONSIDERATIONS FOR REINFORCED AERATED CONCRETE . 332
    Methods of Construction 332
    Flexural Rigidity and the Load Factor against Failure and against
        Cracking 334
    Codes of Practice and the General Design of Flexural Members 337
    Bond and Anchorage 339
    Resistance against Shear 341
    Design for Flexural Rigidity 342

21 AERATED CONCRETE ROOFS, FLOORS AND WALLS 346
    General 346
    Roof Slabs 348
    Floor Slabs 357
    Wall Slabs 359
    Workmanship and Erection 364

22 USE OF AERATED CONCRETE 371
    Block Masonry 372
    Loadbearing Vertical Wall Units 374
    Non-Loadbearing Wall Cladding 378
    Roofs 383

23 LIGHTWEIGHT CONCRETE IN THE DEVELOPING COUNTRIES . . 392

24 CONCRETE BLOCKS 396
    General 396
    Types of Block 396
    Manufacturing Process 398
    Block Machines 399
    Specifications 403
    Difference in Attitude and Practice between British and American
        Block Producers 406

25 LIGHTWEIGHT CONCRETE WALLS 413
    General 413
    Loading 414
    New Materials and Methods of Construction: Design
      Considerations 414
    Principal Factors Influencing the Behaviour of Walls . . 417
    Masonry Walls 423
    The Relationship Between Block Strength and Wall Strength . 426
    Cast-*in-situ* Concrete Walls 430
    Cast-*in-situ* Reinforced Concrete Walls 436
    Limit State Design of Walls 437

APPENDIX: CONVERSION TABLES 441

BIBLIOGRAPHY 443

INDEX 457

CHAPTER ONE

Introduction

Although most readers will no doubt understand in a general way what is meant by 'lightweight concrete', the term has never in fact been uniformly defined. Lightweight concrete is a concrete which by one means or another has been made lighter than conventional concrete, the very familiar product made from sand and gravel or crushed rock and cement, which has for so long been an important all-round building material. This however is a qualitative description rather than a definition. It has been suggested that lightweight concrete may be defined as a concrete made from lightweight aggregate, but this begs the question, because elsewhere lightweight aggregate has been defined as an aggregate which produces a lightweight concrete. In any case, as we shall see later, some lightweight concretes do not in fact contain aggregate in the usual sense. In the face of this difficulty of definition, lightweight concrete has for many years been taken to mean a concrete with a dry density of not more than $1600 \, \text{kg/m}^3$ (100 pcf). However, with the introduction of reinforced concrete structural members employing lightweight aggregate, the density limit has had to be revised, since concrete mixes suitable for such a purpose often means dry concrete densities of up to $1840 \, \text{kg/m}^3$ (115 pcf),[1] or more. This is still lightweight concrete inasmuch as it is significantly lighter than conventional concrete, which usually weighs between 2240 and $2400 \, \text{kg/m}^3$ (140–150 pcf). The Draft International Standard Model Code for Concrete Construction[2] classifies lightweight concrete as having densities between 1200 and $2000 \, \text{kg/m}^3$ (75–125 pcf).

The reader may well ask at this stage why it is necessary, or at any rate desirable, to have lightweight concrete. To answer this we need to examine the characteristic properties of lightweight concrete in comparison with those of the more traditional dense concrete, and in relation to its practical application in construction.

The most obvious characteristic of lightweight concrete is of course its density, which is always considerably less than, and often only a fraction of that of ordinary concrete (Fig. 1.1). There are many advantages in low density, such as reduction of dead load, faster building rates, and lower haulage and handling costs. The weight of a building in terms of the loads transmitted by the foundations is an important factor in design, particularly in the case of tall buildings. The use of lightweight concrete has sometimes made it possible to proceed with a design which otherwise would have been abandoned because of excessive weight. In framed structures,

FIG. 1.1   Dense and lightweight concrete specimens of equal weight.

considerable savings in cost can be brought about by using lightweight concrete for the construction of the floors, partitions, and external cladding.

It has been shown experimentally[3] and by practical experience in the industry that faster building rates can be achieved with lightweight concrete than with the more traditional materials, and for this reason many builders today are prepared to pay considerably more, for example, for lightweight concrete blocks than for burnt clay bricks, for the same area of walling.

With most building materials such as clay bricks the haulage load is limited not by volume but by weight. With suitably designed containers much larger volumes of lightweight concrete can be hauled economically.

A less obvious but nonetheless important characteristic of lightweight concrete is its relatively low thermal conductivity, a property which improves with decreasing density. In recent years, with the increasing cost and scarcity of energy sources, more attention has been given than formerly to the need for reducing fuel consumption whilst maintaining, and indeed improving, comfort conditions in buildings. The point is illustrated by the fact that a 125 mm thick solid wall of aerated concrete will give thermal insulation about four times greater than that of a 230 mm clay brick wall.

Quite apart from their technical advantage in building, some lightweight concretes have the additional merit of providing an opportunity for the utilisation of industrial wastes, such as clinker, pulverised-fuel ash and blast-furnace slag. Apart from agriculture, building is the largest single industry in most countries, and the only one able to absorb vast quantities of industrial wastes of which millions of tons are produced annually. It will be shown in later chapters how these wastes are used for the production of building materials.

Lastly, in many areas, and for a variety of reasons, the traditional concrete materials, sand and gravel, are becoming scarce. Lightweight concrete, even if it had no other merit, would at least supplement the supplies of the older concreting materials in these areas.

Basically, there is only one means of making concrete light—by including air in its composition. This however can be achieved in three distinct ways:

(1) By omitting the finer sizes from the aggregate grading, thereby creating the so-called 'no-fines' concrete.
(2) By replacing the gravel or crushed rock by a hollow, cellular, or porous aggregate which includes air in the mix.
(3) By creating gas bubbles in a cement slurry: after setting, a strong coral-like cellular structure is formed known as 'aerated concrete'.

The three types of lightweight concrete are illustrated schematically in Fig. 1.2. However, concretes can be made which are combinations of these types, for example, no-fines concrete employing lightweight aggregate, and aerate concrete containing a lightweight aggregate filler. The whole range of lightweight concretes is considered in the subsequent chapters, but it will be useful at this stage to review the relationship between these concretes. The scope of the subject can readily be seen from Table 1.1. The reader is also referred to the RILEM classification of lightweight aggregates.[4]

Although lightweight concrete has become much more familiar in recent years, it is in no sense a new class of building material. In the form of clinker it was used in the late nineteenth century in the USA, England and elsewhere. Nor was its use confined to speculative, low-priced housing; clinker concrete was used in the extensions to the British Museum carried out in 1907. Indeed a form of lightweight concrete was frequently used by

TABLE 1.1

GROUPS OF LIGHTWEIGHT CONCRETE

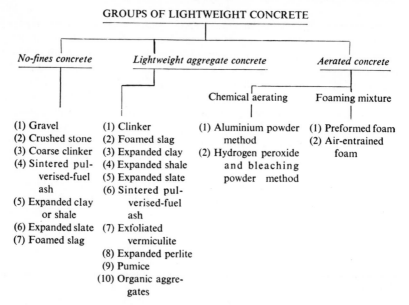

No-fines concrete	*Lightweight aggregate concrete*	Chemical aerating	Foaming mixture
(1) Gravel	(1) Clinker	(1) Aluminium powder method	(1) Preformed foam
(2) Crushed stone	(2) Foamed slag	(2) Hydrogen peroxide and bleaching powder method	(2) Air-entrained foam
(3) Coarse clinker	(3) Expanded clay		
(4) Sintered pulverised-fuel ash	(4) Expanded shale		
(5) Expanded clay or shale	(5) Expanded slate		
(6) Expanded slate	(6) Sintered pulverised-fuel ash		
(7) Foamed slag	(7) Exfoliated vermiculite		
	(8) Expanded perlite		
	(9) Pumice		
	(10) Organic aggregates		

the Romans; the 44 m diameter dome of the Pantheon, built in the second century AD, is composed of cast *in situ* concrete utilising pumice aggregate (Fig. 1.3).

Expanded clay aggregate was used in concrete in the United States for shipbuilding in the First World War, and concrete blocks made with a similar material have been employed continuously in that country since the early 1920s. However, apart from some wartime activities during both World Wars, when it was used for the construction of barges and sea-going ships[5] (Fig. 1.4), it was not until about 1950 that expanded clay aggregate was first used in Britain.

In the middle 1930s foamed blast-furnace slag was introduced into England and has been a major source of lightweight aggregate ever since. Prior to this, natural pumice was sometimes used in Britain and is still employed, principally in block-making.

Although some experimental work on the sintering of pulverised-fuel ash was carried out in the United States more than 30 years ago, the first serious study and subsequent commercial development was done in England, from whence interest has spread to the USSR, Netherlands, France, Germany and elsewhere.

Prior to the Second World War, lightweight aggregate concrete in the United Kingdom was used mainly for non-loadbearing blocks. Later,

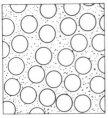

No-fines   Lightweight   Aerated
            aggregate

FIG. 1.2   The three basic types of lightweight concrete.

owing largely to the improved concrete quality which came with the use of better aggregates such as foamed slag and the adoption of British Standards for clinker and other light artificial aggregates, lightweight concrete came to be used for loadbearing purposes—for example, the inner leaf of loadbearing cavity walls, with the approval of the Building Research Station, UK. With the experience which has subsequently been gained, light aggregate concrete is being used for reinforced structural concrete, and indeed for prestressed concrete.

FIG. 1.3   The Pantheon, Rome.

FIG. 1.4 Two thousand ton coaster built in England with expanded clay aggregate concrete.

Parallel with the development of lightweight aggregate concrete, similar progress was being made with aerated concrete. This was first produced in Sweden in about 1929, and in the early days was confined to the production of blocks (Fig. 1.5). Improvements in the properties of the concrete led to the development of reinforced units, so that today more than half the production of Swedish aerated concrete is in that form. Aerated concrete of loadbearing quality was not introduced into the UK until about 1950, and for nearly 10 years there was only one factory, engaged solely in making blocks. There are now many factories distributed over Britain, making building blocks and to a lesser extent reinforced units.

Lightweight concrete is now a firmly established building material throughout the world. Although its use, especially with reinforced concrete and prestressed concrete, has not been without its problems, these are rapidly being overcome. Discussion is now concerned with the measures that control authorities should impose to protect the public. These measures tend to impose restrictive rules, usually to the detriment of lightweight concretes, and often without sufficient cause. There is however no longer any controversy on whether or not these materials can safely be used for loadbearing construction, particularly for reinforced or prestressed concrete work; their general suitability for these purposes has been proved and fully conceded in most countries of the world, developed and developing.

This large step forward was made in a relatively short space of time, and was in no small measure due to the work of research chemists and materials technologists, as well as design and construction engineers who prepared the ground for the industrial production and application of lightweight

FIG. 1.5 Aerated concrete block wall under construction.

aggregates and aerated concretes. In applying the results of research to the production and use of lightweight concretes, industry was diligent and enterprising.

When seen in the entire framework of the concrete industry of Europe the role of lightweight aggregates is important even if lightweight concrete does not as yet represent a large proportion of total concrete production. The total output of aggregate producers in the United Kingdom, for example, is of the order of 80 million m³. (105 million cubic yards) per annum.[6] The output of lightweight aggregates is probably less than 5 per cent of this quantity, including boiler clinker, foamed slag and sintered aggregates.[7] The increasing volume of concrete used in plain and reinforced concrete works as well as economic and social factors point to the urgency of increasing the production of lightweight aggregates and lightweight concretes of various kinds, bearing in mind the need for the economic use of energy. This has become an urgent necessity in order to avoid excessive exploitation of gravel and crushed rock at the expense of the 'whole ecological and amenity balance of our environment'.[8]

One of the important incentives for the development of new types of lightweight aggregate in the UK has been the gradual diminution of clinker supplies to the established concrete block industry. The main source of boiler clinker in the UK is the electricity generating stations of the Central Electricity Generating Board. By the adoption of automatic installations to burn pulverised coal in place of chain-grate stoking boiler plants burning granulated coal, the nature of the waste product has been changed. Instead of furnace clinker, which is a ready-made lightweight aggregate suitable for block-making, pulverised-fuel ash is being produced in increasing quantities. Moreover, the increasing cost of oil as well as of coal will in future encourage the use of nuclear installations, provided these installations can be made sufficiently safe in the human environment. The gradual elimination of boiler clinker, which hitherto has been the cheapest as well as the most plentiful lightweight aggregate in the UK, will leave a gap which cannot as yet be adequately filled by the present production of lightweight aggregates or aerated concrete. Nor is it likely that it can do so for some time to come, for the quantities of lightweight aggregates which will become available on the building materials market will have to be shared between the lightweight block industry and current reinforced and prestressed concrete construction. The principal source of siliceous raw material suitable for the production of high grade lightweight aggregates through thermal processes—in addition to pulverised-fuel ash, blast-furnace slag and clay—is colliery waste or shale, varying in composition throughout the world but invariably containing a sizeable proportion of carbon. This reduces the amount of combustible material (coke, coal, oil or gas) which has to be added to start and to sustain the burning and consequent expansion process needed for the manufacture of the final lightweight product. Unfortunately not all colliery wastes can be used easily or safely for the manufacture of expanded materials: some contain tarry materials which produce a great deal of objectionable smoke and, in addition, tend to condense on the inner linings of ventilating ducts, forming combustible layers. Research on methods of overcoming these difficulties has not yet produced a generally satisfying solution. Yet the utilisation of the massive reserves and current production of colliery waste is essential, for its quantity is of the same order as that of useable coal.

The major cost element for all types of aggregate—normal as well as lightweight—is the cost of transporting the material from the point of extraction or production to the point of use. Some technically highly suitable materials have therefore had to remain unused in the absence of special tariff concessions to allow for the cost of transport. Thus, in the UK, mountains of china clay waste suitable for use as normal weight aggregate have accumulated in Cornwall—a small quantity only being used for block production for local use. The nearest recipient for this material would be the construction industries of south-east England, but the rail network from the south-west to the east is already overloaded, the alternative lines having been dismantled in the course of the economy and 'rationalisation' drive in the late 50s and early 60s. Shipping on the other hand, though practical and cheap, is dependent on adequate port and loading facilities. These are not available and incentives to invest in their construction appear not to have been sufficiently attractive to prevent the necessary capital from being diverted instead to other areas, often outside the UK. An example of unused resources of potential lightweight aggregates in the UK is the intermittent exploitation of Welsh and Scottish waste slate. This is only profitable at times of high economic activity because these materials are found at a considerable distance from centres of major building activity.

It is clear that a rapid growth of the lightweight concrete industry must therefore be largely based on a radical reorientation of the available raw material supplies, to be followed presumably by a reorganisation of the price structure of the industry to take account of increasing costs. In the past, the availability of cheap boiler clinker from the power stations could effectively discourage the development of other types of higher quality but dearer materials in the UK. Those days are almost at an end.

Similar conditions which retarded the development of alternative types of raw material also existed in Germany, where large quantities of pumice concrete blocks and precast reinforced pumice concrete slabs were being manufactured by relatively small and largely unorganised producers. German transport tariff policies traditionally favour mass goods requiring long haulage distances, thus encouraging the use of pumice concrete products over a large area. This system has led to prices which were low enough to discourage the necessary long-term investment of capital in the development of the production of alternative, higher grade lightweight aggregates on an industrial scale. By now the reserves of high grade pumice in the Neuwied-Andernach basin of the Rhine valley have been practically exhausted, but the underlying, much thicker strata of tuff and lava still provide a much heavier but still suitable and cheap source of lightweight aggregate for block-making. This is used locally, and even exported to The Netherlands to supply block works in the Utrecht area and elsewhere. These and similar rocks found in the Eifel Mountains could restrain the utilisation of industrial wastes and other materials for aggregate production. Moreover, the UK and the countries along the western seaboard of Europe as well as Germany present—in periods of high building activity—a ready market for low-priced Greek and Italian high-grade natural pumice, particularly when surplus capacity is available in the world shipping industry, which is notorious for the erratic variations of its freight charges.

There is nevertheless in Germany growing pressure on available supplies of aggregate, especially after the virtual exhaustion of the 'quarries' of brick rubble left as an aftermath of the Second World War in German towns and cities. This is caused not only by the block-making and precasting industries but also by the growing use made in Western Germany and other countries of loadbearing walls cast *in situ* ('Schüttbeton') (Fig. 1.5). To supply this need, the long-established foamed slag industry based on the blast-furnaces of the Ruhr and near Linz in Austria have adopted methods which were originally developed by the late M. Gallai-Hatchard in Britain. Expanded clay is also being made by sintering processes. In addition, a considerable volume of precast, autoclaved products is available from a number of aerated concrete factories originally established both with Swedish technical assistance and independently. The German aerated concrete industry is now considerably larger than any other in Western Europe. Some high-grade expanded clay is also imported from Belgium where it is produced with considerable success. The production of expanded colliery shale aggregate in The Netherlands has largely ceased, as a result of the closure of the coal mines. The increasing cost of other types of fuel may well lead, however, to a re-opening of collieries throughout Western Europe, including France and The Netherlands, and will logically lead to the utilisation of colliery wastes for the production of lightweight aggregate in these countries.

In France, most of the lightweight aggregate production was initially centred around the Alsace iron industry, a limited quantity of foamed slag being produced by methods of production which originated in the UK. A lightweight natural lava aggregate is also being quarried in the Massif Central but its use is not widespread. Turning to other European countries, the vast deposits of scoria and pumice in Central Italy and the Lipari Islands, as well as in Greece, are noteworthy. In Northern Europe the emphasis has been mainly on the development and use of aerated concrete products in the form of blocks and reinforced members, with the exception of Denmark, where lack of natural aggregates led to the development of 'Leca', an expanded clay aggregate produced in rotary kilns. Iceland could be a source of vast quantities of pumice if suitable port facilities could be provided.

In the USA, the large-scale development of lightweight concrete was more rapid than elsewhere. It is governed by the enormous dimensions of that country and the great distances and transport costs involved in moving heavy materials to building sites, coupled with the relatively high cost of labour. Although there does not appear to be an overall shortage of natural dense aggregates, these are frequently at a considerable distance from industrial and population centres and the use of locally-produced lightweight aggregates is then more economical. These factors have led to the development and widespread use of a considerable variety of lightweight aggregates of varying quality. These have been used for a large variety of purposes, from shipbuilding and prestressed bridge girders to block-making and normal cast-*in-situ* applications. By the end of the 50s the production of lightweight aggregates in the USA had reached some 12 million m^3 (15 million cubic yards) per annum. On the other hand, the establishment of an aerated concrete industry has lagged behind other countries, owing—it seems—to local difficulties and misfortunes rather than to any essential technical or policy reasons. With the gradual elimination of these difficulties, the production and use of this material, which is already being made in Canada to the north and Mexico to the south of the USA, could start on a large scale.

The development of all types of lightweight concrete construction in the USSR and countries of Eastern Europe and Asia is conditioned by similar factors as in the USA. Here, too, there are vast distances, great needs to be satisfied in a relatively short time and there is a great variety of raw materials, both natural and artificial. The development of lightweight concretes in these countries is favoured moreover by investment policies which do not necessarily require an immediate financial return on the capital invested in socially necessary production facilities. In addition to the normal investment in new buildings for both industrial and dwelling purposes, there was in Eastern Europe the overwhelming need to replace practically every type of housing, building and civil engineering works lost in the unprecedented destruction experienced during the Second World War. Accelerated industrial expansion in the USSR and elsewhere in Eastern Europe added to economic pressures. Production of both artificial lightweight aggregates—mainly foamed slag and expanded clay—and of autoclaved aerated concrete has therefore been encouraged and is now taking place on a huge scale. More recently, the exploitation of the deposits of natural lightweight aggregates in the Caucasus, mainly in Georgia and Armenia, has led to the increased use of these materials in the USSR.

The development of new types of lightweight concrete and the increasing use made of such materials is reflected, and was itself encouraged and helped by the work of research workers in many research institutions throughout the world. In the UK this work was started at the Building Research Station, Watford, where a series of experimental studies were carried out by Lea, Parker, Newman, Nurse, Bessey and others on the manufacture and properties of foamed slag and other lightweight aggregates, as well as aerated concrete. These investigations were extended to the study of the structural use of lightweight concrete by Thomas and others. Meanwhile the development of new types of aggregate obtained by sintering pulverised-fuel ash, the disposal of which has become a major problem in the national energy supply system, was accomplished at the Building Research Station and elsewhere. The use of these improved lightweight aggregates for structural work was investigated in the USA, Germany and the USSR, as well as in the UK, in research institutions and by individual research workers in universities.

In the USA, pioneering research on the material properties of a large number of different lightweight aggregates and of the concrete made with these materials was undertaken by the National Bureau of Standards. This was followed by research programmes on the structural use of these materials at the Portland Cement Association Laboratories at Chicago carried out by Shideler and others, and also in laboratories in various universities, the earliest being the investigations of Richart and Jensen at Illinois, followed by others at the Universities of Texas, Ohio and Oregon. These workers were mainly concerned with the performance of various proprietary types of lightweight aggregate concrete.

In Germany, research was at first mainly concerned with pumice and foamed slag aggregates and with some types of aerated concrete. Work on the former was being carried out mainly by the Research Institution of the Cement Industry at Düsseldorf, by the Slag Research Institute in Rheinhausen and also at the University of Stuttgart, under the late Professor Graf, and at the University of Munich, under Professor Rüsch, who also inspired a great deal of original work on the structural uses of aerated concrete. Much of the initiative for research on porous types of concrete suitable for loadbearing wall construction (Schüttbeton) came from the Arbeitskreis Schüttbeton led by Schneider-Arnoldi. The larger pumice producers initiated research on pumice concrete by Hart, which dealt with floor and roof slabs with a span up to 4·5 m (15 ft).

Noteworthy work has been carried out at Darmstadt University on the manufacture and properties of expanded clay and sintered materials by Weigler and Karl, while the structural application of lightweight concretes has been studied experimentally by Leonhardt at the Otto Graf Institute near Stuttgart and at the Stevan Laboratory at Delft by Bruggeling in conjunction with workers at TNO, The Netherlands government research organisation.

Much of the initial work on autoclaved aerated concrete owes its origin to the university laboratories in Stockholm and Gothenburg and the Cement and Concrete Institute in Stockholm. The investigations on these materials and their properties were in the main sponsored by the manufacturing companies themselves. The official State Building Research Organisation was responsible for a number of important research programmes relating to the structural performance of aerated concretes of various types, particularly the behaviour of walls and the performance of beams and slabs. Building research in the four Nordic countries is very much an integrated activity with regular consultation between the organisations and individuals concerned. Periodic conferences between the Scandinavian building research workers on proposals for research programmes, and on the progress of existing ones, form an important link in this system.

In the USSR, research on lightweight concrete is mainly carried on at the Building Research Institute in Moscow but lately the interest in their own resources of the more recently developed republics, mainly in the Caucasus is shown by work on their local materials, mainly pumice and sintered clay. There appears to have been, as in other countries, a preoccupation with the properties of the new materials and with production problems; greater interest in problems of their structural application has followed later. The use of aerated concrete for very large panels and the attendant difficulties of providing suitably large diameter autoclaves have been the subject of investigations on an industrial scale.

In industrially advanced countries, increased knowledge of materials technology and of structural performance through research and experience has been reflected in the modern design procedures and practice adopted by the increasing number of scientifically trained professional technologists and engineers employed in the day-to-day work of the building and civil engineering industries. There has been also increasing pressure to maintain some control on the application of this new knowledge and experience, both to protect the safety of the public—a matter for the State—and the reputation of engineers—a matter for the profession. Both these trends— the wider spread and increasing standards of education and competence on the one hand and the need for a uniform approach to the problems raised by the greater range of engineering developments on the other hand—have led in many countries to the establishment of mandatory or non-mandatory standard specifications and codes of practice, as well as Building Regulations having statutory power. In view of the very great importance of the construction industries in any expanding economy—in the UK, for example,[6] they are responsible for about 10 per cent of the gross national product—it is an obvious necessity for these regulations and codes of practice to be adapted to real needs. They should neither be too restrictive, thus throttling new enterprise and development, nor so loose as to encourage standards of building inconsistent with adequate safety and durability; and they must be subject to critical review and revision from time to time.

In this field the most significant, spontaneous professional achievement of the post-war years has been the formulation of the CEB/FIP International Recommendations for Concrete Construction based on limit state design concepts for the safety of structures. These concepts were shown to be equally applicable to other types of civil engineering methods of construction and materials. The work on the International Recommendations was initiated by some of Europe's most experienced and advanced research workers, designers and construction engineers assembled in the Euro-International Committee for Concrete (CEB), in co-operation with the International Federation for Prestressing (FIP). CEB attracted the support of many experts from other countries overseas and the extension of the concepts developed by CEB to other methods of construction is being achieved for structural steelwork and composite steel–concrete construction with the European Convention for Structural Steelwork (CECM), and for timber and masonry construction with the International Council for Building (CIB). The work of CEB and its associated and sister organisations is being promulgated by the International Standards Organisation (ISO); their Code of Practice relating to fundamental requirements is intended to serve as the basis for 'secondary legislation' to be enacted by the great regional organisations of countries for economic cooperation, viz. EEC, CMEA and the Nordic countries.

In the UK, discussion on the interpretation of the various investigations on concrete and on the safety of structures will eventually lead to a revision and integration of existing codes and byelaws in which lightweight concrete is referred to. In fact, the British Standard Code of Practice for Concrete Construction, CP 110:1973,[9] is an important achievement in this direction, based as it is on the CEB Recommendations.

REFERENCES

1. American Concrete Institute ACI 318–71. 'Building Code Requirements for Reinforced Concrete, ACI, Detroit.
2. Euro-International Committee for Concrete (CEB) (1977). 'Draft International Standard Model Code for Concrete Construction', CEB, Paris.
3. Kinniburgh, W. (1948). 'A Work Study on Bricklaying', *National Building Study Technical Paper*, No. 1, HMSO.
4. RILEM (1975). RILEM Recommendations LC1, 'Terminology and Definition of Lightweight Concrete', and LC2., 'Functional Classification of Lightweight Concretes', RILEM, Paris.
5. Anon. (1943). 'Concrete–Steel Barges', *The Engineer*, **176**, 4581.
6. Central Statistical Office (1974), *Annual Abstract of Statistics*, No. 111, HMSO.
7. Gutt, W., Nixon, P. J., *et al.* (1974). 'A Survey of the Locations, Disposal, and Prospective Uses of the Major Industrial By-products and Waste Materials'. Building Research Establishment Current Paper 19/74, Garston, Watford.
8. Advisory Committee on Aggregates, Dept. of the Environment (Verney Committee) (1975). 'Aggregates: The Way Ahead', HMSO.
9. British Standard Code of Practice CP 110: 1973. 'The Structural Use of Concrete', British Standards Institution.

CHAPTER TWO

Chemical Aspects of Lightweight Concrete

SUMMARY

Portland cement is made by calcining a mixture of chalk (or limestone) and clay. At the high temperature of the kiln the minerals combine to form a clinker composed mainly of calcium silicates and aluminates. The product is then finely ground.

The addition of water to Portland cement brings about two types of reaction, hydrolysis and hydration, and new minerals are formed, some of which have cementing properties.

Free lime, as the hydroxide, is one of the products formed by the 'setting' of cement: it is this which maintains the alkalinity in concrete and so inhibits the corrosion of steel reinforcement.

Cement products suffer attack by any soluble sulphates to which they are exposed. Tricalcium aluminate is the component mineral in the cement which is most vulnerable to sulphate attack. Cements made expressly with very low tricalcium aluminate content are marketed as sulphate-resisting cements.

Many chemicals have a pronounced effect on the rate of setting of freshly-made concrete and are known as accelerators or retarders *according to whether they increase or decrease the rate of hardening of the concrete.*

INTRODUCTION

All concretes are cement-bonded products. It is not surprising therefore that many of the common properties of lightweight concrete, such as development of strength, drying shrinkage, carbonation, and resistance to chemical attack are very much influenced by the properties of the cement itself. Even when lime is used as the raw material instead of Portland cement, as is sometimes the case in aerated concrete, the subsequent curing treatment is such that the ultimate binding material is substantially the same as if Portland cement had in fact been used.

The setting of cement, the development of strength in concrete and the subsequent durability of the concrete are chemical matters. It seems fitting therefore at this stage to review briefly the common chemical reactions that occur during the manufacture and use of lightweight concrete, not only for a readier appreciation of such processes as the manufacture of aerated concrete, but to provide a better understanding of the behaviour of

15

concrete. The account given here is much simplified for the convenience of the non-specialist reader. For a comprehensive treatment of the subject see Lea, *The Chemistry of Cement and Concrete.*[1]

TYPES AND NATURE OF CEMENTS

Present-day hydraulic cements may be divided into two broad groups:

(1) Portland cements, which include ordinary Portland cement, rapid-hardening Portland cement, low-heat cement, sulphate-resisting cement and white Portland cement.

(2) The non-Portland cements, which include the various blast-furnace cements, high-alumina cement and numerous other special cements which because of some particular properties have specialised uses. The great bulk of the cement employed in most countries is ordinary Portland cement and most of the lightweight concrete is made with this, though rapid-hardening cement is sometimes used.

Portland cement is made by roasting (calcining) a mixture of calcium carbonate in the form of chalk or limestone with aluminium silicates in the form of clay. At the very high temperature of the kiln (about 1000 °C) the minerals combine to form a clinker composed mainly of calcium silicates and calcium aluminates. As we shall see later, the effect of water on these compounds when finely ground is to create a series of complex products which when fully formed give the binding strength of the set Portland cement.

The chemical composition of minerals is normally expressed in terms of oxides such as SiO_2, CaO, and Al_2O_3. This is a convention and does not imply that the minerals do in fact consist entirely or even mainly of these

TABLE 2.1
COMPOSITION OF A TYPICAL PORTLAND CEMENT

Material	Percentage by weight
CaO (calcium oxide)	64·1
MgO (magnesium oxide)	0·8
Al_2O_3 (aluminium oxide)	4·5
Fe_2O_3 (ferric oxide)	3·1
SiO_2 (silicon oxide)	22·9
K_2O (potassium oxide)	0·6
Na_2O (sodium oxide)	0·5
SO_3 (sulphur trioxide)	2·4
Other materials	1·1

TABLE 2.2

COMPOUNDS PRESENT IN A TYPICAL PORTLAND CEMENT, CALCULATED FROM THE DATA OF TABLE 2.1

Material	Percentage by weight
$3CaO \cdot SiO_2$ (tricalcium silicate)	42·0
$2CaO \cdot SiO_2$ (dicalcium silicate)	34·0
$4CaO \cdot Al_2O_3 \cdot Fe_2O_3$ (tetracalcium aluminoferrite)	9·5
$3CaO \cdot Al_2O_3$ (tricalcium aluminate)	6·7
Other compounds	7·8

oxides. As an illustration of this usage, the composition of a typical Portland cement would be expressed as shown in Table 2.1. The actual compounds present in the cement can be calculated from this analysis and would show the composition given in Table 2.2.

SETTING OF CEMENT

The addition of water to Portland cement brings about two types of reaction. One is 'hydrolysis' and the other 'hydration'. In hydrolysis, water reacts with a compound and splits it into two or more simpler compounds, the water itself being decomposed in the process and its component parts incorporated in the new products. Hydration on the other hand is a process in which one or more molecules of water are 'annexed' to a molecule of the principal compound. The attraction which a compound has for 'hydration water' and the strength of bond with which it maintains this water is a characteristic property of its molecular structure and in particular of its electron configuration. To some compounds the attachment of water, though strictly 'chemical' in nature, is a loose one, and the water may easily be removed, for example by a reduction in the vapour pressure of the ambient air. Other compounds have so great an avidity for water and the resulting association is so intimate that there is the formation of what is virtually a new compound.

Although hydrolysis and hydration are fundamentally different reactions and notionally they occur independently, in practice they take place simultaneously though not necessarily at the same rate. The following equation illustrates the combined effect of hydrolysis and hydration on tricalcium silicate.

$$3CaO \cdot SiO_2 + \text{water} \rightarrow xCaO \cdot ySiO_2(\text{aq.}) + Ca(OH)_2$$

anhydrous tricalcium silicate	a less basic calcium silicate (hydrated)	calcium hydroxide (hydrate of CaO)

The fact that the reaction between cement and water takes place in a number of stages and not all the reactions occur at the same rate is shown by the 'first set', 'final set' and subsequent hardening. The first set is generally held to be due to the rapid solution of the more reactive compounds such as the tricalcium aluminate and tricalcium silicate. The solubility of such compounds is very low and they dissolve with some decomposition, so that a rapid precipitation follows, and this combined with the withdrawal of liquid water due to formation of hydrates results in a stiffening of the paste. The final set and progressive hardening are due to a complex pattern of simultaneous reactions. It is believed that when the final set has taken place the unhydrated cement grains are coated with the hydrated products already formed, and for continuous hardening water must diffuse through this coating in order to reach the unset cement.

In considering the hydration of Portland cement it was demonstrated that the more basic calcium silicates were hydrolysed to less basic silicates with the formation of calcium hydroxide or 'slaked lime' as a by-product. It is this lime which reacts with the aluminium powder to form hydrogen in the making of aerated concrete from Portland cement:

$$2Al \quad + 3Ca(OH)_2 + 6H_2O \rightarrow \quad 3CaO \cdot Al_2O_3 \cdot 6H_2O + \quad 3H_2$$

| aluminium powder | calcium hydroxide | water | tricalcium aluminate hydrate | hydrogen |

In practice other aluminates and degrees of hydration may occur.

The 'free' lime in set cement maintains alkalinity in concrete and so inhibits the corrosion of steel reinforcement; it is also the component in concrete which is most vulnerable to attack by sugar, acid, and very pure water.

Pozzolanas are defined as minerals which, though not cementitious in themselves, contain constituents which will combine with lime at ordinary temperatures in the presence of water to form stable insoluble compounds possessing cementing properties. Materials with strong pozzolanic properties are frequently present in fine aggregates, particularly in lightweight aggregates, and these react with the free lime in set cement, thereby augmenting the strength of the concrete.

CARBONATION

On exposure to the carbon dioxide of the atmosphere, all the compounds which together make up Portland cement would ultimately be decomposed with the formation of calcium carbonate, hydrated silica, alumina and ferric oxide, the cement compound most readily attacked being the calcium hydroxide or free lime. In fact, under ordinary conditions, with well-compacted concrete, the rate of penetration of air into the concrete is so slow that the amount of carbonation which takes place is immeasurably small. However, with lightweight concretes, particularly open-textured products made with semi-dry mixes, and aerated concretes, the penetration of carbon dioxide is quite considerable. This is important because the decomposition of calcium silicate hydrates by carbon dioxide is accompanied by shrinkage which augments the natural drying shrinkage of these concretes. Indeed the carbonation shrinkage may amount to half as much as the drying shrinkage.[2-4] It was first demonstrated that shrinkage of concrete accompanies carbonation by Brady[5] on 1:3 mortar prisms, $\frac{1}{4}$ in. thick. These, after maturing for 7 days in moist air, were partially dried in an atmosphere of 60 per cent relative humidity (r.h.) and then stored in air or in carbon dioxide at the same humidity. The results showed that after the initial drying shrinkage of a concrete is complete, a further shrinkage can take place due to carbonation. Since Brady's original work, a great deal of research has been directed to this complex problem. It has been shown, for example, that although carbonation occurs, no carbonation shrinkage takes place at 100 per cent r.h. or below 25 per cent r.h., and is at its maximum at about 50 per cent r.h.

This applies to initial drying shrinkage: carbonation reduces the reversible moisture movement of concretes cured at normal temperature or in steam at atmospheric pressure but increases the reversible moisture movement in autoclaved products. The volume stability of concrete blocks is improved if the carbonation shrinkage is allowed to take place before the blocks are used. A number of concrete block works use industrial waste gases so that carbonation shrinkage is completed before the blocks are built into a wall, thereby leaving only the true drying shrinkage to take place.

Although the shrinkage accompanying carbonation of concrete is easily demonstrated, and indeed is everyday experience, the mechanism of this is not yet understood. The conversion of calcium hydroxide to calcite leads not to a shrinkage but to an increase of 11 per cent of solid volume, while carbonation shrinkage occurs in hydrated cements containing no calcium hydroxide, such as high alumina cement.

It has been reported by many workers that carbonation markedly increases the compressive strength and tensile strength of cement paste, mortars, and concrete specimens, but studies made by Shideler[6] demonstrated that lightweight concrete blocks made with lean mixes give only a small and variable increase in compressive strength when cured in carbon dioxide. Carbon dioxide, in so far as it penetrates the concrete, leads to some decomposition of the hydrated cement compounds, so it is perhaps surprising that carbonation should increase concrete strength. However, the calcium carbonate formed in such a reaction is itself a strong cementing agent—witness the strength of lime mortar—and it appears that this contributes to the enhanced strength of carbonated concrete.

SULPHATE RESISTANCE

Cement products are attacked to some extent by soluble sulphates to which they are exposed, a common occurrence when concrete is used below ground level. Sulphate solutions attack Portland cement in two ways:

(1) They react with calcium hydroxide in the set cement to form calcium sulphate:

$$Ca(OH)_2 + Na_2SO_4 \cdot 10H_2O \rightarrow CaSO_4 \cdot 2H_2O + 2NaOH + 8H_2O$$

| calcium hydroxide | sodium sulphate hydrate | calcium sulphate hydrate | sodium hydroxide | water |

(2) They react with calcium aluminate to form calcium sulphoaluminate:

$$4CaO \cdot Al_2O_3 \cdot 19H_2O + 3(CaSO_4 \cdot 2H_2O)$$

calcium aluminate hydrate   calcium sulphate hydrate (gypsum)

$$\rightarrow 3CaO \cdot Al_2O_3 \cdot 3CaSO_4 \cdot 31H_2O + Ca(OH)_2$$

calcium sulphoaluminate (ettringite)   calcium hydroxide

The conversion of calcium hydroxide to calcium sulphate more than doubles the solid volume. Likewise, the formation of the highly-hydrated sulphoaluminate is accompanied by a doubling of the volume. It is this large expansion which causes disruption of the concrete which has been exposed to sulphate attack.

All Portland cements have substantially the same components but the proportions vary considerably, and it is well established that low tricalcium aluminate content increases the resistance of cement to sulphate attack. Such a cement with low tricalcium aluminate is marketed as 'sulphate-resisting cement'.

Supersulphated cements are made from granulated blast-furnace slag activated by means of calcium sulphate. Concrete made from such cement has high resistance to sulphate attack, as has concrete with high alumina cement.

Lightweight concretes are not by reason of their composition more vulnerable to sulphate attack than other concretes, but since the most effective defence against sulphate or other aggressive agents is imperviousness, and as this is not characteristic of some types of lightweight concretes, particularly blocks, the latter are not recommended for use below the damp-course in sulphate-bearing soils.

ADMIXTURES

These are materials added in small amount to concrete, usually at the mixing stage, in order to modify the properties of the concrete, either in the fresh or hardened state. Some admixtures are used to reduce the amount of water needed or to improve workability; to accelerate or retard setting, or to increase frost-resistance. Others are employed to reduce permeability or to increase resistance to abrasion, to produce expansion or inhibit shrinkage, or to improve chemical resistance. Some of these additives may be introduced to the concrete by adding them to the cement at the grinding stage.

Accelerators and retarders

The most important accelerator in current use is calcium chloride (or certain proprietary products based on this chemical), and the object of its use is to increase the rate of development of the strength of the concrete at an early age. The intention may be to counteract the effect of low temperature in winter, to reduce the time for moist curing, or to permit earlier removal of form-work. According to Shideler,[7] the effect of calcium chloride on the rate of strength development varies for different Portland cements, temperatures, and water/cement ratio. An addition of 2 per cent calcium chloride to an average Portland cement at 60–70 °F increases the strength of the concrete by some 3–6 MPa (400–800 psi) at 1 day, 5–7 MPa (700–1000 psi) at 7 days, and 3·5–7 MPa (500–1000 psi) at 28 days. Not more than 2 per cent as flake by weight of cement may be added to the concrete. It has been found that at concentrations below 1 per cent, calcium chloride may retard the set, while above 3 per cent it may cause 'flash' set.

In view of the corrosive effect of calcium chloride on embedded steel,[8] particularly on high-tensile steel tendons, this accelerator must be used with great caution. For prestressed concrete it must not be used at all and to avoid the risk of high concentration of this chemical in the concrete near to the steel, the proportion by weight added to ordinary reinforced concrete should not normally exceed 1·5 per cent. In the UK, its use even for reinforced concrete has been discontinued in recent practice.

Sodium chloride produces less change in the setting of cement and the effect is erratic, an acceleration taking place with some Portland cements and retardation with others.

Retarders are intended to prolong the time during which the concrete can be worked by delaying its setting time. Unless the addition of water is suitably controlled, their use is less effective with lightweight aggregate concretes because the particles continue to absorb water during mixing, so that the fresh concrete continues to lose its workability even when the setting of the cement paste has been delayed. Additives used to retard the set of cement are usually based on one of the following:

(1)   Carbohydrates such as sugars and polysaccharides.
(2)   Hydroxylated carboxylic acids and their salts.
(3)   Lignosulphonic acids and their salts.

Workability aids

Some lightweight aggregates can be harsh, and the concrete made from them may as a result have poor workability compared with that made from gravel aggregate. However, certain materials can be added to lightweight concrete mixes to improve the workability. Very fine powders such as pulverised-fuel ash or diatomaceous earth may be added to the extent of a few per cent with beneficial results. However, this benefit can sometimes be partly offset by a necessary increase of the water/cement ratio.

Common air-entraining agents are the alkali salts of pinewood resins, salts of sulphonated aromatic compounds, and hydrolysed proteins. Water-reducing agents, unlike air-retaining agents, are materials which when absorbed on the cement surface make the particles hydrophilic and the water dipoles prevent close approach of the particles, thus facilitating mobility and therefore high workability. Workability aids are also known as 'plasticisers'.

Lime as the binder in aerated concrete

It can be shown that, whether aerated concrete is made from cement and sand or lime and sand, the product after high-pressure curing (autoclaving) is composed largely of tobermorite (monocalcium silicate hydrate). The following equations show that the same product can be derived from lime and sand by synthesis and from dicalcium silicate by hydrolysis.

(1) $Ca(OH)_2 + SiO_2 + xH_2O \rightarrow CaO \cdot SiO_2 \cdot yH_2O$

       slaked lime   silica   water   tobermorite

(2) $2CaO \cdot SiO_2 + xH_2O \rightarrow CaO \cdot SiO_2 \cdot yH_2O + Ca(OH)_2$

   dicalcium silicate   water   tobermorite   slaked lime

If fine silica sand is present in the aggregate, a lime–silica reaction often takes place as a secondary effect when concrete is autoclaved. The product thus formed enhances the strength of the concrete.

REFERENCES

1. Lea, F. M. (1970). *The Chemistry of Cement and Concrete*, Third Edition, Edward Arnold, London.

2. Verbeck, G. J. (1958). 'Carbonation of Hydrated Portland Cement', ASTM Specification Technical Publication No. 205, ASTM, Chicago.
3. Kinniburgh, W. (1960). 'Comparison of Drying Shrinkage of Autoclaved and Air-Cured Concrete at different Humidities', RILEM Symposium on 'Steam-Cured Lightweight Concrete', Gothenburg.
4. Shideler, J. J. (1963). *J. Res. Div. Lab. Port. Cem. Ass.*, **5**(3), 36.
5. Brady, F. L. (1931). *Cement*, **4**, 1105; 'Annual Report, Building Research Board', **1932**, 34; **1933**, 33; **1934**, 38.
6. Shideler, J. J. Private communication.
7. Shideler, J. J. (1952). *Proc. Am. Concr. Inst.*, **48**, 537.
8. Blenkinsop, J. C. (1963). *Mag. Concr. Res.*, **15**(43), 33.

CHAPTER THREE

Mix Design

SUMMARY

The design of lightweight concrete mixes differs considerably from that used for normal dense concrete mixes. In many instances the functional requirements are not merely those of strength and workability, which are specified for normal structural concrete, and each lightweight aggregate must be separately considered.

The grading and other properties of the aggregates influence considerably the properties of concrete made with them.

The mix design of four different types of lightweight concrete is considered, viz.:

1. *No-fines concrete.*
2. *Partially compacted lightweight aggregate concrete.*
3. *Structural lightweight aggregate concrete.*
4. *Aerated concrete.*

The more important properties of each of these types of concrete are dealt with and the choice of the most suitable aggregates, and the way that changes in the mix proportions affect these properties is described.

GENERAL

The design of a concrete mix can be defined as the selection of the most suitable materials, i.e. cement and aggregate, and the most economical proportions of cement, water and the various sizes of aggregates, to produce a concrete having the required physical properties. With ordinary structural concrete made with natural aggregates complying with the requirements of BS 822,[1] the two main properties for which the concrete is designed are degree of workability and crushing strength at 28 days. The workability is of great importance since in normal structural concrete it is essential that the concrete should be fully compacted, whereas in some forms of lightweight concrete, for example, in no-fines concrete or lightweight aggregate concrete used for block-making, the concrete is deliberately made in a partially compacted or porous form.

Dense concrete made with natural normal-weight aggregates has been used increasingly as a structural material since the turn of the century, and

24

much research has been carried out on its properties. It is now known how changes in the properties of the constituent materials and in their relative mix proportions affect the transverse and crushing strength, Young's modulus, shrinkage and thermal movements, resistance to cracking, ability to withstand wearing forces and climatic conditions, and other properties. The effect of changes in the mix proportions on some of these factors is similar to their effect on the crushing strength. Dense aggregate structural concrete is therefore designed to achieve a specified 28-day crushing strength. In 1918 Abrams[2] established the now well-known 'law' that the crushing strength of fully compacted concrete depends primarily on its water:cement ratio, i.e.:

$$\frac{\text{the weight of water in the mix}}{\text{the weight of cement in the mix}}$$

The term 'water/cement ratio' must be qualified as being either the 'free-water/cement ratio', or the 'total-water/cement ratio', depending on whether the water absorbed by the aggregate is allowed for or not. The free-water is the total-water added less that absorbed by the aggregate. It is now more general practice to use the free-water/cement ratio, but since in many cases quoted in this book the absorption of the lightweight aggregates used was not known, the total-water/cement ratio is generally used throughout.

Most methods of mix design for ordinary gravels or crushed rock aggregate concrete are based on the relationships between strength and water/cement ratio. Such relationships are shown in BRS Digest 13,[3] and The Design of Normal Concrete Mixes[4] which replaces Road Note No. 4,[5] which has been widely used in the UK.

One of the factors that is of great importance in deciding on the mix proportions to be used is the grading of the aggregate, particularly that of the fine aggregate. For normal-weight aggregates there is a large range of suitable gradings; this problem is discussed by Newman and Teychenné[6] and in BRS Digest 150.[7] There are differences also in the gradings required for different types of lightweight concrete (Table 3.1). The grading of most fine lightweight aggregates is harsher, and the band of gradings is narrower than for fine natural aggregates (Fig. 3.1).

With different types of lightweight concrete the same considerations of strength and workability do not always apply. For example, lightness in weight is of major importance if the concrete is required for thermal insulation; if the concrete is required for the manufacture of blocks, the ability to be demoulded at once is a factor influencing the choice of mix proportions.

Even with the design of normal gravel or crushed stone concrete mixes, the methods used are only aimed at producing a trial mix, which may or may not fully meet the specified requirements, but will give a starting point

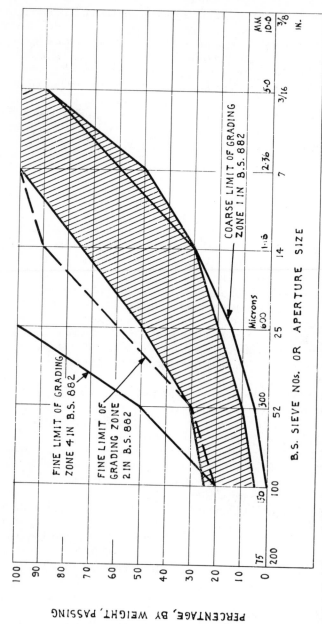

FIG. 3.1 Gradings of fine lightweight aggregates compared with limits specified in BS 882. (Gradings of fine lightweight aggregates generally fall within the shaded zone.)

TABLE 3.1

TYPES AND GRADINGS OF AGGREGATES SUITABLE FOR DIFFERENT TYPES OF LIGHTWEIGHT CONCRETE

Type of lightweight concrete	*Type of aggregate*	*Grading of aggregate i.e. range of particle sizes*
No-fines concrete.	Natural aggregate complying with BS 882. Blast-furnace slag complying with BS 1047. Clinker complying with BS 1165. Other lightweight aggregates may also be suitable if they comply with BS 3979.[16]	Nominal single-sized material between 20 mm ($\frac{3}{4}$ in.) and 10 mm ($\frac{3}{8}$ in.) BS sieves. (The equivalent metric and imperial sizes are not always identical.)
Partially compacted lightweight aggregate concrete.	Clinker complying with BS 1165. Foamed slag complying with BS 877. Expanded clay, shale, slate, vermiculite and perlite. Sintered pulverised-fuel ash and pumice complying with BS 3797.[16]	May be of smaller nominal single sizes or combined coarse and fine [5 mm ($\frac{3}{16}$ in.) down] material to produce a continuous but harsh grading to make a porous concrete.
Structural lightweight aggregate concrete (fully compacted).	Foamed slag complying with BS 877. Expanded clay, shale or slate and sintered pulverised-fuel ash complying with BS 3797.	Continuous grading from either 20 mm ($\frac{3}{4}$ in.) or 14 mm ($\frac{1}{2}$ in.) down to dust, with an increased fines content [5 mm ($\frac{3}{16}$ in.) down] to produce a workable and dense concrete.
Aerated concrete.	Natural fine aggregate. Fine lightweight aggregate. Raw pulverised-fuel ash. Ground slag and burnt shales etc.	The aggregates are generally ground down to a fine powder, i.e. passing a 75 μm BS sieve, but sometimes fine aggregate [5 mm ($\frac{3}{16}$ in.) down] is also incorporated.

TABLE 3.2
PROPERTIES OF DIFFERENT TYPES OF LIGHTWEIGHT CONCRETE

Type of lightweight concrete	Aggregate	Density of aggregate		Density of concrete		Cube crushing strength at 28 days		Thermal conductivity	
		(kg/m³)	(pcf)	(kg/m³)	(pcf)	(MPa)	(psi)	W/m °C	Btu in/ft²/h/°F
Aerated concrete	—	—	—	400-800	25-50	1·5-5·0	200-700	0·09-0·20	0·60-1·4
Partially compacted lightweight concrete	Expanded vermiculite and perlite	60-250	4-15	400-1100	25-70	0·5-3·5	70-500	0·11-0·29	0·75-2·0
	Pumice	500-900	30-55	700-1100	45-70	1·5-4·0	200-550	0·22-0·29	1·5-2·0
	Foamed slag	500-950	30-60	950-1500	60-95	1·5-5·5	200-800	0·22-0·43	1·5-3·0
	Sintered pulverised-fuel ash	650-950	40-60	1100-1300	70-80	3·0-7·0	400-1000	—	—
	Expanded clay or shale	550-1050	35-65	950-1200	60-75	5·5-8·5	800-1200	0·33-0·46	2·30-3·2
	Clinker	700-1050	45-65	1050-1500	65-95	2·0-7·0	300-1000	0·35-0·58	2·40-4·0
No-fines concrete	Natural aggregate	1350-1600	85-100	1600-1900	100-120	4·0-14·0	600-2000	—	—
	Lightweight aggregate	500-1050	30-65	900-1200	55-75	3·0-7·0	400-1000	—	—
Structural lightweight aggregate concrete	Foamed slag	500-950	30-60	1700-2100*	105-130*	10·0-45·0	1500-6000	—	—
	Sintered pulverised-fuel ash	650-950	40-60	1350-1750*	85-110*	14·0-45·0	2000-6000	—	—
	Expanded clay or shale	550-1050	35-65	1350-1850*	85-115*	14·0-45·0	2000-6000	—	—

* These heavier concretes are obtained by replacing some of the lightweight fines by a natural sand.

from which modifications can be made so as to produce the quality of concrete required. This applies even more to lightweight concretes since for given functional requirements there will be a number of equally suitable mixes, depending on the aggregates used and on the methods used in the manufacture of the concrete. Although, as already stated, the grading of lightweight aggregates is more restricted, their other physical properties vary considerably for different types of aggregate. These properties include particle shape, surface texture, bulk density, absorption and hardness or inherent strength. One method of comparing the strength of an aggregate is the '10 per cent fines' test described in BS 812.[8] Typical values for these properties of lightweight aggregates used in the United Kingdom are given by Teychenné.[9]

A further complication lies in the fact that some types of lightweight concrete are not fully compacted and it may be difficult to reproduce the same degree of partial compaction. For example if the cement content of a mix is increased, the strength usually also increases, but if the concrete with the higher cement content was less compacted than the leaner concrete, then the strength of the richer concrete may be lower.

Table 3.2 gives the range of some of the physical properties of different types of lightweight concrete. It is not possible at this stage to describe specific methods of designing concrete mixes with different lightweight aggregates, but some guidance can be given on the way that the choice of aggregates and mix proportions will affect the properties of the concrete produced. Since the functional requirements for different types of lightweight concrete differ, it is necessary to consider each of the following four types of concrete separately.

(1) No-fines concrete.
(2) Partially compacted lightweight aggregate concrete.
(3) Structural lightweight aggregate concrete.
(4) Aerated concrete.

The partially compacted lightweight aggregate concrete may be considered as being structural, in that in many cases it is loadbearing. The essential difference between the two types of lightweight aggregate concrete is this, that whereas type 3 'structural' lightweight aggregate concrete, as used in reinforced concrete, is fully compacted, type 2, partially compacted concrete, is not.

NO-FINES CONCRETE

This material is discussed in some detail in Chapter 7. It is mainly used for both loadbearing and non-loadbearing external and partition walls in houses and flats. The mix design requirements are such that the concrete should have a crushing strength at 28 days of at least 2·75 MPa (400 psi) to comply with the requirements of BS Code of Practice CP 111,[10] and when placed in the wall it should maintain its large voids and not form layers of laitance or cement film. Such layers would destroy the non-capillary character of the material and so provide a path for moisture to travel through to the inside of the wall.

The aggregate used for no-fines concrete should be graded to meet the following requirements: at least 95 per cent should pass the 20 mm ($\frac{3}{4}$ in.) BS sieve, not more than 10 per cent should pass the 10 mm ($\frac{3}{8}$ in.) BS sieve and nothing should pass the 5 mm ($\frac{3}{16}$ in.) BS sieve. Natural aggregates complying with BS 882, blastfurnace slag complying with BS 1047, clinker complying with BS 1165 or foamed slag complying with BS 877 may be used for no-fines concrete and other aggregates such as expanded clay or shale or sintered pulverised-fuel ash complying with BS 3797 are also suitable. Most experience has been obtained in the UK using natural aggregates, blast-furnace slag and clinker.

The strength of no-fines concrete depends on the aggregate which is used as well as on the cement content; as in the case of ordinary concrete, the strength of no-fines concrete is increased as the cement content is increased. Most no-fines concrete is made with a cement/aggregate ratio between 1:6 and 1:10 by volume depending on the aggregate used and on the crushing strength required. In multi-storey structures economies can be made by varying the cement content at different storey heights. Figure 7.2 shows such a structure where the mix proportions varied from 1:6 at the lower levels to 1:10 at the top storey.

Unlike dense concrete, no-fines concrete is very sensitive with respect to water content. A range of water contents cannot therefore be used for a given no-fines concrete mix; for each type of aggregate the most suitable water content must be determined by trial mixes. The correct water content for a particular no-fines concrete mix is judged from its appearance. The aggregate particles must be coated with a shining film of cement grout so as to produce a 'metallic gleam'. If insufficient water is used, there is lack of cohesion between the particles and a subsequent loss of strength; if too much water is used, the cement film will run off the aggregate to form laitance layers, leaving the bulk of the concrete deficient in cement and correspondingly weaker.

As a starting point in making trial mixes it is recommended to use a 1:8 mix by volume of natural or dense aggregates with a water/cement ratio of about 0·45; for lightweight aggregates a richer mix, say 1:6 by volume, may be more suitable with a water/cement ratio of between 0·40–0·60, depending on the absorption of the aggregate. The aggregate should always be wetted first, before adding the cement. The concrete should be placed as soon as possible after mixing, preferably within five minutes. Further recommendations on the use of no-fines concrete are given in Chapter 7 and in Post-War Building Studies No. 1.[11]

PARTIALLY COMPACTED LIGHTWEIGHT AGGREGATE CONCRETE

There are two main uses for this type of concrete:

(1) In precast concrete blocks, or panels.
(2) For casting *in situ* roofs and walls for insulation purposes.

The most important characteristic of each type of aggregate and the properties of the concrete made with it are discussed in detail in Chapter 8. The main requirements for this type of concrete are that it should have adequate strength, a low density—to obtain the best thermal insulation— and a low drying shrinkage, to avoid cracking.

These factors will depend on the aggregate used, the mix proportions, the degree of compaction and the methods used for curing. Tables in Chapter 8 give the properties of concrete made with different aggregates. For a given mix these properties vary depending on the type and quality of the aggregate used and on the method of manufacture. Thus for a 1:6 mix, a partially compacted clinker concrete may have a cube strength at 28 days varying between 4·5 MPa (650 psi) and over 7·0 MPa (1000 psi), depending only on its quality. Also with different aggregates but the same mix proportions the strength can vary from 2·0 MPa (300 psi) to 14·0 MPa (2000 psi) depending on the aggregate used and the methods of manufacture. The density of this type of concrete is a most important factor, the heavier the concrete the higher the strength and the lower its insulation value.

For insulation purposes, the weaker and lighter aggregates such as expanded vermiculite and perlite or lean mixes with heavier lightweight aggregates are used. If the concrete is to be loadbearing according to British practice it should have a crushing strength at 28 days of about (3·0 MPa (400 psi). Partially compacted lightweight aggregate concrete is used extensively in the manufacture of precast concrete blocks. In Britain these should comply with BS 2028[12] which specifies three types of blocks depending on their use, i.e.:

Type A: blocks of density not less than 1500 kg/m^3 (94 pcf) for general building.
Type B: lightweight concrete blocks for loadbearing walls.
Type C: lightweight concrete blocks for internal non-loadbearing walls.

The strength and drying shrinkage requirements differ for each of these types of blocks. Type A blocks can be specified to have an average crushing strength of between 3·5 MPa (510 psi) and 35 MPa (5100 psi) whereas Type B blocks can be specified to have an average crushing strength of either 2·8 MPa (400 psi) or 7·0 MPa (1000 psi). Type C blocks should have adequate strength to avoid breakages in handling and different transverse breaking loads are specified according to the size of the block. The method of manufacture is an important factor in the design of concrete block mixes.[13] Blocks are demoulded immediately after compaction and require an adequate 'green' strength if they are not to deform outside the permitted tolerances. Greater reliance has to be put on the use of trial mixes by the producer to obtain a satisfactory mix for his particular aggregates and manufacturing plant. The use of partially compacted lightweight concrete either cast *in situ* or as precast blocks is discussed further in Chapters 7 and 23.

STRUCTURAL LIGHTWEIGHT AGGREGATE CONCRETE

This type of lightweight concrete differs from the other three types considered in that it is made in a fully compacted state similar to normal reinforced concrete made with natural dense aggregates. This is necessary since it is to be used with steel reinforcement and it is essential that there should be a good bond between the steel and the concrete and that the concrete should provide adequate protection against the corrosion of the steel.

This type of concrete has only been introduced to the UK since the War but there is more extensive experience of its use in the USA. The ways in which the variables in a concrete mix affect the physical properties of structural lightweight aggregate concrete have not yet been as fully investigated as in the case of ordinary gravel concrete. However, data are available from a major investigation carried out at the Building Research Station,[14] and from the producers of the various types of lightweight aggregates. Further details of the physical properties of structural lightweight aggregate concrete made at the Building Research Station[15] are given in Chapter 10.

Aggregates and grading

As indicated in Table 3.1, only the harder varieties of lightweight aggregate are suitable for use in structural concrete. The grading requirements for both coarse and fine lightweight aggregates, excluding foamed slag, are given in BS 3797.[16] Three sizes of graded and single-sized coarse aggregates are given, although in Britain the maximum size used is generally limited to 14 mm ($\frac{1}{2}$ in.) or 10 mm ($\frac{3}{8}$ in.). The grading of most fine lightweight aggregates tends to be rather coarse and is similar to that of a crushed natural aggregate. The outer limits of the two fine aggregate grading zones cover the 'envelope' of typical gradings of fine lightweight aggregate shown in Fig. 3.1. The two fine aggregate grading zones are distinguished from each other by the amount of material passing the 150 μm BS sieve. Grading zone L1 has an upper limit of 19 per cent passing the 150 µm BS sieve, while grading zone L2 raises this limit to 35 per cent and is more applicable to sintered pulverised fuel ash aggregates. The ratio of fine to coarse aggregate depends on several factors but generally this should be less for fine aggregates in grading zone L2 than in grading zone L1.

Workability and water content

One of the essential requirements in designing a structural lightweight concrete mix is that it should be workable so that it can be fully compacted on the site. The shape and texture of the aggregate particles, and the coarse nature of the fine aggregate tend to produce harsh concrete mixes. To avoid this, fine aggregate contents of about 50 per cent are required, and with some materials and lean mixes it is advantageous to use even higher fines contents, an air-entraining agent or to replace some of the fines by a natural sand.

The workability characteristics of lightweight aggregate concrete differ from those of concrete made with natural aggregates. With a given mix using natural aggregates a wide range of workabilities can be obtained by using a wide range of water contents, yet they are still capable of being fully compacted. With lightweight aggregates, the range of water contents and workabilities is reduced. If too low, the mix cannot be compacted and since it does not flow easily prolonged vibration may result in segregation of the lighter coarse particles on the top of the compacted mortar. If too high, segregation may also occur and after compaction the concrete will throw-off water and settle in the mould.

The usual tests for measuring the workability of concrete give a more restricted range of values with lightweight aggregate concrete and different numerical values compared with natural aggregate concrete. Thus concretes having slumps of between 0 and 25 mm (1·0 in.) can easily be compacted. The compacting factor test[17] is a more useful test and a value of 0·8–0·9 indicates a workable structural lightweight concrete. The Swedish VB test,[18] shows the behaviour of concrete under vibration and a workable mix has a VB time of 15 seconds or less.

Figure 3.2 shows the relationships between the total-water/cement ratio and the cement content for various aggregates. The boundary curves are lines of constant water content, which also represent lines of approximately equal workability, the upper boundary (higher water content) indicating a higher workability than the lower boundary.

Crushing strength and water/cement ratio

The crushing strength of structural lightweight concrete depends on the mix proportions in a similar way to concrete made with natural aggregates. The main mix parameter affecting the strength, at a given age, is the water/cement ratio. Typical relationships between the crushing strengths at

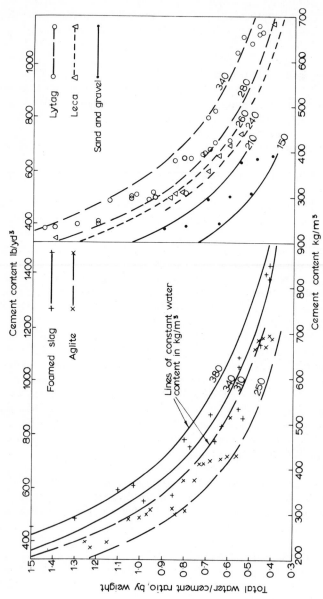

FIG. 3.2 Relationship between the total-water/cement ratio and the cement content.

28 days and the total water/cement ratio are shown in Fig. 3.3. Although structural lightweight concrete follows a similar trend to ordinary concrete a general law cannot be used and each particular type of lightweight aggregate must be considered separately. As with natural aggregates, the strength of structural lightweight aggregate concrete varies during manufacture, and a margin must be added to the specified strength to obtain a target mean strength for mix design. The British Code of Practice, CP 110,[19] requires that this margin should be between 7·5 MPa and 15 MPa (about 1100–2200 psi) for concretes of strength grades of 20 MPa (2900 psi) and over, depending on the quality of control.

The mix design process

The process of designing the mix follows very similar principles and stages as for concrete made with natural aggregates,[4] except that the characteristics of each type of lightweight aggregate are of greater importance. The mix is designed to meet three performance requirements, i.e., crushing strength, workability and relative density.

(1) The crushing strength depends on the aggregate and the water/cement ratio, as shown in Fig. 3.3.
(2) The workability depends on the water content which varies according to the aggregate as shown in Fig. 3.2.
(3) The relative density depends on the aggregate and the cement content as shown in Fig. 3.4.

These three figures are obtained from tests carried out at the Building Research Station,[9] and can be used as a basis for mix design. They show that some combinations of strength and density are not attainable, or are attainable only with particular aggregate.

The design of a trial mix follows the following stages:

(1) Derive the target mean strength from the specified strength and the margin.
(2) From Fig. 3.3 derive the water/cement ratios for the appropriate aggregate to achieve the target mean strength.
(3) For the specified workability use Fig. 3.2 to obtain the cement content at the required water/cement ratio.
(4) From Fig. 3.4 and the cement contents determine the relative density.
(5) From the results of stages (1)–(3) calculate the quantities of materials to produce 1 m³ of fresh concrete.
(6) Prepare a trial mix by deciding on the proportion of fine aggregate in the total aggregate. A fines content of 50 per cent by weight is a useful starting point, but as the cement content is increased, the fines content can be reduced. Most lightweight aggregate manufacturers will give advice on suitable proportions.

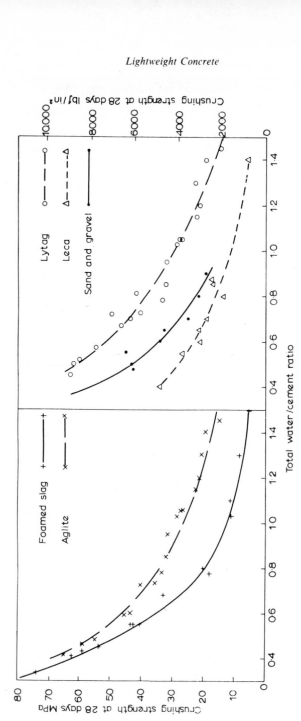

FIG. 3.3   Relationship between the crushing strength of water stored cubes and the toal water/cement ratio.

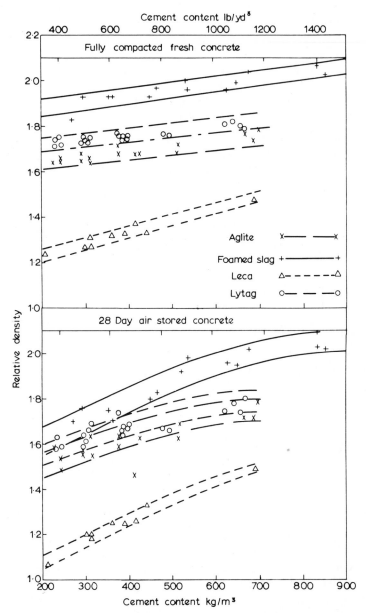

FIG. 3.4 Relationship between the relative density and the cement content.

It must be remembered that Figs. 3.2, 3.3, and 3.4 are based on total-water/cement ratios and dry aggregates. If the aggregates are wet, an allowance must be made for their absorbed water.

Example:

Specified crushing strength at 28 days, 35 MPa (5100 psi).
Specified workability: medium to high.
Specified maximum relative density, 1·8 (1800 kg/m^3 or 112 pcf).
Assume margin of 10 MPa (1450 psi).

(1) Target mean strength = 35 + 10 = 45 MPa (6550 psi). Figure 3.3 shows that this excludes Leca.

(2) From Fig. 3.3 the total-water/cement ratios to meet this target mean strength are:

0·50 for foamed slag
0·60 for Aglite
0·70 for Lytag.

(3) From the upper portion of the bands shown in Fig. 3.2 the cement contents required for the specified workability are:

720 kg/m^3 (45 pcf) for foamed slag.
500 kg/m^3 (31 pcf) for Aglite.
470 kg/m^3 (29 pcf) for Lytag.

(4) At these cement contents the relative densities derived from Fig. 3.4 are:

1·90–2·00 for foamed slag
1·60–1·70 for Aglite
1·65–1·75 for Lytag.

Foamed slag is excluded because its density is greater than that specified. Both Aglite and Lytag would produce a concrete having similar densities and cement contents and the choice of material would depend on their relative cost and availability.

(5) If Lytag is used the relative density of the fresh concrete is 1·75. Thus for 1 m^3 or 1 yd^3 of fresh concrete,

Total weight = 1750 kg (2950 lb)
Cement content = 470 kg (795 lb)
Water content = 0·70 × 470 = 330 kg (555 lb)
Total weight of dry aggregate = 1750 − 800 = 950 kg (1600 lb).

(6) A trial mix should be prepared based on the above values, the fines content being at 50 per cent by weight or at the manufacturer's recommended proportions.

The use of a natural sand as a partial replacement of the fine lightweight aggregate is considered in Chapter 10. The addition of air-entraining agents to improve the workability is not common practice in the UK but is allowed for in the 'Recommended Practice for Structural Lightweight Concrete' proposed by the American Concrete Institute.[20]

Nominal mixes for structural lightweight concrete using different aggregates which meet the strength requirement of the British Standard Code of Practice CP 114,[21] are given in Table 14.1.

AERATED CONCRETE

The manufacture and properties of this type of lightweight concrete are described in some detail in Chapter 17. The general composition is a mortar suitably aerated. There are two distinct methods of effecting aeration; first, a gas can be generated within the mix during its plastic condition by means of a chemical reaction, and secondly air can be introduced either by mixing-in a stable foam or by whipping-in air, using an air-entraining agent. The first method is mainly used in precast concrete factories in which the precast units are subsequently autoclaved in order to produce concrete having a reasonably high strength and low drying shrinkage. The second is mainly used for *in situ* concrete suitable for insulation roof screeds or pipe lagging.

The properties of autoclaved and air-cured concrete differ considerably, as discussed in Chapter 17. The properties of either of these types of aerated concrete will differ according to the mix proportions of cement and siliceous filler used, the amount of aeration and the manufacturing methods used. As shown in Table 3.1, the aggregate or filler generally used consists of a finely ground sand, burnt shale or slag or pulverised-fuel ash, although in some cases some fine aggregate ([5 mm ($\frac{3}{16}$ in.)] down) is also incorporated. The physical properties of aerated concrete are closely related to its density, which can be regarded therefore as the main design criterion. Table 3.3 shows how some physical properties of autoclaved aerated concrete are related to the density.

TABLE 3.3
DENSITY AND OTHER PROPERTIES OF AERATED CONCRETE

Dry density		Cube crushing strength (tested wet)		Modulus of elasticity ($\times 10^3$)		Thermal conductivity	
(kg/m^3)	(pcf)	(MPa)	(psi)	(MPa)	(psi)	($W/m°C$)	($Btu\ in/ft^2/h/°F$)
300	19	—	—	—	—	0·11	0·75
500	31	2·8	410	1·5	220	0·14	1·00
650	41	3·4	490	2·3	330	0·17	1·20
800	50	4·2	610	3·1	450	0·29	2·00

From Table 3.3 it is seen that if it is required to use aerated concrete in load-carrying blocks for which a crushing strength of 2·75 MPa (400 psi) is required, a concrete density of about 550 kg/m³ (35 pcf) is needed.

REFERENCES

1. British Standard 882: Part 2: 1973. 'Coarse and Fine Aggregates from Natural Sources for Concrete', British Standards Institution.
2. Abrams, D. A. (1918). 'Design of Concrete Mixtures', Bulletin No. 1 Structural Materials Research Laboratory, Lewis Institute, Chicago.
3. Building Research Station (1971). 'Concrete Mix Proportioning and Control', Digest No. 13, HMSO.
4. Department of the Environment (1975). 'Design of Normal Concrete Mixes', HMSO.
5. Road Research Laboratory (1950). 'Design of Concrete Mixtures', Road Note No. 4, HMSO.
6. Newman, A. J. and Teychenné, D. C. (1954). 'A classification of Natural Sands and its Use in Concrete Mix Design'. Symposium on Mix Design and Quality Control of Concrete, Cement and Concrete Association, London.
7. Building Research Station (1973). 'Concrete: Materials', Digest 150, Building Research Station, Garston, Watford.
8. British Standard 812: Part 3: 1975 'Methods for Sampling and Testing of Mineral Aggregates, Sands and Fillers', British Standards Intitution.
9. Teychenné, D. C. (1968). 'Lightweight Aggregates: Their Properties and Use in Concrete in the UK', Proceedings of the International Congress on Lightweight Concrete, London. (Also Building Research Station, CP73/68.)
10. British Standard Code of Practice 111:1948. 'Structural Recommendations for Loadbearing Walls', British Standards Institution.
11. 'House Construction'. Post-War Building Studies No. 1, HMSO.
12. British Standard 2028,1364: 1968 'Precast Concrete Blocks', British Standards Institution.
13. McIntosh, J. D. and Kolek, J. (1965). 'Concrete Mixes for blocks', *Concrete Building and Concrete Products*, Vol. 40, No. 2.
14. Teychenné, D. C. (1967). 'Structural Concrete made with Lightweight Aggregates', *Concrete*, 1967, Vol. 1, April. (Also Building Research Station, Current Paper, Engineering 48.)
15. Short, A. (1959). 'The Use of Lightweight Concrete for Reinforced Concrete Construction', *Reinforced Concrete Review*, 5(3).
16. British Standard 3797:1964. 'Lightweight Aggregates for Concrete', British Standards Institution.
17. British Standard 1881:Part 2:1970. 'Methods of Testing Concrete', British Standards Institution.
18. Svenska Cementforeningen (1940). Report on the Test on Concrete carried out with the Vebe Apparatus, Tekniska Meddelanden och Undersokningsrapporter No. 1, Malmö-Stockholm.
19. British Standard Code of Practice 110:Part 1:1972. 'The Structural use of Concrete', British Standards Institution.

20. American Concrete Institute (1958) Committee 613: 'Recommended Practice for Selecting Proportions for Structural Lightweight Concrete, *Amer. Concr. Inst. J.*, **30**(3).
21. British Standard Code of Practice 114:1957 (as amended in 1965) 'The Structural Use of Reinforced Concrete in Buildings', British Standards Institution.

CHAPTER FOUR

Curing of Concrete

SUMMARY

The strength developed by concrete results from the setting of the cement,a complex process involving hydrolysis *and* hydration. *Exposure of the freshly made concrete to conditions of temperature and humidity which are favourable to these reactions is termed* curing. *The forms of curing practised in the industry are* air-curing, *in which the goods are kept moist for a period, usually* 28 *days at normal temperature,* low-pressure steam-curing, *in which the concrete is exposed to steam at atmospheric pressure, and* high-pressure steam-curing *or* autoclaving, *in which the concrete units are subjected for some hours to steam, usually at about* 150 *psi gauge or* 11 *atmospheres.*

The rate of development of strength in concrete is much enhanced by elevated temperatures, particularly at early ages.

With low-pressure steam-curing, a high early strength is obtained, but the gain at later ages is somewhat reduced, so that the strength which is ultimately attained is rather less than would have been obtained by curing at ordinary temperature. Such curing does not reduce drying shrinkage.

High-pressure steam-curing not only gives high early strength but will usually give strength beyond that attainable by air-curing. Moreover, it generally leads to the reduction of drying shrinkage and improves resistance to sulphate attack.

FUNDAMENTALS

Before discussing the curing of concrete it would be well to recall the brief account of the chemistry of setting cement and the mechanics of strength development given in Chapter 2.

Portland cement is composed of a number of compounds, the majority of which are complex in structure. The most important, and by far the most abundant of these compounds are the silicates, aluminates, and aluminoferrites of calcium. When these react with water, two chemical reactions take place: the first we call 'hydrolysis' and the second 'hydration'. These reactions take place simultaneously so that the cement compounds are decomposed and water is progressively combined. For example, when water reacts with tricalcium silicate, calcium hydroxide is formed as well as a hydrated, less-basic calcium silicate. The latter is the compound which

42

gives the set cement the greater part of its bonding strength and therefore provides the functional strength of the concrete. It is clear therefore that the processes of hydrolysis and hydration are extremely important. 'Curing' is the procedure which is followed to ensure that the hardening concrete is maintained in conditions of temperature and humidity which will permit the chemical reactions to proceed efficiently.

Detectable improvement in concrete strength can go on for more than 20 years in the presence of water, but most of the strength development takes place in the early stages. Good working strength is attained in about 28 days and there is little gain after 90 days. Cement grains and water combine chemically to form the hydration product, cement gel (see Chapter 2). This gel can be precipitated only into water-filled voids and occupies about 2·4 times the space occupied by the original cement grains. It follows therefore that for total hydration one volume of cement must have available 1·4 volumes of water, and the gel cannot be precipitated into air-filled spaces. Following this up, Powers[1] has shown that for relative humidity below 80 per cent, little hydration takes place: at this humidity the water-filled capillaries begin to empty, and since hydration-gel can be precipitated only into water-filled spaces, hydration virtually ceases. It is well known from practical experience that concrete develops better strength when stored in water than when stored in air.

Calcium silicate hydrates are relatively stable compounds and are formed over a wide range of temperature, while some of the other hydrates are less stable and are decomposed at higher temperatures. This, together with certain physical changes, results in differences between concrete which is cured at ordinary temperatures and that which is steam-cured.

The fact that the reaction between cement and water takes place in a number of stages, and that not all the reactions occur at the same rate, means that the practical results of such reactions also manifest themselves in stages. For example, there is a 'first set' which takes place soon after wetting. This is generally held to be caused by a rapid solution of the more reactive components of the cement. However, the solubility of such compounds is very low and they mostly dissolve with some decomposition. A rapid precipitation therefore follows, and this, combined with the withdrawal of liquid water and its combination as hydrate, results in a stiffening of the cement paste. Later there is the final set and thereafter a progressive hardening. It is believed that when the final set has taken place the unhydrated cement grains are coated with the hydrated products already formed and that the continued hardening must therefore take place by the diffusion of water through this coating in order to reach the unset cement. It is therefore important, in order to obtain the best conditions for subsequent hardening, that curing conditions should be maintained for a sufficient time.

Having considered briefly the theoretical basis of curing, we may

Lightweight Concrete

summarise by saying that the strength of the concrete is developed by maintaining it in moist conditions for some time. Such treatment may be a prolonged period at ordinary temperature in moist air or in water, or for a shorter term at some elevated temperature.

EXPERIMENTAL WORK

We have now seen that the development of strength in concrete is the consequence of a series of chemical reactions and the progress of such reactions (mainly hydrolysis and hydration) must depend on an excess of water and favourable temperature conditions. Lea[2] and others have shown that the rate of development of strength of concrete is much affected by variations in temperature, particularly at early ages. This is shown in Table 4.1.

Raising the temperature not only increases the rate of reactions which are already taking place, but if high enough may initiate certain reactions which would not otherwise occur. There is therefore a strong argument for curing at elevated temperatures, particularly in the case of precast products. (Clearly, there are difficulties in curing *in situ* concrete with heat, but electrical heating can be used: alternating current can be passed

TABLE 4.1

EFFECT OF STEAM PRESSURE AND DURATION OF STEAMING ON COMPRESSIVE STRENGTH

Steam pressure (*MPa*)	0·46		0·71		1·35		*Period of curing in moist air (days)*	
(*psi*)	68		103		197			
Period of steaming (hr)	18	42	18	42	18	42	7	28
Compressive strength, MPa (psi)								
Cement A	18·3	37·8	36·9	49·2	48·1	52·4	36·4	43·7
	(2650)	(5480)	(5350)	(7140)	(6970)	(7600)	(5280)	(6340)
Cement B	22·9	34·8	35·3	37·7	41·4	48·5	37·8	42·8
	(3330)	(5040)	(5120)	(5470)	(6000)	(7030)	(5480)	(6200)
Cement C	24·5	37·7	32·8	46·0	46·4	46·8	18·9	35·0
	(3550)	(5470)	(4760)	(6670)	(6730)	(6790)	(2740)	(5080)
Cement D	23·9	39·7	38·5	49·4	42·1	46·6	17·7	35·0
	(3460)	(5760)	(5580)	(7160)	(6110)	(6760)	(2560)	(5080)

through the concrete, employing either steel plates on the surface or any reinforcement, as electrodes.)

Experience has shown that by maintaining the concrete at ordinary temperature for a few hours before subjecting it to heat, better strength development takes place. As an explanation of this, it has been suggested that in the very early stages the principal reaction is hydrolysis, which tends to be inhibited by any considerable amount of hydration; as hydration is differentially favoured by elevated temperatures there is advantage in maintaining the product at relatively low temperatures in the early stages. During the subsequent period, whether it is 28 days at ordinary temperature or a few hours of steam-curing, it is the hydration which is the predominant reaction.

In fully compacted, structural lightweight concrete the water absorbed by the aggregate is available to give a certain degree of self-curing of the concrete. Tests by Teychenné[3] have shown that a reduction in the length of the initial period of moist curing has a smaller effect on the strength at 28 days with lightweight concrete than with sand and gravel concrete. The average reduction in the 28-day strength of sand and gravel concrete having only 1 or 2 days of moist-air curing instead of 7 days, before subsequent storage in air at 18 °C and 65 per cent r.h., is about 20 per cent; the corresponding reduction for lightweight aggregate concrete is only about 8 per cent. Figure 4.1 shows that generally there is only a small increase in the 28-day strength if the period of initial moist curing is increased from 2 to 7 days.

It was mentioned earlier that steam-curing can initiate reductions which would not occur, at any rate not perceptibly, at ordinary temperatures. For example, in high-pressure steam-curing, quartz sand will react with lime formed by the setting of the cement to form a cementing material which contributes to the strength development of the product. Moreover, if pozzolanic materials are present, then reaction with lime is greatly enhanced, even at temperatures below 100 °C. Incidentally, a study[2] of the effect of mineralogical composition of aggregates on the tensile strength of mortars cured in high-pressure steam at 150 °C has shown that minerals containing combined silica give substantially lower strength than aggregates containing free silica as flint or quartz. This must be attributed to a reduction in the lime–sand reaction.

It is not difficult to recognise the advantages to be gained from hastening the curing process. Moulds and pallets can be released quickly, thereby reducing the numbers to be carried and maintained. The large absorption of capital, not only in accommodating but in withholding from the market 28 days' production is avoided, and in certain circumstances superior products are obtained. On the other hand, the capital and running cost of steam-curing equipment is considerable.

While a high early strength is obtained by curing at 100 °C, the gain at

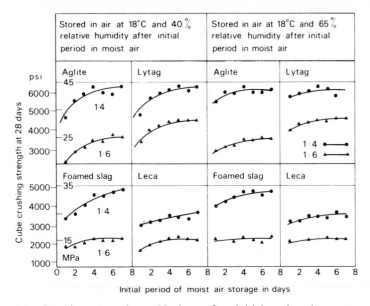

FIG. 4.1 Crushing strength at 28 days after initial moist air storage and subsequent storage at 18 °C and 65 % r.h.

later ages is somewhat reduced, particularly for gravel aggregate concrete, so that the strength which is ultimately attained is rather less than would have been obtained at ordinary air temperature. This loss of strength is somewhat less in the case of lightweight concrete. When the benefit to be gained from the rapid development of strength is such as to make sacrifice of final strength worthwhile, as in the manufacture of precast blocks, low-pressure steam-curing is often used.

While the effect of steam-curing may be influenced by many factors, Nurse[4] has shown that strength can be expressed roughly as a function of the product of temperature and the duration of steam-curing. Figure 4.2 shows the time–temperature product expressed as a percentage of the strength of concrete attained at 3 days at normal curing (18 °C).

The relationship shown in Fig. 4.2 applies in a general way to concretes made from aggregates which are not reactive at low-pressure curing temperatures (50–100 °C), but some aggregates have pozzolanic properties and will produce concrete with enhanced strength even under 100 °C. As has been mentioned elsewhere, under the conditions of high-pressure steam-curing considerable reaction can take place between lime and quartz, and curing under the latter conditions may then provide in a few hours strengths higher than those which would be attained after 28 days by curing at ordinary temperature. According to Lea[2] there is in general not much

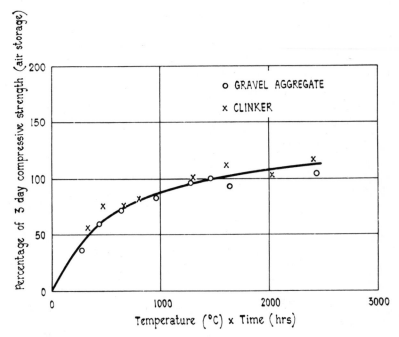

FIG. 4.2   Relationship between strength development and time–temperature in steam curing of concrete.

extra gain in strength to be obtained by curing at gauge pressures above 150 psi (1 MPa) for periods of autoclaving, at the maximum pressure, of more than about 8–12 hours; at higher pressures, strengths sufficiently close to the maximum are obtained in 6–8 hours. Autoclaving at pressures below 100 psi (0·7 MPa) does not result in such high strengths except for extended steaming periods. These figures can only be a rough guide for they are influenced by the cement, the aggregate, the concrete mix, and by additions such as ground silica.

Low-pressure steam-curing has little effect on drying shrinkage, but high-pressure curing (autoclaving) reduces the shrinkage to half or even less of what it would be after normal moist air-curing. The reason for this reduction of drying shrinkage of cement products when cured at high-pressure may be explained briefly as follows.

Set cement, being composed principally of hydrated silicates, is technically a gel, and as such displays the characteristic gel-like property of swelling on absorbing water and shrinking on drying out. In a dense concrete of the conventional type, in which gravel or crushed rock is the aggregate, the latter, because of its rigidity, restrains in a large measure the alternating expansion and contraction to which set cement is prone when exposed to changes of moisture. Such a concrete typically has a low drying shrinkage and moisture expansion. Lightweight aggregates being less rigid impart less restraint to the movements of the cement matrix; concretes made from such aggregates show somewhat higher drying shrinkage. In the case of aerated concrete, where little or no aggregate is used apart from a fine filler, very high shrinkage is the rule *unless high-pressure steam-curing is used.* During the process of such curing, whether in aerated or aggregate concrete, mineral changes take place in the matrix which result in its transformation from a gel-like structure to one of more crystalline character; the latter has greater dimensional stability, a property which is reflected in the concrete of which it is a part. This is further discussed in Chapter 5.

Apart from its effect on strength and drying shrinkage, high-pressure steam-curing improves the resistance of concrete to attack by sulphate water, making it almost completely resistant to the action of sodium sulphate and calcium sulphate, and increasing greatly its resistance to magnesium sulphate.

This is illustrated in the Table 4.2, due to Lea.[2]

TABLE 4.2

TIME REQUIRED FOR EXPANSION OF 1:10 CEMENT–SAND MORTARS IN SULPHATE SOLUTION

Solution	Linear expansion (%)	Temperature of saturated steam-curing (24 hr)				
		21°C	100°C	125°C	150°C	175°C
2·1% Na_2SO_4	0·02	3 days	10 days	1 year	1 year	1 year
Saturated $CaSO_4$	0·02	7 days	18 days	1 year	1 year	1 year
1·8% $MgSO_4$	0·10	5 days	13 days	25 days	25 days	65 days
	0·20	6 days	32 days	75 days	130 days	1 year

PRACTICAL CURING METHODS

Air curing
When precast concrete in the form of blocks or other units is air-cured it is usually stored in the yard without cover of any kind. This is of course the easiest way of approaching the objective, because the concrete would have to be stockpiled in any case. But the curing conditions are no more certain than the weather. In dry periods the units may have to be repeatedly hosed down in order to maintain the moisture ambience required for curing.

Sometimes the stacks are covered with tarpaulins or polythene sheets to help stabilise the curing conditions. A much more satisfactory arrangement is to store the units indoors, in warehouses maintained at high humidity. Because of the high cost this is rarely used. In any event the products should be maintained in a damp condition for 28 days and thereafter allowed to dry out. This drying out period is of considerable importance, although it is rarely enforced, as dried blocks lead to less subsequent trouble from cracking. In other words it is better for the blocks to dry out in the stockyard than when they have already been built into the wall.

In the case of *in situ* work the concrete obviously cannot be treated in the same way as the precast units. With such concrete, rapid drying out can be prevented, or at any rate minimised, by spraying the surface with 'curing compounds' with a view to providing a moisture-proof film. More often the surfaces are covered with wet hessian sacks or other suitable covering material such as polythene sheeting.

Low-pressure steam-curing

As we saw in an earlier part of this chapter, there is much virtue in curing concrete at elevated temperatures. The method of steam-curing most widely used for precast concrete products is that described as low-pressure curing, that is curing at atmospheric pressure, the temperature being in the range 60–80 °C, though in North America 90 °C or even higher temperatures are often used. Curing may be operated as a continuous process or more commonly as an intermittent one. In the continuous process the plant consists of a tunnel through which the blocks or other concrete wares are transported on bogies. Saturated steam at about 0·1–0·3 MPa (about 20–50 psi) is led into the tunnel and the condensation, as well as the sensible heat of the steam, maintains a high temperature. In order to minimise the loss of steam and indeed to avoid heat loss generally, the ends of the tunnel are closed by flap-doors which permit the entry of a bogie at one end and the exit of another at the other. The rate of travel of the bogies through the tunnel is regulated to give the goods the required period of exposure to the steam. Continuous curing as distinct from intermittent kilns has the merit that, owing to the very considerable thermal capacity of the tunnel, the temperature is more or less constant; once the structure is heated up the input of heat is virtually limited to that required to replace the sensible heat carried out of the tunnel in the concrete and to make up for radiant heat loss.

In the intermittent steam-curing process the goods are stacked in chambers or kilns into which steam is introduced. These may be quite small, but may sometimes be as much as 4 m (13 ft) wide and 7 m (23 ft) deep or more, and may hold many tons of concrete. In a modern works the goods are set in the chambers by fork-lift trucks. A number of such chambers are employed simultaneously as a battery in which one chamber is being filled while another is being emptied, the remainder standing at various stages of the curing cycle (Fig. 4.3). The cycle times of each chamber in the battery can be controlled by preset time-switches which operate the steam valves by relays. The principal disadvantage of this method is that the chambers fall to near normal temperatures between discharging and recharging and the heat represented by the thermal

Fig. 4.3　A battery of steam curing chambers being loaded by a fork-lift truck.

capacity of the kilns is largely lost. The intermittent method however has the advantage of flexibility in that with fluctuating output only the number of kilns required at any one time needs to be brought into service. Moreover, the use of separate chambers enables close control of the temperature pattern to be maintained. This is of considerable importance since the rate of temperature rise has a significant effect on the quality of the concrete.

A great deal of care is necessary in designing the curing kilns, particularly with respect to the type and position of the steam jets, if the best results and the highest efficiency are to be obtained. For example, it is now believed that steam introduced at ceiling level gives more uniform moisture distribution than when introduced at floor level, while very high jet velocity may damage the goods, particularly if there is entrained water. For the highest efficiency the steam input should be dry and saturated or slightly superheated.

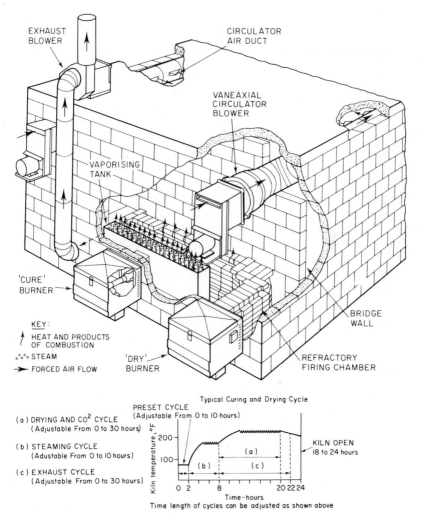

FIG. 4.4   Typical carbonation process, shown schematically.

As mentioned earlier, it is customary to maintain the concrete at ambient air temperature for a period of a few hours after casting before commencing the steam heating. The length of this period varies considerably but is most frequently about 3 hours.

The temperature rise of the concrete lags behind that of the kiln in the early stages, but gradually gains on the latter until they finally reach equilibrium at about 70–80 °C. At this point the steam is shut off and the temperature is allowed to fall slowly, preferably at about 3–5 °C per hour. In this way the 'soaking' period will last for about 16 hours.

A modified form of low-pressure curing plant employs carbon dioxide from the combustion gases of the steam-raising equipment. This is intended to effect carbonation of the concrete and thereby to avoid subsequent 'carbonation shrinkage' (see Chapter 2).

It is not easy to see how this amount and concentration of carbon dioxide can be very effective in bringing about any significant degree of

FIG. 4.5 A battery of carbonation units.

carbonation, yet one proprietary design alone has been installed in some 250 curing units by 30 block-making companies in the USA. It is clear however that opinion in the United States concrete industry is sharply divided on the effectiveness of artificial carbonation in limiting shrinkage. If the process results in a considerable carbonation of the free lime normally present in concrete it should not be used with reinforced concrete units, since the protection of the reinforcing steel against corrosion depends largely on a high concentration of free lime in the concrete, i.e. high alkalinity.

Figure 4.4 shows schematically one design of carbonation equipment. Figure 4.5 gives the general appearance of an actual battery of such units.

High-pressure steam-curing

By high-pressure steam-curing is meant curing in an autoclave at pressures between 0·7 and 1·2 MPa (100–170 psi). The autoclaves are cylinders 2–4 m (6–12 ft) in diameter and 15–45 m (50–150 ft) in length, and may have doors at both ends, which is a great advantage. However, as the doors must be very elaborate in order to combine easy opening with complete safety, these are in consequence very expensive. Therefore, autoclaves more often than not have doors at one end only, and these are of the quarter-turn or breech-lock pattern. A battery of such autoclaves is shown in Fig. 4.6. Since the autoclaves operate at pressures considerably above atmospheric pressure, they cannot be run continuously.

FIG. 4.6   High-pressure steam chambers (autoclaves).

Before the concrete is placed in the autoclave, it is customary to allow a hardening period of a few hours at normal temperature, although for some products manufacturers submit the goods to low-pressure curing for 3–6 hours before transferring them to the autoclave. Premature steaming at high pressure results in poorer development of strength and often hair-cracking.

When the concrete has been placed in the autoclave and the door securely locked the steam is admitted and the pressure is increased slowly; usually it takes up to 5–6 hours to reach maximum pressure. The time of treatment at maximum pressure ranges from 4 to 18 hours according to the nature of the goods, the longer periods being given to aerated concrete.

Quite rapid release of pressure is usually employed in commercial practice for quick drying of the concrete. It is claimed that rapid pressure drop from 0·8 to 1·1 MPa (110–155 psi) to atmospheric pressure in the case of lightweight concrete is often sufficient to dry the blocks down to near air-dry condition. On the other hand, it is held by some that rapid release of pressure, particularly with aerated concrete, may cause damage by creating fissures. It has been found that if the release of pressure is controlled to take place over 10–15 min, this gives adequate drying without adverse effect on lightweight concrete blocks.

There is no doubt that both the capital cost and the subsequent running expense of autoclaving is high, yet over the past 20 years some 250 blocks plants in the USA have changed over from low-pressure to high-pressure curing. For a number of reasons Europe, including the UK, has been slow to adopt autoclaving, except of course in the manufacture of aerated concrete.

A modification in autoclave plant, introduced in the USA some years ago is the 'boilerless autoclave'. In principle this is closer to the ordinary domestic pressure cooker than to conventional autoclave equipment, in as much as the goods are placed in the chamber with a quantity of water and heat is applied from without. In practice the water is heated by circulating hot oil through coils within the autoclave, the oil having been heated externally. Several autoclaves are operated as a battery and the hot oil can be diverted from one autoclave to another, according to the state of the respective vessels within the heating cycle. Moreover, the hot water (at about 360 °C) is recovered from each operating cycle and stored in a condensate recovery tank for use in the next autoclave to be charged. A plant of this kind lends itself to automatic control.

Summarising, we may say that in order to develop strength and other desirable properties, concrete after setting must be maintained in conditions which are conducive to the continuance of certain essential chemical reactions. Maintenance of such conditions is termed curing. Curing may be simple storage in damp conditions, low-pressure steam-curing, or high-pressure steam-curing (autoclaving). Autoclaving gives very high strength in a very short period and in some cases gives higher strength than would be realised by air-curing. Moreover, in most instances the drying shrinkage is much reduced. Low-pressure steam-curing does not affect the drying shrinkage but gives high early strength, although the strength of the concrete at later ages is usually less than would be obtained by air-curing in moist air.

REFERENCES

1. Powers, T. C. (1947). 'A Discussion of Cement Hydration in Relation to Curing of Concrete'. *Proc. Highways Research Board*, HIRPA, Vol. 27.
2. Lea, F. M. (1956). '*The Chemistry of Cement and Concrete*, Second Edition, Edward Arnold, London.
3. Teychenné, D. C. (1967). 'Structural Concrete made with Lightweight Aggregates', *Concrete*, **1**. (Also Building Research Station, Paper No. 48.)
4. Nurse, R. W. (1949). 'Steam-Curing of Concrete', *Mag. Concr. Res.*, **1**(2).

CHAPTER FIVE

Drying Shrinkage and Cracking

SUMMARY

All cement products show some small changes in their dimensions in response to changes in moisture conditions. When concrete is first dried it undergoes a shrinkage, usually termed initial shrinkage, *and on subsequent wetting and drying shows alternate expansion and contraction, generally called* reversible moisture movement.

The practical result of shrinkage is the tension stress which is set up in restrained structures which, should it exceed the tensile strength of the concrete, may lead to cracking.

The shrinkage of concrete blocks and other units can be reduced by curing these in high-pressure steam. Precautions can be taken in the design of buildings to minimise the effect of shrinkage.

NATURE OF SHRINKAGE MOVEMENTS AND STRESSES

All cement products show some small changes in their volume in response to changes in moisture conditions. Though small in magnitude, these changes are of considerable importance. The mechanism of shrinkage in cement and its products has been dealt with very comprehensively by Lea,[1] but for the present purpose a much more concise presentation will be sufficient.

Shrinkage is affected mainly by the quantity of cement paste in the mix, the quality of the cement paste, and the type of aggregate used. Neat cement paste, being a gel, has a high drying shrinkage, so that, all other things being equal, the richer the mix the greater is the shrinkage. Gravel concrete with its hard dense aggregate usually shows relatively small shrinkage, the movements due to the cement being restrained in a large measure by the rigidity of the aggregate. In the case of lightweight aggregate concrete, however, where weaker and less rigid aggregates are used, much less restraint is imposed on the cement paste, and this is reflected in the higher drying shrinkage in these concretes—generally about twice that observed in heavy aggregate concrete. This is the general case but research[2] has shown that a few natural aggregates have themselves marked drying shrinkage, so that instead of restraining the shrinkage they in fact contribute to the shrinkage of the concrete in which they are used.

55

Aerated concrete, which is really an aerated rich mortar, has a very high shrinkage *unless the products are high-pressure steam-cured;* by this treatment changes of a physicochemical nature take place in the cement minerals, which in turn lead to a reduction in drying shrinkage. This is further discussed in the chapters dealing with curing and aerated concrete.

Concrete when first dried undergoes a shrinkage which is usually termed 'initial drying shrinkage'; and on subsequent wetting and drying shows alternate expansion and contraction, generally called 'reversible moisture movement'. The increase in dimensions due to wetting prior to further drying is known as 'wetting expansion'. Generally the expansion which occurs on rewetting does not result in its reaching the original dimension, so that the initial drying shrinkage is usually greater than the subsequent moisture movement. In some Standards which include limits for moisture movements, a greater tolerance is allowed for drying shrinkage than for wetting expansion. This reflects the general experience of the dimensional behaviour of concrete under the influence of moisture changes so far as dense heavy aggregate concrete is concerned. However, work in recent years has demonstrated that because of the physical character of lightweight concretes, these in many respects behave differently from conventional heavy concrete. Response to moisture change is such a case. Records over the years in Britain have shown that with lightweight concrete the reversible moisture expansion is frequently as high as, or in some instances higher than the initial drying shrinkage. This has been recognised in the most recent revisions of BS 2028 'Precast concrete blocks'[3] and BS 1180 'Concrete bricks and fixing bricks',[4] in which the reversible moisture expansion requirement has been omitted as not meaningful, except for products made from clinker aggregate. The object of retaining the moisture expansion requirement in the latter case is to reveal the presence of unsound or chemically unstable clinker, but it is doubtful if this requirement will be long retained, as the occurrence of unsound clinker is very infrequent (see Chapter 8).

For many years the British Standard test for drying shrinkage provided for the measurement of the shortening which took place in a block or prism in the course of drying from complete saturation (4 days immersion in water) to oven dryness (17 per cent r.h. and 50 °C). But testing houses frequently found anomalies arising from this procedure and it was found that in routine testing the level of 17 per cent r.h. was difficult to maintain. As the result of research, a rather more elaborate method of conditioning the specimens was evolved. This is described in great detail in BS 2028.[2] However, although the procedure has been amended, the original basic principle remains the same. In practice, of course, the concrete will seldom, if ever, experience the very great change of conditions represented by saturation followed by oven drying, but the test is not intended to reproduce practice but to be an index to behaviour.

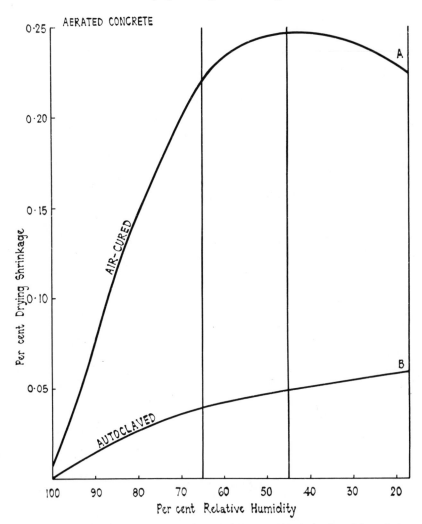

FIG. 5.1   Relationship between drying, shrinkage and relative humidity of air-cured and autoclaved aerated concrete.

Work done at the British Building Research Establishment has shown that lightweight concretes can be divided into two groups with respect to their behaviour during drying, those which have been autoclave-cured and those which have been air-cured.[5] The autoclaved products show an almost straight-line relationship between the humidity level and the amount of drying shrinkage, while the air-cured products, apart from having a higher drying shrinkage, show their maximum shrinkage at about 40–50 per cent r.h. This is believed to be due to carbonation and it is suggested that this difference in behaviour results from two complementary causes:

(1) Autoclaved concrete is bonded by well-crystallised tobermorite which is less vulnerable to carbon dioxide than the disorganised form of silicate characteristic of air-cured material.

(2) The favourable conditions for carbonation provided by the conditions 45 per cent r.h.

Summing up, it may be said that autoclaved products show lower shrinkage when dried at 45 per cent r.h. than at 17 per cent r.h. This is illustrated in Fig. 5.1.

The practical result of shrinkage is that tensile stresses are set up in the concrete if it is dimensionally constrained, for example, in plain concrete such as block walls and *in situ* work, and in reinforced concrete, particularly in hyperstatic structures. If the shrinkage stresses exceed the tensile strength of the concrete, cracking results. The shrinkage stresses can be relieved to some extent by the elastic extensibility and creep of the concrete.

In reinforced concrete the presence of steel reinforcement cannot prevent shrinkage cracks, but ensures that these are of lesser width and more closely spaced than in plain concrete where the formation of a single crack of considerable width can relieve tensile stresses caused by shrinkage along a corresponding length of concrete.

In prestressed concrete, shrinkage cracks are avoided by the introduction of an initial compression in the concrete. Dimensional changes due to shrinkage of the concrete merely reduce that compression somewhat but for the appropriate classes of structure (see Chapter 10), not sufficiently to result in cracking in the tension zone of the concrete, even when combined with losses in prestress due to other causes.

BLOCK WALLS

Unless precautions are taken to limit the amount of cracking or to distribute it in the form of fine inconspicuous cracks, the appearance of the building may be marred. Shrinkage cracking in walls generally occurs more or less vertically, and they appear for the most part as a result of stress concentration where the cross-section of the wall is suddenly reduced, as for example above or below the corners of windows and above door openings. Cracking may take one or other of two forms—that running straight through the block and joint continuously (crack A in Fig. 5.2) or it may take a zigzag path following the joints (crack B in Fig. 5.2). Which of these two forms of crack actually occurs in any instance depends very largely on

FIG. 5.2   Typical cracking in block wall construction.

the relative strength of the blocks and the mortar in which they are set, as well as on the bond strength between block and mortar. Since the form of cracking shown at B is more easily repaired, it is better to make the joint weaker in tension than the block itself. Moreover, there is the added advantage with the weaker mortar that this permits the blocks to shrink individually, thereby giving relaxation of stresses by a redistribution of the internal forces in the wall. Thus there is a tendency for hair-cracks to form around each block, rather than for wider and more conspicuous cracks to occur at greater intervals.

It is necessary to consider the amount of shrinkage which might be expected to take place in given circumstances. Weak points in a wall are openings such as windows and doors. These in house construction will usually occur at intervals of about 3–4 m (10–12 ft). With a maximum permissible shrinkage of 0·06 per cent the total possible shrinkage over 4 m is about 2·4 mm ($\frac{3}{32}$ in.), assuming a moisture change from the saturated to the oven-dried condition. If this total movement were to occur as one crack it would be disfiguring to the wall, but such a moisture change is unlikely to occur, and because of this and other alleviating conditions the total crack width rarely exceeds a quarter of the maximum possible, and would thus be 0·6 mm in the above example. The magnitude of the drying shrinkage varies according to the composition of the concrete, the nature of the curing treatment it has received before delivery and the moisture changes to which it is submitted.

The limits allowed in the current BS 2028:1968 for drying shrinkage are shown in Table 5.1. American standards are discussed in Chapter 21.

TABLE 5.1
LIMITS ON DRYING SHRINKAGE ALLOWED IN BS 2028:1968

Block type	Average compressive strength		Block density (kg/m^3)	Maximum drying shrinkage (%)
	(MPa)	*(psi)*		
A	Less than 10·5	Less than 1500	All	0·05
	10·5 and above	1500 and above	All	0·06
B	Less than 7·0	Less than 1000	Over 625	0·07
			625 and less	0·09
	7·0 and above	1000 and above	All	0·08
C	All blocks		Over 625	0·08
			625 and less	0·09

Formal compliance of a type of block with the requirements of the appropriate British or other national standard does not imply that there will be no risk of shrinkage cracking in a wall. It does mean, however, that the blocks have been made in such a manner that the coefficient of shrinkage, as judged by the appropriate standard test, has been reduced as far as practicable within the economic framework of commercial production and with the present understanding of cause and effect. Precautions must likewise be taken by the *user* to keep down the shrinkage and to distribute stresses in such a way that the incidence of serious cracking is reduced to a minimum. The following precautions should be taken and are based on the British *Building Research Station Digest No.* 6.[6]

(1) *Storage.* Blocks should be kept on the site in such a manner that they will be reasonably dry when required for use. If they must be held in stock for any considerable time, the stacking should be such as to permit air circulation in order to assist further drying, and they should be covered over with polythene sheeting or other suitable material to keep out the rain.

(2) *Wetting.* When being laid, some types of blocks need wetting on the surface in order to reduce their 'suction'; otherwise the mortar is dehydrated and the blocks are difficult to lay. Such wetting should be done sparingly and then only when absolutely necessary; the body of the blocks should on no account be saturated with water.

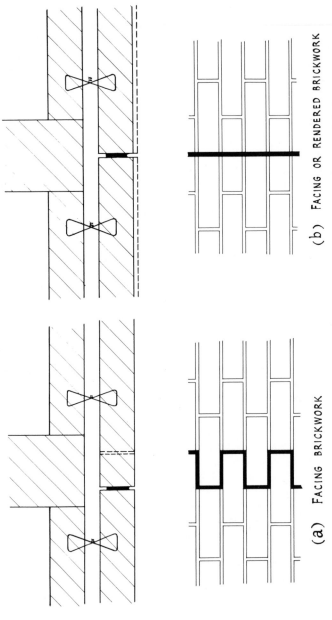

(a) FACING BRICKWORK (b) FACING OR RENDERED BRICKWORK

FIG. 5.3 Arrangements of vertical joints in walls of domestic buildings to allow for shrinkage movement.

(3) *Mortar*. As mentioned earlier, the mortar should be relatively weak, a mix of one part of Portland cement with 2 parts hydrated lime and 8 parts of sand (by volume) is generally suitable. A somewhat stronger mix (1:1:5–6) may be desirable when work is being carried out in winter or in special conditions. Alternatively, one part of Portland cement and 8 parts of sand by volume with a plasticiser may be used instead of the 1:2:8 mix, or one part of Portland cement and 5 or 6 parts of sand by volume, with a plasticiser, in place of the 1:1:5–6 mix. Mixes with a lower proportion of cement (e.g. 1:3:10–12) are suitable for internal walls built in summer. There is in practice a wide latitude in mortar composition which can be used without materially affecting the strength of the wall. (For a discussion on the strength and stability of walls generally and the effect of mortar strength on wall strength, see the British *Building Research Station Digest No.* 61.[7]) Increasing use is being made of special masonry cement–sand mixes and of ready-mixed sand–lime mortar.

(4) *Design*. Where the design of the building permits, dividing the wall into suitable lengths or panels with freedom from restraint at the ends will reduce the risk of cracking. This may take the form of continuous vertical contraction joints formed at suitable intervals along the length of the wall. The design details of such contraction joints are shown in Fig. 5.3. The joints may with advantage be situated behind rainwater pipes or as a dividing feature between the individual houses constituting a terrace. In order to exclude wind and rain from the gap which is formed, some kind of barrier or stopping must be used. The required effectiveness of such exclusion will depend on the design of the wall, for example, whether it is a cavity wall or a solid wall.

In facing work, the joint may be caulked with a mastic compound; this is

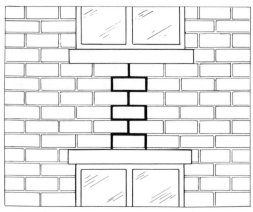

FIG. 5.4   Dry sand joints left to accommodate shrinkage movement.

one of the most satisfactory methods. In rendered work, a vertical damp-course felt may be set in the gap as the wall is built and the rendering brought up to the projecting felt on both sides of the joint. As an alternative, giving absolute exclusion of wind and rain, a V-section strip of copper may be fixed to the wall so as to bridge the gap, the limbs of the folded strip being subsequently embedded in the rendering. This method gives a neat and pleasing appearance but is rather expensive and quite difficult to fix in position. The latter methods are of course suitable only for straight joints.

Yet another method is to make a vertical break at the mid-point of the windows between sills and lintels, leaving dry joints to be mortared up later, after the structure has ceased to shrink. This is shown in Fig. 5.4.

In most cases cracking is important in blockwork only because of its effect on appearance. It does not in general affect the structural stability materially nor in cavity walls does it lead to rain-penetration. The cracks usually develop, if at all, during the first summer after building.

REFERENCES

1. Lea, F. M. (1970). *The Chemistry of Cement and Concrete*, Third Edition, Edward Arnold, London.
2. Snowdon, L. C. (1961). 'Moisture Movement of Natural Aggregate and its Effect on Concrete'. RILEM Symposium on 'The Durability of Concrete', Prague.
3. British Standard, BS 2028.1364:1968 (amended 1970). 'Precast Concrete Blocks', British Standards Institution.
4. British Standard, BS 1180:1970. Concrete Bricks and Fixing Bricks, British Standards Institution.
5. Kinniburgh, W. (1960). 'Comparison of Drying Shrinkage of Autoclaved and Air-cured Concrete at Different Humidities', RILEM Symposium on 'Steam-Cured Lightweight Concrete', Gothenburg.
6. Building Research Station Digest No. 6 (First series) Revised 1959. 'The Avoidance of Cracking in Masonry Construction of Concrete or Sand–Lime Bricks', Building Research Station, Garston, Watford.
7. Building Research Station Digest No. 61 (Second series) 1965. 'Strength of Brickwork, Blockwork and Concrete Walls', Building Research Station, Garston, Watford.

CHAPTER SIX

Functional Properties of Lightweight Concrete

SUMMARY

The properties of lightweight concrete considered in this chapter are: thermal insulation, fire protection, durability, water absorption, rain penetration, and acoustic characteristics.

Properties are defined, tests are described and typical values given.

THERMAL INSULATION

A difference of temperature between the inside and the outside of a building must result in a transfer of heat from the warmer to the cooler zone, so that there is a progressive difference of temperature across the thickness of the wall; the steepness of the temperature drop is termed the temperature gradient. Any wall separating these zones will offer some resistance to, but will not completely prevent, the flow of heat. Thermal insulation may be regarded as the coefficient of resistance to heat transfer.

In recent years, even in Britain and other countries of mild climate, more attention has been given than formerly to reducing fuel consumption whilst maintaining or improving comfort conditions in buildings. To this end effort has been concentrated on improving the efficiency of heating appliances and the thermal insulation of buildings. In this book we are not concerned with heating equipment but only with the properties of materials of construction, and here in particular with the conductivity of lightweight concrete.

One of the striking features of lightweight concrete is the relatively high thermal insulating values which they exhibit, the insulation being more or less inversely proportional to the density of the material. Most inorganic structural building materials have very similar chemical composition, principally a mixture of silicates, and so have very much the same true density and thermal conductivity. Differences in the apparent density and the effective thermal conductivity of concretes arise from differences in their porosity. In other words, voids filled with air contribute nothing to the weight of the concrete, while the overall conductivity of a porous concrete is the resultant of the thermal conductivity of the silicate structure and that of the air contained in it. It is for this reason that the thermal conductivity of the concrete is related to the apparent density.

Because thermal conductivity, or rather insulation, is so much a feature of lightweight concrete, it is essential that engineers and architects should be in a position to assess the value of these materials in this important respect when designing and specifying. For this reason it is considered that a short section on thermal insulation will assist in interpreting the figures quoted for the various classes of lightweight concrete.

Reference must be made to textbooks of physics for a fundamental consideration of thermal conductivity, but an adequate exposition of the subject for engineers, architects and builders has been given by Handisyde and Melluish.[1] In this chapter discussion will be confined largely to what is necessary for the application of the quantitative information on lightweight concrete materials given elsewhere in this book.

Definition of terms

The following are definitions of some of the terms which are used in thermal studies and referred to in the literature.[1-3]

Calorie (cal). For practical purposes this is the quantity of heat required to raise the temperature of one gram of water through 1 °C. A kilogram calorie is 1000 calories.

British thermal unit (Btu). For practical purposes this is the quantity of heat required to raise the temperature of one pound of water through 1 °F.

Conduction. This is the method by which heat passes through a solid material or flows from one material to another in intimate contact with it. (Air is a poor conductor so that lightweight concretes, which are porous, and thus contain much still air, are good insulators. It is easy to see why thermal insulation is closely related to the density of the material, as the more air it contains the lighter it is.)

Convection. Unlike solids, gases alter very markedly in density with changes in temperature. The lighter gas thus tends to rise over the heavier, so that currents, termed 'convection currents' are set up. The rising gas, being warmer, transports its sensible heat to the upper zone of the space in which it is circulating. Transfer of heat in this way is called 'convection'. In the definitions given above it was implied that conduction is a characteristic of solids only. In fact, gases do conduct heat, but except in very narrow spaces, convection is so predominantly the mode of heat transfer in gases that it is convenient to consider conduction to be essentially a property of solids.

Radiation. When heat is emitted from the surface of a solid material and transmitted as energy across a space, the process is termed 'radiation'. Radiant energy is to be regarded as a wave motion, the wavelength of which depends on the temperature of the radiating surface.

Heat is *conducted* through a wall and dissipated at the surface partly by *radiation* and partly by *convection*.

Thermal conductivity (k). This is the quantity of heat in the steady-state* condition passing in unit time through an area forming part of a slab of the uniform material of infinite extent and with flat and parallel faces. It is proportional to the area A and to the difference in temperature θ between the faces, and inversely proportional to the thickness L of the slab. Thus,

$$q = \frac{kA(\theta_{s_1} - \theta_{s_2})}{L},$$

where q is the quantity of heat flowing in unit time under the conditions prevailing at that time, and θ_{s_1} and θ_{s_2} denote the temperatures at the inner and outer surfaces, respectively.

Expressed somewhat differently, thermal conductivity is a measure of the ability of a material to conduct heat, and in metric units is expressed as heat flow (in watts) through a square metre of the material when a temperature difference of 1 °C is maintained between opposite surfaces of a metre thickness of the material. The thermal conductivity k is expressed in the following metric dimensions:

$$(\text{W/m}^2) \times (\text{m/}^{\circ}\text{C}) \qquad \text{or} \qquad \text{W/m } ^{\circ}\text{C}$$

Time, which is explicitly stated in the imperial system of units, is hidden in the SI expression: when using the imperial units, the watt, being a *rate* of heat flow, is replaced by Btu/h, and the unit of thermal conductivity is thus:

$$\text{Btu in/ft}^2 \text{ h } ^{\circ}\text{F.}$$

Thermal resistivity ($1/k$). In calculations, it is more convenient to use the reciprocal value of thermal conductivity, i.e. thermal resistivity. The thermal conductivity is a measure of the ability of a material to conduct heat, so thermal resistivity expresses its ability to resist the transfer of heat.

In metric units $1/k$ is given in m °C/W, in imperial units in ft^2 h °F/Btu in.

Thermal conductance (C). This is the thermal transmission through unit area of a material or of a structure divided by the temperature difference between the hot and cold faces in steady-state conditions. It is expressed thus: W/m^2 °K in SI units, and Btu/ft^2 h °F, in imperial units.

Thermal transmittance (U). This is the thermal transmission through unit area of a given structure divided by the difference between the effective ambient temperature on either side of the structure in steady-state conditions. Transmittance differs from conductance because the

---

* If the quantity of heat flowing into a body is exactly equal to the quantity flowing from it, then, although the temperature will differ at different points within the body, the temperature of any given point will remain constant. The condition is termed the 'steady state' and refers only to those cases where the temperature at any given point within the body is independent of time. Therefore, the quantity of heat in such a body is also independent of time.

temperature is measured at different positions. For conductance the temperature difference is that between the surfaces of the material on opposite faces of the structure; for transmittance, it is the difference between the effective ambient temperature on either side of the structure. Thus the thermal transmittance U of a structure involves both the thermal conductance and the surface coefficients of the structure. In SI units it is expressed in W/m^2 °C, and in imperial units in Btu/ft^2 h °F.

Standard U values.[3] In the past, U-values have been obtained by a variety of methods—by measurement, by adjustment of measured values, or by calculation from the thermal resistance of component parts. As a result, different sources often quoted different values for the same construction. In fact, the U-value of a structure does vary to some extent from one situation to another; amongst other things it depends upon the moisture content of the component materials, wind speed and internal room conditions.

In order to provide a common basis for comparing constructions or for meeting a stated figure specified by the client or by regulations, standard U-values are required and the use of standardised values is now accepted.

Standard U-values are calculated from the resistances of the component parts of a structure; these in turn are based upon standard assumptions about moisture contents of materials, rates of heat transfer to surfaces by radiation and convection, and air-flow rates in ventilated spaces. The effects of heat bridging through the structure also have to be taken in a standard manner.

The thermal transmittance of a building element is obtained by combining the thermal resistance of its component parts and the adjacent air layers. Thermal transmittances of walls and roofs composed of parallel slabs are obtained simply by adding thermal resistances and taking the reciprocal, thus;

$$U = \frac{1}{R_{si} + R_1 + R_2 + \cdots R_a + R_{so}},$$

Where U = thermal transmittance; R_{si} = inside surface resistance; R_1, R_2 = thermal resistance of structural components; R_a = air space resistance; and R_{so} = outside surface resistance.

Inside surface resistance R_{si} for concrete walls can be taken as $0.123 \, m^2$ °C/W $(0.7 \, ft^2$ h °F/Btu). Outside surface resistance R_{so} for concrete walls can be taken as (for sheltered, normal, and severe exposure, respectively) 0.08, 0.055, and $0.03 \, m^2$ °C/W $(0.45$, 0.31, and $0.17 \, ft^2$ h °F/Btu).

Heat bridging. The inclusion of a metal rod or other member of high conductivity in a concrete masonry structure increases the heat loss. In simple cases, the thermal resistance can be found by calculating the thermal transmittances of the different portions of the construction separately and combining them in proportion to their relative areas.[1]

THERMAL CONDUCTIVITY VALUES AND THEIR MEASUREMENT

Thermal conductivity values for insulating materials can be obtained from the *IHVE Guide, Book* A. These materials are intended for use in dry situations and their thermal conductivity in dry air conditions is appropriate.

For materials commonly used as masonry, such as lightweight concrete, there is a relationship between bulk dry density and thermal conductivity, but the effect of moisture must be considered. Table 6.1 sets out for a range of dry densities some average thermal conductivities at moisture contents appropriate to concrete, either protected from the rain or exposed to it, e.g. in the inner and outer leaves of cavity walling. It should be noted, however, that an outer leaf with external rendering is regarded as protected from rain.

TABLE 6.1
THERMAL CONDUCTIVITIES OF CONCRETES

Bulk density		Thermal conductivities			
(kg/m^3)	(lb/ft^3)	$(W/m°C)$		$(Btu\,in/ft^2\,h\,°F)$	
		3% moisture (protected)	5% moisture (exposed)	3% moisture (protected)	5% moisture (exposed)
400	25	0·15	0·16	1·03	1·10
500	31	0·17	0·18	1·17	1·24
600	38	0·19	0·20	1·31	1·38
700	44	0·21	0·23	1·45	1·59
800	50	0·23	0·26	1·59	1·80
900	56	0·27	0·30	1·87	2·07
1 000	63	0·30	0·33	2·07	2·28
1 100	69	0·34	0·38	2·35	2·63
1 200	75	0·38	0·42	2·63	2·91
1 300	81	0·44	0·49	3·04	3·39
1 400	88	0·51	0·57	3·53	3·95
1 500	94	0·59	0·65	4·08	4·50
1 600	100	0·66	0·73	4·57	5·05
1 700	106	0·76	0·84	5·26	5·82
1 800	113	0·87	0·96	6·02	6·65
1 900	119	0·90	1·09	6·23	7·55
2 000	125	1·13	1·24	7·83	8·59
2 100	131	1·28	1·40	8·87	9·70
2 200	138	1·45	1·60	10·04	11·08
2 300	144	1·63	1·80	11·29	12·47
2 400	150	1·83	2·00	12·68	13·86

TABLE 6.2
MOISTURE FACTORS FOR USE WITH TABLE 6.1

Moisture content by volume	1	3	5	10	15	20	25
Moisture factor	1·3	1·6	1·75	2·1	2·35	2·55	2·75

In conditions of driving rain and where condensation occurs, much higher moisture can be expected to occur. Table 6.2 gives moisture factors that can be used to adjust the values shown in Table 6.1 to other moisture contents. In applying these factors it must be borne in mind that the figures of Table 6.1 already incorporate a moisture factor. Thus, to calculate the conductivity of a material of 1000 kg/m³ (63 pcf) density with a moisture content of 25 per cent, select from Table 6.1 the value for 1000 kg/m³ at 3 per cent, i.e. 0·30 W/m/°C, divide this by the factor it already includes and multiply it by the factor for the required moisture content (Table 6.2).

TABLE 6.3
THERMAL TRANSMITTANCE (*U*-VALUE) OF SOME WALL SYSTEMS

System	$W/m^2 °C$	$Btu/ft^2 \ h \ °F$
Solid wall, unplastered, 220 mm (8½ in.) brick	2·2	0·39
Solid wall, with 16 mm (0·63 in.) plaster on inside face, wall thickness 220 mm (8½ in.), lightweight plaster	1·8	0·32
Same as above but with dense plaster	2·0	0·35
Cavity wall (unventilated), 105 mm brick outer leaf, 100 mm (4 in.) lightweight concrete block inner leaf, with 16 mm (0·63 in.) dense plaster on inside face. Wall thickness 260 mm (10 in.)	0·90	0·16
Same as above but with 13 mm (0·5 in.) expanded polystyrene board in the cavity	0·62	0·11
Solid wall, 150 mm (6 in.) aerated concrete block, with tile hanging externally and with 16 mm (0·63 in.) plaster on the inside	0·90	0·16
Cavity wall with 75 mm (3 in.) aerated concrete block outer leaf, rendered externally, 100 mm (4 in.) aerated concrete block inner leaf and with 16 mm (0·63 in.) plaster on inside face, 50 mm (2 in.) cavity	0·79	0·14
Cast dense concrete, 200 mm (8 in.)	3·0	0·52

Thus:

$$\frac{0\cdot30 \times 2\cdot75}{1\cdot6} = 0\cdot51$$

It was implied at the beginning of this chapter that the object of improved insulation was economy of fuel and maintenance of warmth. Whilst this is true, the provision of insulation is not only a question of comfort; unless there is adequate insulation, condensation will occur in cold weather on inside surfaces of walls and roofs and in the body of absorbent materials of construction. This can lead to the corrosion of any embedded reinforcement where it is imperfectly protected. Moreover, moisture reduces the natural insulation value of the material, as shown in Table 6.1.

We saw earlier that the low conductivity of lightweight concrete was due to air-filled pores which it contained, air being a very poor conductor of heat. Since water has a conductivity about 25 times that of air, it is clear that when the air in the pores has been partially displaced by water, the concrete must have greater conductivity. The extent of this effect is shown in Tables 6.1 and 6.2.

In the UK, the thermal conductivity of building materials is usually determined by a steady-state method in which the guarded hot-plate is used.

Essentially this apparatus consists of an electrically-heated hot-plate 304 mm (12 in.) square and two liquid-cooled plates of the same dimensions. Two slabs of the material to be tested, also 304 mm square, of thickness not exceeding 50 mm (2 in.), are placed one on each side of the hot-plate and these sandwiched between the cold plates. The hot-plate proper is 203 mm and is surrounded by a guard-ring, a co-planar area 50 mm wide all round, thus making up the assembly to 304 mm square. It is essential that all the heat generated by the hot-plate should pass directly through the test area of the two specimens without lateral loss. It is to prevent such loss that the guard-ring is provided. Further, to avoid heat-exchange between the hot-plate and the guard-ring, the latter is electrically heated to match the temperature of the hot-plate. The whole equipment is contained in an insulated cabinet. The guarded hot-plate assembly within the cabinet is shown in Fig. 6.1. When thermal equilibrium is reached, the conductivity is calculated from measurements of the amount of heat passing through the area of the slab in unit time, and of the temperature difference between the two faces of the slab and its thickness.

This method has the advantage that the situation is under the direct control of the operator, that the concept is simple and that a good standard of reproducibility and accuracy can be achieved. The method and apparatus are covered by British Standard 874:1965, and the equipment used at the British Building Research Station has been described by Pratt and Ball.[4]

Fɪɢ. 6.1   Guarded hot plate apparatus for thermal conductivity measurement.

One of the main drawbacks of the steady-state, guarded hot-plate method is the length of time required before steady conditions are attained. This effectively prevents its use as a control procedure for monitoring the quality of commercial production and severely restricts its usefulness for measuring damp specimens because of the redistribution of the moisture within the specimen which takes place during the settling-down period. For this reason, methods of measuring thermal conductivity have been devised which do not require the establishment of such precisely-defined, steady thermal conditions. These have the advantage of producing a result much more rapidly than steady-steady methods and hence can be used for measurements on damp specimens without causing excessive moisture redistribution. A brief review of such transient-state methods is given below.

Transient-state methods of conductivity measurement may be conveniently divided into two broad categories, namely, those using a line source of heat and those employing one or more plane sources of heat. In both categories the usual procedure is to apply a steady heat flux to the specimen, which must be in thermal equilibrium initially, and to measure the temperature rise at some point in the specimen resulting from this applied flux. The equation governing the temperature increase is expressed as a series of exponential terms, most of which can be ignored except at very small values of the time variable. Thus by avoiding the initial settling period, the duration of which depends upon the material and dimensions of the test specimen, a reasonably simple temperature–time relationship may be used.

In the line-source method, the source is either a wire or a thin cylindrical probe which is inserted into the test sample. The temperature rise resulting from the heat input is usually measured at a fixed distance from the source. In either case, i.e. with wire or probe, after the initial settling period, referred to above, the temperature rises linearly with the logarithm of time, the slope being equal to $Q/4\pi k$, where Q is the rate of heat emission from unit length of the source and k is the thermal conductivity of the material. Various workers throughout the world have used the line-source technique for the measurement of thermal conductivity.

A probe incorporating heat source and thermocouple for temperature measurement is available commercially. The particular advantage of the line-source method, in addition to those in common to all transient state methods, are the simplicity and portability of the apparatus required and the fact that, above a lower limit that may be specified, the size and shape of the specimen are not critical. Disadvantages of the method are the fragility of the probe if it is to be thin enough to represent a line-source adequately, and the difficulty of ensuring a low and uniform thermal contact resistance between the probe and the specimen.

Vernotte[5] determined the equations for calculating the thermal conductivity from the time–temperature relationship at the centre of a stack of four identical specimens arranged with heaters placed between the upper and lower two specimens. Thermocouples were used to measure the temperature rise at the central interface which approximates to a non-conducting plane.

A transient-state method of thermal conductivity measurement which requires only two specimens and one heater was devised at the Building Research Station in England.[6] The single plane heater is sandwiched between the two identical sheet specimens; the unheated faces of the specimens are in contact with heat sinks so are kept at a substantially constant temperature.

ACOUSTIC PROPERTIES

Noise nuisance may be avoided by suppression of the sound at its source or by isolating it when it has been created. The greatly increasing use of noise-producing equipment such as radio and television often precludes suppression of noise as a measure against nuisance, while the tendency towards closer proximity of separate dwellings in the populous areas makes the isolation of noise not only desirable but more difficult. Isolation of noise is more than the simple matter of providing an insulating barrier such as a party wall, as noise is transmitted in many ways other than by transference through a membrane. Nevertheless it will be convenient in this short review to confine attention to walls as the principal insulation for transmitted sound.

Sound is a form of energy and as such it can be measured objectively by physical instruments. The sound reduction factor is defined as the ratio of the energy of the sound at its source to that at any other location, and is expressed as decibels (dB). It is important to note that the scale of decibels is logarithmic, that is, an increase of 10 dB means a reduction of sound to one-tenth, 20 dB a reduction to one-hundredth, and 30 dB to one-thousandth. The sound reduction factor is a means of assessing the relative efficiency of different forms of materials and constructions as insulators of sound of different frequencies. In considering noise abatement in buildings, the concern is with the reduction of noise levels and for this some criterion is necessary, either in terms of residual noise level or of noise reduction.

In considering the acoustic properties of building materials it should be realised that there is not a single insulating value which is valid for the whole range of audible frequency. Sound transmission through a wall may be tolerable at one frequency and intolerable at another. Nearly all structures provide better insulation at the higher than at the lower frequencies, and cavity walls are usually superior to solid walls of the same weight at high frequencies but not at low frequencies. The system of classifying sound barriers now in use specifies the insulation value at all frequencies. The effectiveness of solid walls in transmitting sound is taken to be approximately proportional to the weight of the wall.

Lightweight concretes have not been considered to have any special sound insulating value but tests made on full-scale walls constructed of Lytag concrete[7] have indicated a somewhat higher sound insulation than might be expected from the 'mass law'. Until more information becomes available, solid partitions of lightweight concrete can be expected to follow the established mass–insulation curve so long as they are not porous to sound—in other words, airtight. To be airtight, lightweight concrete blocks have to be plastered, not only because they are often porous themselves, but because they frequently leak sound through imperfect formation of joints. Plastering on one side may well be sufficient, but a dense sheet such as plasterboard fixed to battens is not a satisfactory alternative to plaster intimately bonded to the lightweight concrete wall.

Sound absorption is quite a different property from sound insulation. Sound absorbing materials reduce the sound reflection from a surface, while sound insulating materials reduce the sound passing through.

Except where they have sealed surfaces, most lightweight concretes show moderately good sound absorption. Stacey[8] has given the values shown in Table 6.4 for the absorption coefficient over a range of frequencies of 75 mm (3 in.) clinker concrete, unplastered.

TABLE 6.4
ACOUSTIC ABSORPTION COEFFICIENT AT VARIOUS FREQUENCIES
(75 mm (3 in) CLINKER, CONCRETE, UNPLASTERED)

Frequency Hz (cps)	125	500	2 000	4 000
Absorption coefficient	0·2	0·6	0·5	0·5

One of the advantages of absorbent lightweight concrete over denser material when used in cavity construction is the 'built-in' absorption which is provided in the cavity, thus giving the effect of a sound-absorption quilt—a sound-attenuating expedient which is sometimes used in cavity walls.

Building regulation grades

Regulations for building in Britain incorporate mandatory requirements which control sound transmission between dwellings. The classification is in Grades and in no case is the required performance below that given for Grade 1. However, lower Grades denoting lower performance than Grade 1 may be accepted for improvements of existing dwellings and may be useful in defining the performance in other types of building for which there are no mandatory requirements for sound insulation.

The Grades of sound transmission given in the British Building Regulations[9] are given below.

Party-wall grade

This Grade is based on the performance of the one-brick party wall. It reduces the noise from neighbours to a level that is acceptable to the majority; a lower standard certainly could not be justified on present evidence. A higher standard is not yet practicable, mainly because at this level of insulation flanking transmission is usually about equal to direct transmission and there is little to be gained from improving only direct transmission.

Grade I

This is the highest insulation that is practicable at the present time *vertically* between flats. It is based on the performance of a concrete floor construction with a floating floor, which gives the best floor insulation obtainable by normal structural methods. Noise from the neighbours causes only minor disturbance; it is no more of a nuisance than other disadvantages which tenants may associate with living in flats.

Grade II

With this degree of insulation the neighbours' noise is considered by

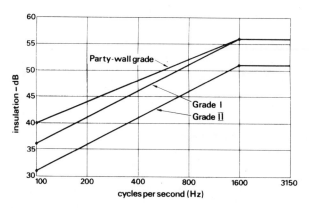

FIG. 6.2   Grade curves for airborne sound insulation.

many of the tenants to be the worst thing about living in flats, but even so at least half the tenants are not seriously disturbed.

The grade curves

The levels of airborne and impact sound insulation that satisfy the party-wall grade and Grades I and II are given in Figs. 6.2 and 6.3. To qualify for a particular airborne sound grading, the insulation should be *not less than* the value shown at each frequency in Fig. 6.2. To meet an impact grading, the measured noise levels produced underneath a floor by a standard impact machine operated on the floor should not *exceed* the value shown at each frequency in Fig. 6.3.

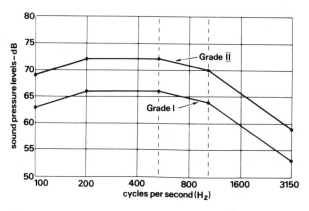

FIG. 6.3   Grade curves for impact sound insulation.

TABLE 6.5

GRADINGS OF PARTY WALLS IN TRADITIONAL DWELLINGS

Solid walls	Finishing[a]	Weight including any plaster kg/m^2	(psf)	Grade[b]
One-brick wall	pbs	415	83	P-W
In situ concrete or concrete panels with joints solidly grouted	plaster optional	415	83	P-W
175 mm concrete at 2320 kg/m³ (145 pcf)	without plaster	—	—	P-W
175 mm concrete at 2080 kg/m³ (130 pcf)	pbs	—	—	P-W
Lightweight concrete or other material	pbs	415	83	P-W
300 mm lightweight concrete at 1 200 kg/m³ (75 pcf)	pbs	—	—	P-W
225 mm no-fines concrete at 1 600 kg/m³ (100 pcf)	pbs	—	—	P-W
200 mm no-fines concrete at 1 600 kg/m³ (100 pcf)	pbs	365	73	I
Lightweight concrete	pbs	220	44	II
Half-brick wall	pbs	220	44	II

Cavity walls, with wire ties of butterfly pattern and plastered on both sides	Cavity width (mm)	Weight including any plaster		Grade
Two leaves consisting of: 100 mm brick, block or dense concrete	50	415	83	P-W
Lightweight aggregate concrete— sound-absorbent surfaces to cavity (see text)	50	300	60	P-W
Lightweight aggregate concrete— sound-absorbent surfaces to cavity (see text)	75	250	50	P-W
Lightweight aggregate concrete— sound-absorbent surfaces to cavity (see text)	50	250	50	I
50 mm lightweight concrete at 1280 kg/m³ (80 pcf)	25	—	—	II
100 mm hollow concrete blocks	50	—	—	III

[a] pbs = plastered on both sides
[b] P-W = Party-Wall Grade

Wall constructions are required to meet the grade for airborne sound only; floor constructions, in order to be classified under a particular grade, must satisfy that grade for both airborne and impact sound insulation.

Measured insulation curves seldom follow the grade curves exactly and measurements satisfying grade requirements over most of the frequency range may very likely fall short at one or two frequencies; it is not intended that constructions should be condemned or graded down on account of minor faults that may have little significance, and in practical grading assessments a suitable tolerance is allowed. For strict grading purposes, such as conformity to Building Regulations, tolerances must be accurately defined, and it is also necessary to correct, or normalise measurements to standardised conditions; without this correction a construction would for example vary in its insulation value depending on whether it was measured in an occupied or an empty dwelling, because of the different amounts of absorption present.

All the gradings in this chapter are based on measurements made in accordance with BS 2750:1956, normalised to 0·5 sec. reverberation time in the receiving room. The permitted tolerance for compliance with a particular grade is a total adverse deviation from the grade curve at all $\frac{1}{3}$-octave frequency bands between 100 and 3150 Hz (cps) of not more than 23 dB. The performance of party wall and party floor constructions is given in terms of their sound insulation grading relative to the grade curves.

The sound insulation gradings of various forms of construction for party walls are shown in Table 6.5. The values given are based on the assumption that the remainder of the construction is traditional, with all structural elements firmly bonded together.

Cavity walls

Cavity walling of two half-brick leaves, separated by a 50 mm (2 in.) cavity was formerly recommended for party walls on the basis of the higher single-figure insulation. All available evidence now shows that this has no sensible advantage over the one-brick solid wall; indeed, unless the cavity width is maintained as a minimum and wire ties of butterfly pattern are used, the Party-Wall Grade will not be attained.

Materials other than brick (e.g. concrete or stone) used for the leaves of a cavity wall will attain Party-Wall Grade if the wall is plastered and its overall weight is not less than 415 kg/m² (83 psf).

If lightweight aggregate concrete is used, presenting sound-absorbent surfaces to the cavity, the weight of the wall can be reduced to 300 kg/m² (60 psf) with a 50 mm (minimum) cavity. If the width of the cavity is increased to 75 mm or more, the weight of the wall can be further reduced to 250 kg/m² (50 psf).

In all cases, the requirements already stated regarding plastered walls and ties must be met.

FIRE PROTECTION

So far the thermal insulation of lightweight concrete has been discussed mainly in terms of retaining warmth within buildings. Another important application of thermal insulation is in the protection of structures against fire damage. In order to appreciate this aspect of thermal insulation it will be helpful to consider briefly the general question of fire protection.

Materials are classified as combustible and non-combustible, the criterion being that a combustible material when once ignited contributes to the severity of the fire by producing heat, while a non-combustible material does not. Inorganic materials such as stone, brick and concrete are non-combustible; organic materials such as timber are combustible.

In considering combustibility in relation to fire protection two important points must be borne in mind.

(1) Although the combustibility of a building material is very important, and the designer should consider this property when selecting materials, the severity of a fire generally derives not so much from the fabric of the building as from its contents.

(2) Although a building material may not be combustible, it may suffer from the fire in such a manner as to be rendered unfit for the functional duty for which it was chosen. This usually means loss of strength through chemical or physical changes.

The basic object of fire protection design is to ensure that once a fire has started, its rate of development and the extent of spread will be so limited that time will be permitted for occupants to escape, and for fire-fighting action to become effective in preventing the fire reaching a severity which will lead to irreparable damage or spread to adjacent property. A structural element of a building is a definable member such as a wall, column or beam. A column functions only as a means of support while a loadbearing wall acts both as a support for a superimposed load and also as a barrier to the spread of fire. On the other hand a column, although it does not itself contain the fire, may have the duty of supporting a wall which is a fire barrier. It is clear from this that the fire resistance of a material as such, is meaningless, as in this context it is a property not of a material, but of an assembly of materials that make up a structural element of specific dimensions and function.

The effect of fire on a structural element of a building depends on the temperature reached, the duration of the fire and of course on the nature of the unit and its intrinsic resistance to thermal damage. In the fire-resistance test, prescribed in British Standard 476,[10] the structural element is placed in a furnace which reproduces conditions similar to an actual fire and the period of time, reckoned in hours, which the unit can remain exposed to the fire of standard severity without functional failure is used as an index of fire

FIG. 6.4 Commencement of fire-resistance test on aerated concrete block wall.

resistance. Thus the element is said to have a fire resistance of 1 hour, 2 hours, etc. (see Fig. 6.4).

Buildings are classified according to the potential heat-producing character of their normal contents and constructional materials. This factor, expressed in units of $kcal/m^2$ or Btu/ft^2, is termed the 'fire-loading' and is defined as the quantity of heat which would be produced by complete combustion per unit area of floor area, assuming a calorific value for the cellulosic materials in general of $4460\,kcal/kg\,(8000\,Btu/lb)$. Fire-loadings range from $13\,550\,kcal/m^2$ ($50\,000$ Btu/ft^2) to $54\,200\,kcal/m^2$ ($200\,000$ Btu/ft^2).

TABLE 6.6
FIRE LOAD AND FIRE RESISTANCE

Fire load density[a]		Equivalent period of fire resistance
kg/m^2	psf	(*Hours of standard test*)
Up to 61	12·5	1·0
61–122	12·5–25	1·5
122–244	25–50	2·0

[a] Weight of fuel per unit floor area assuming calorific value of 4460 kcal/kg (8000 Btu/lb).

If the fire resistance of an element corresponds to the fire loading of the building in which it is proposed that it should be used, the element is said to be 'fully protected'. This, of course, is only true if all supporting elements are similarly protected.

A structural element having a low fire resistance can in many cases be improved in this respect by suitable protection. For example, the 2-hour fire resistance of a 115 mm ($4\frac{1}{2}$ in.) brick wall can be raised to 6 hours by the application of a special plaster.

In framed structures, structural steel and aluminium alloys will not for long withstand exposure to fire, because when the temperature of steel reaches 550°C and aluminium about 200–250°C, the strength of these metals becomes so reduced that they can no longer support the loads they are expected to carry. This can happen in the first few minutes of a fire. However, with appropriate protection they can be given virtually any amount of fire resistance.

Gypsum plaster is non-combustible and much of its resistance to the effects of fire is to be attributed to the proportion of chemically bound water which it contains and which has to be removed before failure of the plaster takes place. Gypsum plaster containing such lightweight aggregates as exfoliated vermiculite or expanded perlite, by virtue of its high thermal insulation, very substantially increases the fire resistance of a structural element to which it is applied, provided the plaster is securely bonded to its surface.

It is usual to encase structural steel in concrete, providing a cover of not less than 50 mm (2 in.) thickness, to increase fire resistance. However spalling of the concrete cover owing to heat reduces the potential fire resistance of such members, and to prevent this the concrete can be reinforced with a light mesh. Lightweight concrete provides a more effective fire protection than dense aggregate concrete as it is less liable to spalling and has a higher thermal insulation. There is a wide range of lightweight casings which provide efficient protection for steel, such as slabs and blocks of concrete employing artificial aggregates (foamed slag, explanded clay, or sintered pulverised-fuel ash) or slabs of aerated concrete. The use of such lightweight concrete in place of gravel concrete increases the fire resistance of the structures by 30–40 per cent.

As examples of fire tests on lightweight concretes, Tables 6.7, 6.8 and 6.9, Reference 11, give representative values. The test results are given in terms of the time in minutes from the start of the test until failure has occurred under one or all of the criteria—stability, integrity, and insulation—as prescribed in BS 476. As an example, a test showed the following results:

Stability	120
Integrity	120
Insulation	15

This means that the specimen failed in respect of insulation after 15 min but complied with the other requirements for at least 120 min.

DURABILITY

This may be defined as the ability of a material to withstand the effects of its environment. In a building material this may be interpreted as chemical attack, physical stress and mechanical assault.

Chemical attack is usually encountered as aggressive ground-water, particularly sulphate, polluted air and spillage of reactive liquids. Lightweight concrete has no special resistance to these agencies: indeed, as it is generally more porous than the more conventional concretes, it is, if anything, more vulnerable. For this reason lightweight concrete would not be recommended for use below damp-course. Except in the most polluted exposure, the chemical attack from the air is not significant, and in any case lightweight concrete would usually, for other reasons, be rendered or otherwise protected. A chemical aspect of durability is the stability of the material itself, particularly in the presence of moisture. Furnace clinker is probably the only material used in lightweight concrete which in practice might lead to failure, and occurrences of this are not very common.

Physical stresses to which lightweight concrete is exposed are principally frost action and shrinkage and temperature stresses.

The climate of the British Isles is not severe and long periods of very low temperatures are not common. This cannot be said of some countries in which lightweight concrete is used, but if suitably protected by rendering this material does not appear to suffer noticeably from frost. Specimens of the unprotected lightweight concrete exposed in shallow trays of water over a number of years, thus experiencing many cycles of freezing and thawing, have not generally shown significant damage, while unrendered aerated

TABLE 6.7

NON-LOADBEARING MASONRY WALLS

FROSI No., Date & Sponsor	Construction		Test results			Fire resistance grading (hr)
			Stability (min)	Integrity (min)	Insulation (min)	
No. 2545 1963 Durox Building Units Ltd	Reinforced aerated concrete 'Durox'	3in	187	187	187	3
No. 248(c) 1951 British Gypsum Ltd	'Fletton' bricks 1 in. vermiculite gypsum plaster	This wall had previously been heated for 6 hr in connection with another test SI No. 248(a) during which dehydration had occurred	240	240	240	4 (plaster face)

No. 468 1954 Lignacite (North London) Ltd	Lignacite building blocks $\frac{3}{16}$ in. gypsum plaster on heated face		262	262	247	4
No. 4438 1967 Lignacite (North London) Ltd	Lignacite hollow blocks		240	240	240	4

TABLE 6.8
NON-LOADBEARING MASONRY WALLS

FROSI No., Date & Sponsor	Construction		Test results			Fire resistance grading (hr)
			Stability (min)	Integrity (min)	Insulation (min)	
No. 248(a) 1951 British Gypsum Ltd	'Fletton'bricks ¼in.	1 in. vermiculite/gypsum plaster both sides	360	360	360	4
No. 248(b) 1951 British Gypsum Ltd	Clinker blocks 3in.	1 in. vermiculite/gypsum plaster both sides	360	360	360	6

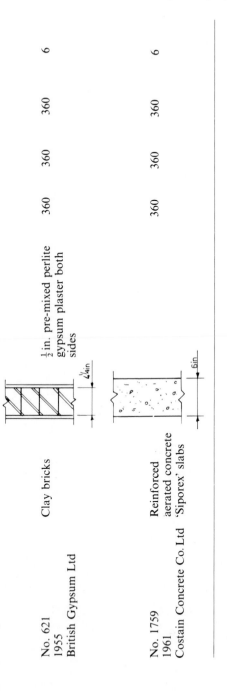

| No. 621
1955
British Gypsum Ltd | Clay bricks | ½ in. pre-mixed perlite gypsum plaster both sides | 360 | 360 | 360 | 6 |
| No. 1759
1961
Costain Concrete Co. Ltd | Reinforced aerated concrete 'Siporex' slabs | | 360 | 360 | 360 | 6 |

TABLE 6.9

NON-LOADBEARING MASONRY WALLS

FROSI No., Date & sponsor	Construction	Test results			Fire resistance grading (hr)
		Stability (min)	Integrity (min)	Insulation (min)	
No. 738 1956 Thermalite Ltd.	Thermalite— Ytong aerated concrete blocks	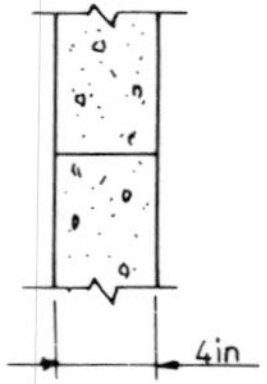 276	276	262	4
No. 1021 1957 Moler Products Ltd	'Bimol' hollow blocks ½ in. render & plaster skim both sides 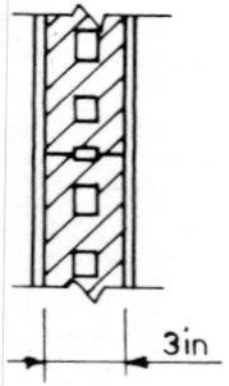	260	260	253	4

No. 2434 1963 Leca (GB) Ltd	'Lecalite' lightweight concrete panels	[3½ in]	Lightweight plaster skim both sides	330	330	321	4
No. 2542 1962 Durox Building Units Ltd	'Durox' aerated concrete building blocks	[4 in]		245	245	245	4

concrete has been known to withstand several severe winters in Sweden without suffering unduly.

Stressing may be due to the drying shrinkage of the concrete or to differential thermal movements between dissimilar materials or to other phenomena of a similar nature. Drying shrinkage commonly causes cracking of lightweight concrete if suitable precautions are not taken.

Mechanical damage can result from abrasion or impact but it might also arise from excessive loading of flexural members.

The lightest grades of aerated concrete are relatively soft so that they would be subject to some abrasion were they not for other reasons protected by rendering. This can also lead to impact damage of completed buildings, although the principal risk of this kind is in the handling of components before or during erection.

Avoidance of damage through overloading is not specific to lightweight concrete and in any case is a matter for design.

An aspect of durability which is not a property of the material itself, but nevertheless of great importance, is the spalling of lightweight concrete as the result of corrosion of steel in reinforced units.

WATER ABSORPTION

Lightweight concretes, particularly those used in blocks, are somewhat porous and so have a higher water absorption than dense concrete. This is not considered to be of great importance in practice, since lightweight concrete exposed to the weather is not generally used without a suitable protective rendering. The question of protection of reinforcement in porous concrete is discussed elsewhere.

Lightweight aggregates themselves are more porous than gravel aggregate and so absorb a great deal more water during the making of the concrete. This is not of great practical importance in concrete-making as a whole, but where lightweight concrete is used in insulating roof screeds, and where it is desirable that there should be relatively quick drying, high absorption of water by the aggregate is a disadvantage. Methods of waterproofing lightweight aggregate are known but it has not yet been demonstrated that these methods are acceptable economically.

RAIN PENETRATION

An essential function of walls is their ability to exclude rain-water. Where cavity walls are used the question of rain penetration hardly arises but there are several forms of construction which employ single-skin walls and then resistance to the passage of rain-water is of great importance. A limited

FIG. 6.5   Artificial rain penetration test on rendered wall of lightweight concrete blocks.

amount of experience has been gained from laboratory work on the resistance of lightweight concretes to rain penetration and on the whole these have been satisfactory, especially when the walls were protected by an external rendering. It is important to realise that when a wall permits the passage of rain-water, the penetration is seldom through the body of the concrete but through capillary cracks in the joints and the more impervious the concrete the greater is the risk of moisture penetration through these cracks. Lightweight concrete, being generally more porous, if used in sufficient thickness and if protected by a porous rendering, will give good resistance to rain penetration even when used as a single thickness. In the UK, cavity wall construction is the general rule and so there is little experience of rain penetration in practice except in cases of faulty design detail or careless workmanship. On the other hand, no-fines concrete, which is used on quite a large scale in Britain, is normally employed as a single skin and there appears to be little trouble with rain penetration. In many countries single-skin construction in aerated concrete is common and appears to give satisfaction. In certain areas of the British Isles single-skin aerated concrete walls are permitted.

In order to assess the likelihood of rain penetration through any particular walling system, standard tests are carried out. These vary somewhat from one country to another but essentially they involve the spraying of water on to the face of the wall at a predetermined rate, either continuously or intermittently, with or without artificially simulated wind pressure (Fig. 6.5). Ability to withstand this treatment for some standard period of time without showing moisture stains on the back of the wall is deemed to constitute satisfactory resistance to rain penetration.

REFERENCES

1. Handisyde, C. C. and Melluish, D. J. (1971). *Thermal Insulation of Buildings*, HMSO.
2. British Standard, BS 874:1973. 'Determining Thermal Insulating Properties, with Definitions of Thermal Insulation Terms', British Standards Institution.
3. BRS Digest No. 108 (1972). 'Standard *U*-values', Building Research Station, Garston, Watford.
4. Pratt, A. W. and Ball, J. M. E. (1956). 'Thermal Conductivity of Building Materials: Methods of Determination and Results', *J. Inst. of Heat. Ventil. Engnrs*, **24.**
5. Vernotte, P. (1937). *Comptes Rendues Acad. Sci.*, Paris, 563.
6. Ball, E. F. (1967). 'A Transient-Flow Method of Measuring Thermal Conductivity and Diffusivity', Building Research Station Current paper, Research Series No. 65, Building Research Station, Garston, Watford.
7. Lytag Ltd., Private Communication.
8. Stacey, E. F., Building Research Station, Private Communication.
9. Building Regulations (England and Wales) 1965. HMSO.
10. BRS Digest No. 102 (Second series). Revised 1971.
11. Smart, P. M. T. and Fisher, R. (1974). 'Sponsored Fire Resistance Tests on Building Elements', Building Research Establishment, HMSO.

CHAPTER SEVEN

No-Fines Concrete

SUMMARY

The term no-fines *concrete means a concrete composed of cement and a coarse* 19–9 mm ($\frac{3}{4}$–$\frac{3}{8}$ *in.*) *aggregate only, the product having many uniformly distributed voids. It is used for loadbearing external and internal walls, non-loadbearing walls, infilling walls for framed structures, and underfloor filling for solid floors. The mix commonly used is* 1:8, 1:10 *or* 1:12 *by volume and the compressive strength attained is up to about* 11·0 *MPa* (1600 *psi*).

The drying shrinkage of no-fines concrete is usually considerably less than that of all-in aggregate concrete made with the same materials.

The thermal conductivity of no-fines concrete is comparable with that of conventional brickwork.

GENERAL

The term 'no-fines' concrete generally means concrete composed of cement and a coarse 19–9 mm ($\frac{1}{4}$–$\frac{3}{8}$ in.) aggregate only, and the product so formed has many uniformly distributed voids throughout its mass. This is shown in Fig. 7.1. The term is also used sometimes to denote concrete made not with 19–9 mm aggregate, but aggregate from which the fines below 5 mm (0·2 in.) only have been removed from an otherwise normal grading. This is apt to lead to confusion. Strictly speaking, the latter definition is quite appropriate and the 19–9 mm ($\frac{3}{4}$–$\frac{5}{8}$ in.) aggregate concrete would be more properly described as a 'single-size' aggregate concrete, but as the term 'no-fines' is so firmly associated with the 19–9 mm aggregate concrete, it will be used throughout this book.

No-fines concrete is used for loadbearing, cast *in situ* external and internal walls, party walls, non-loadbearing walls, infilling walls for framed structures, and underfloor filling for solid ground floors. When this type of concrete is used for external walls, rendering is necessary, owing to its open texture, but, by virtue of this open structure, capillary attraction of water is eliminated and the concrete forms an excellent base for rendering or plastering. A two-coat rendering is usually sufficient but three coats are sometimes used for high-rise buildings. The mix used for the rendering must not be too rich in cement otherwise excessive racking could occur in

FIG. 7.1   No-fines concrete made with gravel aggregate.

the rendering, allowing rain-water to penetrate through the cracks without being able to evaporate from the surface of the wall. Owing to its low thermal conductivity, no-fines concrete is particularly suitable for external walls. Its sound insulation is not very good but it may be used for party walls. No-fines concrete solid party walls made of gravel or crushed rock are satisfactory if they are not less than 190 mm ($7\frac{1}{2}$ in.) thick and have a plaster coat on both sides.

HISTORY AND DEVELOPMENT

No-fines concrete probably had its origin in Holland and was introduced into the UK in 1923, when 50 houses were built in Edinburgh, followed a few years later by 800 or more in Liverpool, Manchester and London, all built with no-fines concrete. An extensive study of this form of concrete and its mode of use was made at the British Building Research Station as early as 1928, and from this a very substantial body of knowledge and experience was gained. In the years immediately preceding the war, and indeed during it, many hundreds of houses were built in Scotland using gravel or whinstone no-fines concrete. Since 1945 it has become a generally accepted material and is now used extensively, not only in Britain, but also in Germany, Holland, France, Belgium and the USSR. That no-fines concrete has proved to be competitive with the more traditional materials, is determined by the fact that 25 per cent of the houses built in Scotland in 1974 were constructed of no-fines concrete[1] and, one British firm alone (Wimpeys) has built the equivalent of over 300 000 houses with this material between 1945 and 1974 in the UK, apart from large contracts overseas.[2]

In Britain the use of loadbearing, no-fines concrete is generally confined to buildings of less than 5 storeys, although as a non-loadbearing material, it

FIG. 7.2   Multi-storey block of flats built in Coventry with loadbearing walls of
no-fines concrete.

is also used for infilling for high multi-storey framed structures. However,
following the construction in Germany of a number of tall blocks of flats up
to 20 storeys in height in loadbearing, no-fines concrete, 10-storey flats were
built in Glasgow in a similar manner with no fines concrete made with
gravel aggregate.[1] In these buildings the walls are 305 mm (12 in.) thick
throughout their height, and the richness of the mix varied from 1:6 by
volume (cement:aggregate) at the lower levels to 1:10 at the top (Fig. 7.2).

STRENGTH

In practice nowadays, most no-fines concrete is made principally by weigh-
batching; the mix is almost always 1:8 or 1:10 by volume with a
water/cement ratio of 0·40, using gravel aggregates. Strengths recorded
from regular testing of laboratory cubes show the average results given in
Table 7.1, and Fig. 7.3 indicates the approximate correlation found
between the density of gravel aggregate no-fines concrete and its strength.
No-fines concrete walls fail in compression at about half the cube strength
of the concrete.

The modulus of deformation of no-fines concretes tends to diminish
somewhat with age. It depends on density, as in the case of concrete made
with lightweight aggregates. For a 1:8 by volume concrete mix, for
example, the modulus of deformation is about 15 000 MPa ($2·2 \times 10^6$ psi).

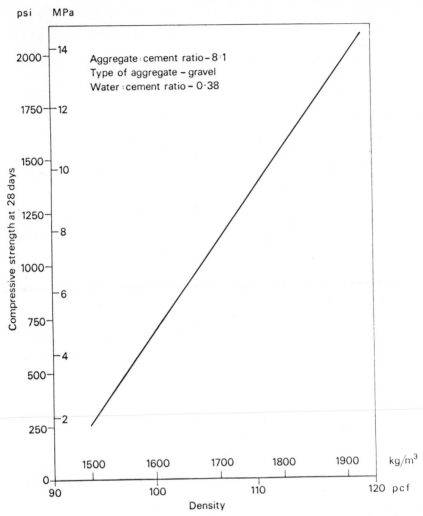

FIG. 7.3 Relationship between compressive strength and density of no-fines concrete.

The effect of the size of the aggregate particles on the strength obtained is shown in Fig. 7.4 for variable cement contents. The strength of no-fines concrete increases with decreasing aggregate size.

The effect of the water–cement ratio on strength can be considerable. With variations of the water–cement ratio the strength of the same mix may vary between 11 and 28 MPa (1600–4000 psi). Figure 7.5 indicates that for

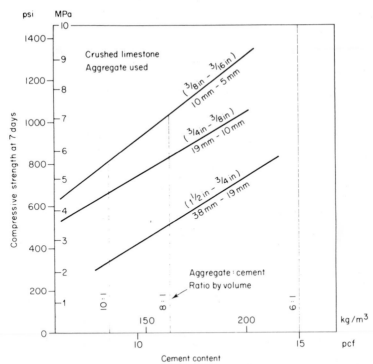

FIG. 7.4   Effect of aggregate size and cement content on compressive strength of no-fines concrete.

TABLE 7.1

COMPRESSIVE STRENGTH OF NO-FINES CONCRETE AS OBTAINED FROM 150 mm (6 in.) CUBES[2]

Aggregate	Dry density		Compressive strength at 28 days	
	$(kg/m^3,$ approx.)	(pcf)	(MPa)	(psi)
Rounded quartz gravel	1840	115	8·6	1250
Irregular flint gravel	1540	99	4·8	700
Crushed limestone	1830	114	6·9	1000
Crushed granite	1700	106	7·6	1100

Typically, a density of about 1600 kg/m³ (100 pcf) corresponds to a compressive strength of about 5 MPa (700 psi) and a density of about 1850 kg/m³ (115 pcf) to a strength of about 8·5 MPa (1250 psi).

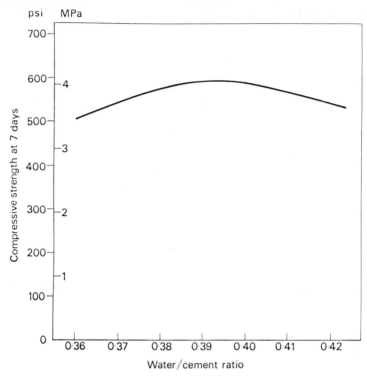

F<small>IG</small>. 7.5   Effect of variation of water/cement ratio on compressive strength of no-
fines concrete.

given materials and mix proportions there is an optimum water–cement
ratio for maximum compressive strength.

DRYING SHRINKAGE

Unlike other forms of lightweight concrete, the drying shrinkage of no-
fines concrete is particularly low: indeed, it is often no more than about 60
per cent of the shrinkage of compacted concrete made with fully graded
material (Table 7.2).

The rate of drying shrinkage of no-fines concrete is much more rapid than
that of dense concrete. It has been shown that in no-fines concrete, 80 per
cent of the total shrinkage movement takes place within 100 days, but in the
same period, only 60 per cent of the final shrinkage takes place in dense
concrete. When the lower overall shrinkage of no-fines concrete is
considered, together with its higher rate of drying when exposed to

TABLE 7.2

COMPARISON OF THE DRYING SHRINKAGE OF NO-FINES AND COMPACTED FULLY
GRADED CONCRETES MADE WITH DIFFERENT TYPES OF AGGREGATE

Aggregate	Mix proportions (cement: aggregate, by volume)	Water/cement ratio (by weight)	Drying shrinkage (per cent 50°C and 17 per cent r.h.)
Natural river gravel	1:8	0·40	0·018
Natural river gravel	1:10	0·45	0·018
Natural river gravel	1:12	0·50	0·018
Natural river gravel	1:2:4 dense concrete		0·035
Whinstone	1:8	0·35	0·022
Whinstone	1:10	0·40	0·023
Whinstone	1:12	0·45	0·028
Whinstone	1:2:4 dense concrete		0·049
Air-cooled slag	1:8	0·40	0·025
Air-cooled slag	1:10	0·45	0·020
Air-cooled slag	1:12	0·50	0·022
Air-cooled slag	1:2:4 dense concrete		0·038
Crushed limestone	1:8	0·40	0·016
Crushed limestone	1:10	0·45	0·019
Crushed limestone	1:12	0·50	0·022
Crushed limestone	1:2:4 dense concrete		0·033

moderate humidity, it is apparent that the effective shrinkage which will take place after the rendering and plastering of a no-fines concrete wall will be much less than with a wall of dense concrete.

Practical experience with no-fines concrete made with heavy aggregate shows that the drying shrinkage is sufficiently small for semi-detached houses to be built without the inclusion of vertical contraction joints. Because of the somewhat higher drying shrinkage experienced with concrete made from some of the lighter aggregates, however, it is recommended that even semi-detached houses should have contraction joints where these materials are used.

THERMAL CONDUCTIVITY

The thermal conductivity (k-value) of no-fines concrete varies with the type of aggregate used, and is in the same range as that of conventional brickwork. However, any changes in the thermal conductivity caused by changes in the type of aggregate are, by comparison with the various lining systems, of marginal significance for the thermal transmittance coefficient or U-value of the finished wall system. The lining systems employed are

TABLE 7.3

CALCULATED THERMAL CONDUCTANCE (*U*-VALUE) FOR SOME TYPICAL NO-FINES
CONCRETE WALLS

Internal lining system	No-fines concrete wall system		U-value for normal exposure	
	(mm)	(inch)	(W/m² °C)	(Btu/ft² h °F)
38 mm (1½ in.) plasterboard-cavity-plasterboard with a	200	8	0·78	0·16
low emmissivity surface towards the no-fines concrete	250	10	0·73	0·15
20 mm (¾ in.) thick expanded polystyrene and lightweight	200	8	0·83	0·17
plaster	250	10	0·78	0·16
38 mm (1½ in.) thick plasterboard-cavity-plasterboard	300	12	0·88	0·18

chosen to comply with the thermal insulation requirements of the British
Building Regulations (Second Amendment).

The range of calculated thermal conductances (*U*-values) for a few
typical wall constructions based on a 1:8 no-fines concrete mix, are given in
Table 7.3. All these walls were assumed to be finished externally with a
20 mm (¾ in.) thick cement-and-dash rendering.

MOISTURE PENETRATION

A solid no-fines concrete wall with a suitable rendering and good detailing
is comparable to a wall constructed in 280 mm (11 in.) cavity brickwork as
regards resistance to moisture penetration. Owing to the cellular structure
of no-fines concrete, capillary moisture migration virtually does not exist,
and it has been estimated that in the absence of exceptionally powerful
driving wind, water penetrating the wall is limited in its inward travel to
about twice the diameter of the largest aggregate. At worst, an external
solid no-fines concrete wall may become saturated to about one-third of its
thickness. Thus, an external wall of rendered no-fines concrete is made up
of a wall with no capillary attraction faced with a rendering which has
substantial capillary attraction and there is therefore no tendency for water
to be drawn into the wall from the rendering. There is, however, the danger
of water entering the wall due to faulty detailing at windows and door

openings, or through cracks in the rendering. (The risk of cracking is increased by the use of too-rich mixes for rendering.) However, water entering the wall through either of these faults will drain towards the foot of the wall, where it will flow away through weep holes. These must be provided above the damp-course and kept clear of obstruction. Where lintels intervene, these must be inclined over part of their upper surface downwards towards the outside face of the wall and the normal precautions of inserting a damp-proof course must be taken, otherwise draining water is as likely to be diverted to the inside of the wall as to the external face. The damp-course should not be wholly sloped towards the outer face; at least two-thirds of the area should form a level bearing.

Tests carried out at the Building Research Station have indicated that rendered panels of no-fines concrete 230 mm (9 in.) thick are not subject to rain penetration. Experience over many years of houses having clinker no-fines concrete walls 230 mm (9 in.) thick treated externally with roughcast confirms this result. 200 mm (8 in.) walls of heavy aggregate with external roughcast have been equally satisfactory over several years. The uneven open textured surface of no-fines concrete walls is a good base for rendering external walls; 2 coats suffice for normal use but 3 coats are needed for high-rise buildings.

As stated above, it is a mistake to use cement-rich renderings, for this leads to hair-cracking through which water can readily penetrate but cannot escape through evaporation. For normal conditions a 1:1:6 or 2:1:9 cement–lime–sand mix will serve well. A rough surface texture is needed.

MAKING NO-FINES CONCRETE

Suitable aggregates are those complying in the UK with BS 882 for natural aggregates, BS 1047 for blast-furnace slag or BS 877 for foamed slag. Newer lightweight aggregates covered by BS 3797 are also suitable for no-fines concrete in certain circumstances, including sintered pulverised-fuel ash, expanded clay, expanded shale and expanded slate. The grading of the aggregate should be such that not more than 5 per cent is held on a 19 mm ($\frac{3}{4}$ in.) sieve, and not more than 10 per cent passes a 9 mm ($\frac{3}{8}$ in.) sieve. Any grading within these limits is considered to be satisfactory. The aggregate should be free from any coating of clay or dust and it should be rounded or roughly cuboid and not of a flaky character like shale. (The Flakiness Index is usually limited to 30 per cent.)

The proper consistency for no-fines concrete when being placed is such that the mixture should be of a uniform colour, with all the aggregate modules coated with cement grout. This cannot be so if insufficient water is used, whilst too much water will cause the cement to run and separate from the aggregate. This not only leaves insufficient grout for the satisfactory bonding of the aggregate, but results in deposits of dense concrete at the lower levels, or else the loss of cement grout through the shuttering. The effect of the water cement ratio on strength is shown in Fig. 7.5.

Mix design is largely empirical, based on builders' experience. Using dense gravel or crushed rock aggregates, about 180 kg cement is required for each cubic metre of aggregate (1 cwt cement for 10 ft³ aggregate), giving a 1:8 mix by volume. The corresponding recommended quantities for lightweight aggregates are 250 kg cement for each cubic metre of aggregate (1 cwt cement for 7 ft³ aggregate), giving a 1:6 mix by volume. Such mixes used with a water–cement ratio of about 0·4 will give a cube crushing strength of 2·8–3·5 MPa (400–500 psi). Densities corresponding to cube strengths higher than 7 MPa (1000 psi) for no-fines concrete are not desirable except for special structural purposes, since at such a density the thermal insulation properties of the material become seriously impaired.

The mixing procedures used for no-fines concrete structures have been arrived at from long experience on many sites. The aggregate should be damp or wetted before adding the cement, but the limiting water content should be carefully watched. Mixing must then be continued until all particles are fully coated with the cement–water matrix. Where lightweight aggregates are used, two points must be carefully watched. First, lightweight aggregates are water absorbent; the effective water–cement ratio is thus variable and not easy to determine. This may lead to excessively wet or excessively dry mixes being used. Secondly, some lightweight aggregates, being more friable than gravel, tend to be abraded in the mixer and to produce a mass of fine material if mixing is allowed to continue for too long. With drum mixers it is advisable to pour some water into the drum before the dry material is added. The rest of the water is then poured. This makes for a more uniform mix and prevents it from sticking to the sides of the drum. With open pan type mixers, the solids are placed in the pan first and the water is added since the mix is scraped off the side of the pans in the mixing process.

No-fines concrete made with gravel pours as easily as loose ballast and so is more or less self-packing. It is not recommended to rod the concrete after placing, as this can lead to the creation of local high density. The concrete dries rapidly, and it is therefore important to pour continuously. No-fines concrete will not normally segregate so it can be dropped from a greater height than fully graded concrete. This allows the use of greater lifts in one operation and therefore fewer horizontal joints.

It is possible to pour the walls of a house to 3-storey height in one day, so obviating construction joints. Pouring at uneven depths should be avoided, otherwise diagonal joints will be formed which are a source of weakness in the finished walls.

Horizontal reinforcing rods are sometimes placed above and below the

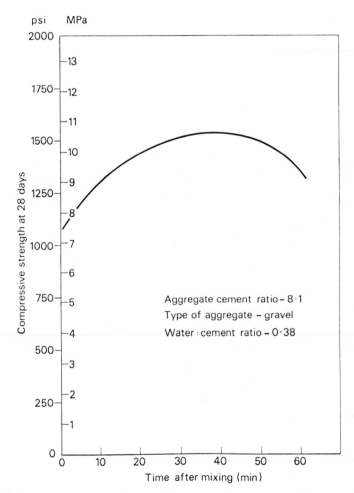

FIG. 7.6 Effect of delays between mixing and placing on compressive strength of no-fines concrete.

openings, and diagonal shear reinforcement across the angles, but more often the reinforcement is confined to a ring at eaves level. When reinforcement is used, an application of cement grout to the reinforcement reduces the risk of corrosion. The external rendering must, however, be regarded as the main protection against penetration of water to the steel.

The density of no-fines concrete is about two-thirds to three-quarters of that of normal concrete made from the same aggregate. The pressure of no-fines concrete on formwork is therefore very much less than that of dense concrete. Because of the reduced pressure and the absence of 'fines' less robust and so less expensive shuttering may be used. Such shuttering usually takes the form of plywood on a light timber frame with steel walings or perforated sheet or wire mesh suitable framed.

Delays between mixing no-fines concrete and placing the wet mix on site affect the compressive strength (Fig. 7.6). Maximal strength is normally obtained by placing about half and hour after the mixing process has been completed.

FIG. 7.7   Two-storey no-fines concrete houses during construction, showing details of the shuttering system used.

With no-fines concrete the amount of skilled labour required is much less and the construction more rapid than for many other forms of wall construction. However, owing to the cost of the shutters, no-fines concrete construction is only economical if design is based on repetition of the floor-plan. Figure 7.7 shows no-fines, cast *in situ* concrete houses in the course of construction, and the shuttering system used.

DESIGN

The design of no-fines concrete structures is guided by similar considerations to those for other lightweight concrete structures (Chapters 9 and 14). Reinforcement has not been employed often with no-fines concrete in the past because resistance to corrosion of embedded steel is difficult to ensure. In most cases, however, the basic structural concept of no-fines concrete buildings must be in harmony with the conditions which determine the strength and stability of a monolithic box construction. In low rise structures the risks of progressive collapse due to accidental loading (such as explosions) are not considered to be critical although some code authorities require special measures against progressive collapse even for low-rise structures. Peripheral steel reinforcement in the walls, or special

Fig. 7.8 Use of peripheral reinforcement at floor levels for no-fines concrete walls.

reinforcement to provide tension-resistant joints between vertical and horizontal loadbearing membranes, have not been required hitherto. Nevertheless, as a measure of additional safety against collapse and loss of serviceability some horizontal reinforcement —usually welded steel mesh— has been incorporated at floor levels, even in two-storey houses (Fig. 7.8). It seems doubtful if such reinforcement can be effective over more than a limited period in an environment exposed to the weather unless it is specially protected against corrosion. This is unlikely to lead to disruption of the concrete by corrosion products, however, since the diameter of the steel bars is normally slight. It would seem that in areas liable to seismic disturbances specially designed reinforcement, adequately protected to ensure durability, would have to be provided. Alternatively, in such circumstances a cast-*in-situ* or precast structural frame would be needed to resist seismic forces.

Reinforcement must be provided over openings in the wall; in German practice a type of lintel has been provided by using fully graded concrete in the wall over openings, reinforced with embedded bars. The dense concrete can provide protection against corrosion which cannot be given by the no-fines concrete, which rapidly becomes carbonated. Reinforcing bars embedded in no-fines concretes should always be anchored at the ends with hooks. In addition to bars over openings, it is considered advisable, for safety against accidents, to provide some reinforcement at sills under window openings. This is accepted practice in Germany and France.

The fixing of heavy appliances to no-fines concrete walls presents similar problems to those with other lightweight and particularly with aerated concrete walls. Fastenings which can be safely used with ordinary concrete or brick walls could pull out, together with parts of the wall itself, when fitted to such low-strength materials. It is therefore usually necessary for such appliances—wash basins, lavatory and bidet pans, machine fixings etc.—to be attached by bolting through the wall to encased wood or metal anchor plates. It is evident, however, that whatever fixing method is used, its effectiveness and reliability will depend largely on the care and workmanship with which the work is carried out on the site. Lighter fittings—pipes, shelves etc.—can be screwed or nailed to wood blocks embedded in the concrete, having been fastened to the shuttering before pouring the concrete. Similarly, cavities, chases and openings for services, ducts etc. should be formed by inserting suitable cores in the shuttering before casting the concrete. Cutting finished no-fines concrete should be avoided since it is likely to lead to extensive damage.

For the structural design of loadbearing, no-fines concrete walls a load factor of about 5·5 is considered acceptable in ordinary conditions of use. This means that for simple ordinary walls having a slenderness ratio, (i.e. height/thickness) of less than 15, using a concrete mix of 1:8 by volume, the 28-day cube strength should be not less than 5·5 times the working design stress in the wall. For such a concrete mix 180–190 kg cement is normally used for each cubic metre of aggregate.[3]

TESTING NO-FINES CONCRETE

To arrive at the controlled strength of no-fines concrete in a uniform and comparable way, a special British Standard method and apparatus have been developed for testing no-fines concrete.[4] The specimens must be made within 5 min of mixing the concrete, which is placed in two equal layers in the mould, each being tamped by 10 blows from a given height with a standard rod (Fig. 7.9). The cubes are cured at 20 per cent r.h. and $20 \pm 2\,°C$ for 16–24 hrs in their moulds under tarpaulins or plastic sheeting.

(a)

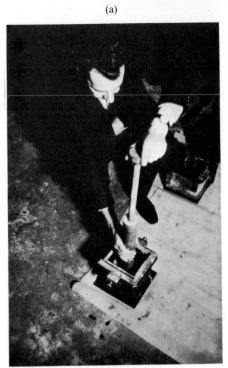

(b)

FIG. 7.9   Test method and equipment to obtain the cube strength of no-fines concrete.

Demoulding may be delayed by a further 24 hrs. The surfaces of the specimens are then wetted and dried; after being kept in polythene bags for 6 days, they are stored in bags in dry air in the testing laboratory. Not less than 3 cubes are crushed for each age of testing.

REFERENCES

1. Scottish Special Housing Association, Private Communication.
2. Wimpey Laboratories Ltd, Private Communication.
3. British Standard Code of Practice, CP 111:1970. 'Structural Recommendations for Loadbearing Walls', British Standards Institution.
4. British Standard, BS 1881, Part 3:1970.

CHAPTER EIGHT

Lightweight Aggregate and Loadbearing Lightweight Aggregate Concrete

SUMMARY

A description is given of the properties and mode of manufacture of lightweight aggregates suitable for the making of loadbearing concretes. Typical values are given for the properties of lightweight aggregate concrete.

INTRODUCTION

The consumption of aggregates of all types has been increasing in recent years in most countries at a rate far exceeding that suggested by the growth rate of their economy or of their construction industries. In part at least, this is caused by the increasing tempo of road building, the aggregate for which has to be added to the consumption of aggregate in construction concrete. Artificial, manufactured aggregates are normally more expensive to produce than normal natural aggregates, but the overall cost of aggregate is more sensitive to transport charges than to the cost of manufacture. The cost of transporting lightweight aggregate is naturally lower than that of transporting dense aggregates. When, therefore, the available source of natural aggregates is at a considerable distance from the point of use, manufactured aggregates at a lesser distance may even have a cost advantage.

There are however other factors to be considered. The continued and expanding extraction of natural aggregate is accompanied by serious environmental problems. Often it leads to irremediable deterioration of the countryside. It is known that the extraction of crushed rock aggregate from suitable quarries is 30–60 times more efficient in obtaining material than the digging of gravel from pits, in relation to disturbed surface area. On the other hand, artificial aggregates can be produced often from industrial wastes such as slag, colliery waste shale, slate waste, and pulverised-fuel ash. In industrial areas, therefore, the use of these kinds of artificial material would relieve industry of troublesome pollutants, a social benefit of rapidly increasing importance.

In this chapter each of the lightweight aggregates are considered in turn,

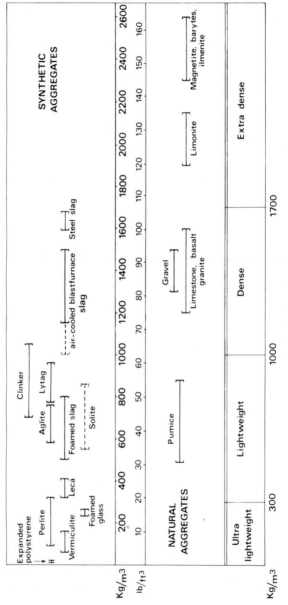

FIG. 8.1 Loose bulk density of various coarse aggregates.

but in order to show at a glance how each stands on the scale of density, this information is given in Fig. 8.1.

FURNACE CLINKER

The British Standard 1165:1966, 'Clinker aggregate for plain and precast concrete', defines clinker as 'well-burnt furnace residues which have been fused or sintered into lumps and excludes residues from furnaces fired with pulverised fuel'. This wording is intended expressly to prevent the use of coal ashes from domestic grates, as these have not been heated to a high enough temperature, so are too fine and too soft for use as an aggregate. This in effect limits the material defined to that produced by high-temperature boiler furnaces using chain-grate stokers such as those still employed at many power stations, although locomotive ashes can sometimes be used. The term 'breeze' is frequently used when 'furnace clinker' is intended; the former name is more properly applied to the fine fraction of coke and the indiscriminate use of the word 'breeze' leads to confusion, particularly as coke breeze was formerly used quite extensively in making lightweight concrete blocks.

Clinker has its origin in the mineral matter, principally calcite, kaolinite and pyrites, invariably present in coal and which after burning has a chemical composition such as that shown in Table 8.1. This table indicates

TABLE 8.1
CHEMICAL COMPOSITION OF COAL CLINKER
(PER CENT)

Silicon oxide (SiO_2)	25–50
Aluminium oxide (Al_2O_3)	20–40
Ferric oxide (Fe_2O_3)	0–30
Calcium oxide (CaO)	1–10
Magnesium oxide (MgO)	0·5–5
Titanium oxide (TiO_2)	0–3
Alkali ($Na,K,)_2O$	1–6
Sulphur trioxide (SO_3)	1–12

the elements present and the proportions in which they occur. This is a conventional mode of expression and is not intended to imply that the minerals are present solely or mainly as oxides; indeed, they occur largely as silicates of aluminium, although oxides of calcium and iron are normally present.

Most of the clinker used as aggregate is derived from chain-grate stokers. In this type of plant, the fuel is ignited on the surface of the fire-bed, and if the temperature is high enough to fuse the ash, this will drip through the bed and freeze into glassy globules in the cooler zone below. If, however, the softened ash remains plastic for a long time, it may coalesce into large clinkers. The behaviour of the ash is complicated by the fact that coal ash is not homogeneous, but consists of two components—a highly refractory portion derived from the kaolinite and like minerals, and the more readily fusible pyrites together with the fluxing agent calcite. Consequently the clinker consists of glassy masses with inclusions of refractory fragments, together with nodules of unburnt fuel, the latter being thereby protected from combustion. The significance of this brief reference to the chemical composition and mode of formation of clinker will be appreciated in the subsequent discussion on the imperfections of clinker as an aggregate, and the precautions necessary with its use in concrete.

Clinker has been used as an aggregate in Britain for about 90 years and it is still an important aggregate in terms of quantity used. The popularity of clinker has been due to its low price and the very great quantities which have hitherto been available. Its availability has however been much affected by the increased use of pulverised coal, and in many areas it is no longer cheap or plentiful. In the USA, clinker, (known as 'cinder') has been used for about as long as in Britain, and it is still widely employed in spite of the large output and wide range of alternative aggregates. Clinker at its best makes a very good aggregate, if somewhat high on the scale of density, but it varies widely in quality. The poorer grades can readily lead to building failures and have consequently earned the material an indifferent reputation, notwithstanding which it still has a widespread use for the reasons already given. Poor quality clinker containing a large proportion of combustible matter yields concrete of poor strength and high drying shrinkage. For example, Lea[1] in 1929 showed that the general quality of clinker concrete decreased as the combustible matter contained in the aggregate increased. After an interval of nearly 30 years the Building Research Station made a study of contemporary clinker and obtained results in close agreement with the earlier work. The results of the more recent investigation are summarised in Table 8.2.

The combustible matter in well-fused clinker may be as low as 1–2 per cent, but values of 15–25 per cent are more common and 60 per cent fuel content is not unknown. An estimate of the combustible matter in clinker can be made with sufficient accuracy by the loss-on-ignition test described in the British Standard 3681:1973.[2] The specification lays down that when tested by the prescribed method, the loss-on-ignition shall not exceed the values given in Table 8.3. The American Standard ASTM C331 permits 3·5 per cent of combustible matter in cinder for aggregate.

When concrete of high potential drying shrinkage is used in the form of building blocks, the large shrinkage movements which take place as the wall continues to dry out after plastering often lead to cracking of the

TABLE 8.2
EFFECT OF COMBUSTIBLE CONTENT ON THE PROPERTIES OF CLINKER CONCRETE

Combustible content of aggregate (per cent)	Mix proportions cement:aggregate (by volume)	Compressive strength at 28 days		Drying shrinkage (per cent)	Moisture expansion (per cent)
		(MPa)	(psi)		
5·4	1:6	7·4	1 075	0·045	0·039
	1:10	3·2	460	0·036	0·034
18·4	1:6	5·4	790	0·066	0·060
	1:10	1·9	270	0·052	0·053
31·4	1:6	4·5	650	0·082	0·076
	1:10	1·2	175	0·065	0·071

plaster. Another and more serious trouble which sometimes accompanies the use of clinker concrete is a progressive expansion of the hardened concrete. This may cause cracking in *in situ* concrete of such severity that walls become fissured and often quite unsafe. Likewise expansion in floors and roof screeds has caused displacement of walls and parapets to an extent which has made reconstruction necessary. Clinkers causing such expansion in concrete are termed 'unsound'.

Lea[3] has shown that unsoundness is due to the presence of certain types of coal in an unburnt or slightly burnt condition. Not all coals behave in this way and even the coals which he described as 'dangerous' will not cause expansion if they have been well carbonised. The total amount of combustible matter in a clinker is therefore not an indication of the likelihood of unsoundness, since such combustible matter may vary from unburnt coal to fully-carbonised material, and in any case the coal itself may belong to the dangerous or non-dangerous class. British Standard 3681:1963[2] prescribes the method for carrying out the soundness test, which consists essentially of observing the stability of a hardened mortar-pat made up of Portland cement, plaster of Paris and powdered clinker,

TABLE 8.3
PERMISSIBLE LIMITS FOR LOSS-ON-IGNITION IN CLINKER

Class	Use	Loss-on-ignition (per cent)
A1	Aggregate for use in plain concrete for general purposes	Not greater than 10
A2	Aggregate for use in *in situ* concrete for interior work not exposed to damp conditions	Not greater than 20
B	Aggregate for precast clinker concrete blocks	Not greater than 25

cast on to a glass plate. Radial cracks and lifting of the edges of the pat are deemed to indicate unsoundness.

Spalling of clinker concrete is caused by the swelling which accompanies the hydration of hard-burnt lime,[4] magnesia or calcium sulphate, which may occur as particles in the clinker. Although this kind of defect does not lead to any structural hazard it often occurs after walls built of clinker concrete have been plastered and decorated, so that inconvenience and expense is incurred in making good spalled plaster and paintwork. Also, oxidation of iron compounds such as pyrites may cause staining of clinker concrete. To avoid these troubles, it is recommended that the clinker should be exposed to the weather for a few months. This helps to hydrate the lime, magnesia, and anhydrite, and to oxidise the iron compounds, so that they have reached a stable state before they are incorporated in the concrete mix.

Provided that the sulphur content does not exceed about 1 per cent, expressed as sulphur trioxide, little trouble is to be expected from this element, and the British Standard for clinker limits the acid soluble sulphur content to this amount. However, in combination with other factors, sulphur compounds accelerate the corrosion of steel reinforcement, and in Great Britain, for this reason, clinker is not permitted for reinforced concrete; nor is its use allowed in any position in contact with steelwork.

It has already been stated that clinker at its best is a very satisfactory aggregate, but that much of the clinker which is offered to the concrete industry is far from satisfactory, particularly on account of the high proportion of fuel which it contains. As the supply of clinker is diminishing many users are forced to be less discriminating, and clinker which formerly would have been discarded is now being used, so that the general quality of the material is tending to deteriorate. According to the Building Research Station most of the combustible matter is present in the finer material and it has been shown that the fuel content of a clinker can often be reduced from more than 30 per cent to 5 per cent by screening and discarding the fines. Alternatively, flotation or pneumatic and jigging table separation can be employed. The Station has also explored the possibility of removing the excess fuel by re-burning on a sinter-strand with a strong air draught. Experimental work in which the fuel content was reduced in this way from 57 per cent to 3 per cent gave improvements in clinker quality as shown in Table 8.4.

It has sometimes been argued that the cleaning of clinker would be uneconomical because such a low-priced commodity could not bear the cost; it is, however, this low initial purchasing price which would make the cost of processing tolerable. Whilst clinker formerly had little competition from other lightweight aggregates of greater technical merit, this situation is rapidly changing, and clinker, in so far as it continues to be available, will sooner or later have to compare favourably in quality with the newer

TABLE 8.4
EFFECT OF RE-BURNING CLINKER

Aggregate	Mix proportions cement: aggregate (by volume)	Compressive strength of concrete at 28 days		Drying shrinkage (per cent)	Moisture expansion (per cent)	Dry density of concrete	
		(MPa)	(psi)			(kg/m³)	(pcf)
Raw clinker (57% fuel)	1:6	5·27	765	0·061	0·056	1 040	65
Re-burnt clinker (3% fuel)	1:6	6·96	1 010	0·026	0·021	1 344	84

aggregates or its use in concrete will cease. It is very unlikely that the cost of cleaning or otherwise improving the quality of clinker would raise its price beyond the ruling prices for other processed aggregates which possess the desired properties.

Typical properties of clinker concrete are summarised in Table 8.5.

TABLE 8.5
PROPERTIES OF CLINKER CONCRETE

Dry density of concrete		Compressive strength at 28 days		Drying shrinkage (per cent)	Thermal conductivity, k-value	
(kg/m³)	(pcf)	(MPa)	(psi)		(W/m °C)	(Btu in/ft² h °F)
1 040– 1 520	65–95	2·0–6·9	300– 1 000	0·04–0·08	0·33–0·56	2·4–4·0

FOAMED BLAST-FURNACE SLAG

In the operation of a blast-furnace, the iron oxide ore is reduced to metallic iron by means of coke, while the silica and alumina constituent combine with lime (included in the furnace charge), to form a molten slag which collects on top of the iron. This slag has a composition somewhat as shown in Table 8.6.

The slag issues from the furnace as a molten stream at 1400–1600 °C. If this is allowed to cool slowly, it solidifies to a grey, crystalline stony material, known as 'air-cooled slag', which is used as road-stone and as an aggregate for heavy concrete.[5] Cooling of the slag with a large excess of

TABLE 8.6

COMPOSITION   OF   BLAST-FURNACE   SLAG
(PER CENT)

Calcium oxide (CaO)	30–50
Silicon oxide (SiO_2)	28–38
Aluminium oxide (Al_2O_3)	8–24
Magnesium oxide (MgO)	1–18
Iron oxide (Fe_2O_3)	0·5–1
Sulphur trioxide (SO_3)	2–8

water produces 'granulated slag', a more friable material. Chilling with a controlled amount of water, applied in such a way as to trap the steam in the mass, gives a porous product of pumice-like character, termed 'foamed slag', or 'expanded slag', which on cooling is used as a lightweight aggregate (Fig. 8.2). This basic process with several modifications of varying degrees of sophistication has been used in the several countries which produce this aggregate. In Britain the manufacturer employs a large pond or foaming bed in the bottom and sides of which are water sprays and into which an entire ladle of molten slag is tipped in one operation. Figure 8.3 shows the stages of the operation. The foaming period is a matter of moments and the mass of foamed slag can be removed by a mechanical drag-line almost immediately, thereby vacating the pond for the next charge. For a time an American method, the Kinney–Osborne Process,

FIG. 8.2   Foamed slag aggregate.

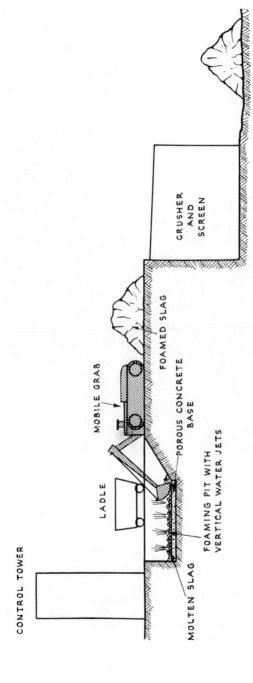

FIG. 8.3   Schematic drawing of the Gallai–Hatchard slag foaming plant.

FIG. 8.4   The foaming jets in the Kinney–Osborne process.

was also used in the UK. This employed a series of jets which directed
compressed air, steam, and water spray against a falling stream of molten
slag (Fig. 8.4). Whichever method of foaming has been employed, the
product is crushed and screened to sizes suitable as lightweight aggregate.
The gradings currently produced are Coarse Aggregate, 14–3 mm ($\frac{9}{16}$–
$\frac{1}{8}$ in.), and Fine Aggregate, 3–0 mm ($\frac{1}{8}$–0 in.).

The chemical analysis of foamed slag is very little different from that of
the original molten slag except that the sulphur content is somewhat lower,
this reduction having resulted from reaction of the sulphides with water and
the liberation of sulphur gases. The mineralogical composition may,
however, suffer considerable change during the transition from liquid to

solid, such changes being relating to the conditions of cooling. For example, Parker[6] has shown that foaming removes 'unsoundness' in almost all slags, and that a slag which when air-cooled may 'fall' or dust by β to γ dicalcium silicate inversion is rendered stable by foaming. British Standard 877, 'Foamed blast-furnace slag for concrete aggregate', limits the lime (CaO) content to 50 per cent, and also limits to 0.5 per cent the sulphate available to extraction under certain conditions which are specified.

TABLE 8.7
PROPERTIES OF FOAMED SLAG CONCRETE

Mix proportions cement: aggregate (by volume)	Dry density		Compressive strength at 28 days				Drying shrinkage (per cent)	Thermal conductivity, k-value	
			Semi-dry for blocks		Fully compacted mixes				
								(W/m °C)	(Btu in/ ft² h °F)
	(kg/m³)	(pcf)	(MPa)	(psi)	(MPa)	(psi)			
1:4			—	—	22·7	3 300	0·07	—	—
1:5			—	—	17·2	2 500	0·06	0·43	3·0
1:6			6·2	900	11·0	1 600	0·05–0·055	0·35	2·4
1:8	960– 1 760	60– 110	4·8	700	7·6	1 100	—	—	—
1:10			3·4	500	—	—	0·045–0·05	0·29	2·0
1:12			2·1	300	—	—	0·03–0·04	—	—
1:15			1·7	250	—	—	—	—	—
1:20			1·4	200	—	—	—	0·24	1·7
1:24			1·2	180	—	—	—	—	—

The only significant chemical property of foamed slag when used as a concrete aggregate is its hydraulicity. It is not as active as granulated slag but many foamed slags do exhibit hydraulic activity, and when mixed with lime or Portland cement, develop cementing action which augments the strength of concretes in which they are used.

The foaming of slag was first carried out by Karl Schol in Germany in 1911, but it was not until 1935 that the process was introduced into the UK, where it is second only to furnace clinker in terms of quantity used.

At the Building Research Station and elsewhere a great deal of investigation has been carried out on foamed slag, and this together with 40 years of practical experience has given the material a reputation as a good and reliable aggregate. Table 8.7 gives some typical results of tests on foamed slag concrete.

In Britain at the present time, foamed slag is used as an aggregate in concrete building blocks and in insulating concrete roof screeds. About two-thirds of the aggregate is employed in blocks and the remainder mainly in screeds although a limited amount is used for *in-situ* loadbearing walls in 2-storey houses. A new process has been developed in England for the production of pelletised foamed slag but this is not yet available commercially.

EXPANDED CLAY AND EXPANDED SHALE AGGREGATE

When certain clays and shales are heated to a semi-plastic stage, often termed 'the point of incipient fusion', they expand or 'bloat' to as much as seven times their original volume, owing to the formation of gas within the mass of the material at the fusion temperature. The cellular structure so formed is retained on cooling and the product may be used as a lightweight aggregate. For the production of such aggregate, the clay should soften at a temperature which can be reached and maintained economically and at the same time it should contain constituents which will produce gases at such temperature. If such constituents are not present naturally in the clay, they may be incorporated during manufacture.

The relationship between the chemical composition and the ability to bloat has been studied by many workers ever since Jackson[7] put forward his theories in 1903. A very comprehensive account of an investigation was given by Riley[8] in 1950. There can be no doubt that a thorough understanding of the factors which contribute to bloating is very desirable, but for practical purposes, the empirical assessment of clays in regard to their 'bloatability' is much speedier and more directly informative than expensive mineral analyses. A first indication of the bloating characteristics of clays and shales can be obtained by heating individual pellets of the material at various temperatures over the range at which such bloating is likely to take place. It is essential that the clay should be raised to the operative temperature very rapidly, and it is very convenient if the required range of temperature can be obtained in a single furnace. Such a furnace has been designed at the Building Research Station. In this there are 12 temperature zones between 120 and 1350 °C. A separate sample for each temperature level (consisting of two pellets) is fired for 5 min and then quickly removed from the furnace. When cool, the pellets are measured and the expansion computed. Thus the optimum temperature for the bloating can be assessed.

Expanded clays and shales have been used in the USA and continental Europe for many years. In the USA, expanded shales were used as aggregate for concrete ships in the First World War.[9] The well-known product 'Haydite' was produced in the early 1920s and is still being produced from shale or clay in rotary kilns fired by oil, gas, or pulverised fuel.

Expanded shales and clays are also produced on sintering hearths, and have been so made for many years, the first being manufactured in 1931 under the name Lytag, (not to be confused with a present-day product of the same name made in England, which is a sintered pulverised-fuel ash aggregate.) A more recent aggregate produced in the USA from clay expanded on a sintered hearth is Aglite.

In North America to-day there are probably about 60 different brands of expanded clay and shale aggregates and perhaps 100 or more separate plants. The best-known of the expanded shales in the USA are, Basalite, Crestlite, Rocklite, Materialite, Lite-rock, Galite, and Nytralite, and the expanded clays, Aglite and Gravelite. The brand names Haydite and Solite are used for both shales and clays.. In Canada, the expanded shales are Herculite, Saturnalite, and Aggrite, and the expanded clays Solite, Lite-rock and Echo-lite.

In Europe, the Danish-produced Leca has been made for more than 35 years, and is now produced under licence in many other countries. This is a light, rounded, smooth-skinned clay product made in a rotary kiln.

FIG. 8.5   The sintering hearth used in the process for producing Aglite.

FIG. 8.6 Rotary kiln used in the production of Aglite.

Expanded shale aggregate is manufactured in Holland, Germany, Poland, USSR, and elsewhere in Europe.

No doubt because of the large supplies of furnace clinker and foamed slag which have for so long been available in the UK, there was formerly limited interest in expanded clay, although there was some production for ship-building during the Second World War. (See Fig. 1.4). In the early 1950s, however, production of expanded clay was started under licence from LECA of Denmark. This is still an important aggregate in England.

For nearly 20 years Aglite has been produced in Britain as well as in the USA, by the sintering-hearth method. In the UK, this aggregate is being made from clay mixed with ground coke, but is also being manufactured from shale-bearing waste from coal-washing plants. Figure 8.5 shows the sintering hearth, and Fig. 8.6, the rotary kiln.

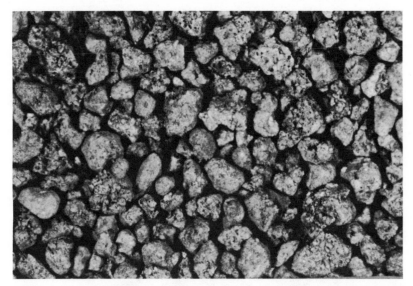

Fɪɢ. 8.7   Aglite expanded clay aggregate manufactured on sinter-strand.

As with other lightweight aggregates, concrete produced from expanded clay or shale depends for its strength not only upon the inherent strength of the aggregate, but also upon the degree of compaction, which in turn is influenced by the shape and grading of the aggregate. It is sometimes said that fragmental aggregate is capable of giving the greater strength, but that the rounded material gives better workability and so may often lead

TABLE 8.8

PROPERTIES TO BE EXPECTED FROM VARIOUS DENSITY GRADES OF FULLY-COMPACTED EXPANDED CLAY CONCRETE

Dry density of concrete		Compressive strength of concrete at 28 days		Drying shrinkage (per cent)	Thermal conductivity, k-value	
(kg/m³)	(pcf)	(MPa)	(psi)		(W/m °C)	(Btu in/ft² h °F)
960	60	9·0	1 300			
1 120	70	11·0	1 600			
1 280	80	13·8	2 000	0·04–0·07	0·22–0·58	1·5–4·0
1 440	90	22·0	3 200			
1 600	100	40·0	5 800			
1 760	110	62·0	9 000			

FIG. 8.8 Leca expanded clay aggregate made in rotary kiln.

indirectly to stronger concrete, if only by permitting a lower water/cement ratio. Practical experience, however, seems to show that it is the shape of the fine fraction and the grading of this which influences the workability of the mix and the fines derived from a so-called rounded aggregate may be as harsh and irregular as that from a fragmental aggregate. The workability of a harsh aggregate can usually be improved by the use of air-entraining agents in the mixing water. Figure 8.7 shows the irregularly shaped aggregate produced on the sinter-strand, and Fig. 8.8 the smooth rounded sort obtained from the rotary kiln.

With careful grading and good compaction, the lighter types of expanded clay aggregate can produce remarkably strong concrete at modest density (Table 8.8). Indeed, the strength to be expected from a mix depends very much on the grading, the water/cement ratio and the degree

TABLE 8.9

PROPERTIES OF SEMI-DRY MIXES OF EXPANDED CLAY CONCRETE

Type of aggregate	Dry density of concrete		Compressive strength at 28 days		Drying shrinkage (per cent)	Thermal conductivity, k-value	
	(kg/m³)	(pcf)	(MPa)	(psi)		(W/m °C)	(Btu in/ft² h °F)
Light clay aggregate 1:6 mix	720	45	2·4	350	0·045	0·20	1·4
Expanded shale aggregate 1:6 mix	1 280	80	13·4	1 950	0·05	0·49	3·4
1:9 mix	1 200	75	5·4	800	0·05	0·40	2·8

of compaction. The mix design of lightweight concrete is dealt with in Chapter 3.

Semi-dry partially-compacted mixes suitable for block-making give much lower strengths. Some typical examples are given in Table 8.9.

EXPANDED SLATE

Slate is a low-grade metamorphic rock which has usually been derived from fine-grained sediments such as shale, or in some cases from fine-grained volcanic tuffs. Under the influence of the metamorphic stresses minute crystals of flaky minerals grew with their platy surfaces at right angles to the direction of maximum compressive stress. The rock thus developed a preferential split direction or slaty cleavage parallel to the flat surfaces of the grains.

In Britain 75 per cent of the Welsh slate is used as roofing slates, but there is an increasing demand for larger slabs of slate for architectural decoration.

Slate is won from quarries, and the process produces a high proportion of waste at all stages; in blasting from the quarry face, in cutting up the large blocks, and in the final splitting, which is still carried out manually with hammer and chisel. Overall the proportion of waste to marketable slate is about 20 to 1, though in difficult seams it may be much higher.

About 1·2 million tonnes of slate waste are produced annually in Wales alone. Apart from the current production, old tips in this area hold 300–500 million tonnes.

Just as heat treatment of certain clays and shales causes them to expand
so as to give a product suitable as an aggregate for lightweight concrete, so
some slates have been found to behave in much the same way. When heated
quickly to a sufficiently high temperature, these slates lose their
characteristic close laminar structure and expand to several times their
original thickness, thereby giving a product containing a large number of

FIG. 8.9   Slate expanded by heat in comparison with raw slate.

minute cavities sufficiently light to float on water. Figure 8.9 shows the
effect of heating a single piece of slate. The expansion is due to the
generation of gases from the decomposition of certain constituents of the
slate, the evolution of these gases taking place when the slate is in the plastic
state.

The useful employment of slate-waste could substantially change the
economic situation of the slate industry. This has been realised for many
years and investigations into the production of expanded slate as an
aggregate were carried out at the Building Research Station as early as
1932. An account of the employment of expanded slate as lightweight
aggregate was given by Coleman in 1936.[10]

For successful expansion, the slate must be of such composition that it
commences to fuse just before the evolution of the gas. The rate of heating
must be rapid, otherwise the gases will be generated so slowly that they will
be dissipated without expanding the slate. An examination of Welsh slates
showed that those occurring amongst the Ordovician and Silurian

formations expanded most readily. Suitable slates show expansion of 3–7 times their original volume. Anything less than a three-fold expansion would not give an aggregate which would be regarded as satisfactory from the point of view of lightness.

When broken across, a nodule of expanded slate is seen to be composed of small cells separated by glassy walls, the whole being covered by a vitrified skin, by virtue of which it is impervious to water in spite of its porous interior.

In making a lightweight aggregate from slate-waste, the raw material is first crushed and then heated in a rotary kiln. By proper grading of the crushed material before firing, it is possible to produce an aggregate of the required grading, consisting solely of nodules having a vitreous skin. By this means, a somewhat more impervious aggregate is obtained than would be possible by crushing large lumps after burning, since the crushing breaks through the fused skin, thereby exposing the more porous interior. Nevertheless, aggregate which has been crushed after firing is not particularly absorbent, for example, broken nodules held under water for a week will, after release, float for two months or more, before sufficient water has been absorbed to cause them to sink. Slate crushed after being expanded tends to break along laminar planes which are retained in the material.

The strength obtained from expanded slate aggregate concrete is comparable with that from other lightweight concretes of similar density, while the drying shrinkage is better than for most lightweight concretes. Table 8.10 gives a summary of the values to be expected from expanded slate aggregate concrete.

In the USA many plants manufacture lightweight expanded slate

TABLE 8.10
PROPERTIES OF EXPANDED SLATE CONCRETE

Mix proportions cement: aggregate (by volume)	Dry density of concrete		Compressive strength at 28 days		Drying shrinkage (per cent)	Thermal conductivity, k-value	
	(kg/m³)	(pcf)	(MPa)	(psi)		(W/m °C)	(Btu in/ft² h °F)
Semi-dry mixes							
1:6	640–1 280	40–80	3·1–6·2	450–900 }	0·03–0·04	0·14–0·29	1·0–2·0
1:11	560–960	35–60	1·4–2·1	200–300 }			
Compacted mixes reported by US Bureau of Standards							
1:2·8	1 360	85	27·6	4 000 ⎤		0·49	3·4
1:3·7	1 296	81	23·8	3 450 ⎟	0·08–0·09	0·43	3·0
1:5·2	1 184	74	15·9	2 300 ⎟		0·40	2·8
1:9·0	1 168	73	9·0	1 300 ⎦		0·40	2·8

aggregate, and the production of these in 1968 was 630 000 tonnes. Examples are Penlite, made in Pennsylvania, and Verlite, produced in Vermont.

SINTERED PULVERISED-FUEL ASH

Pulverised-fuel ash may be described as the residue from the combustion of powdered coal in the modern boiler-furnaces such as are used in many of our power-generating stations to-day. It is a grey powder much resembling Portland cement in fineness and in general appearance. Being so fine, the ash is gas-borne and can be removed from the flue-gas only by electrostatic precipitators, cyclone separators or wet scrubbers, or some combination of these. The ash consists mainly of minute spherical glassy particles as can be seen in Fig. 8.10. By heat treatment, these small particles can be made to cohere, thus forming porous pellets or nodules which have considerable strength. The process of causing this cohesion is termed 'sintering'. A much enlarged cross-section of a sintered pellet is shown in Fig. 8.11.

The output of pulverised-fuel ash in the UK is now over 10 million tonnes per annum and is increasing year by year, as powdered coal comes more and more into favour as a boiler fuel. This has necessarily had the effect of

FIG. 8.10   Pulverised-fuel ash seen under the microscope.

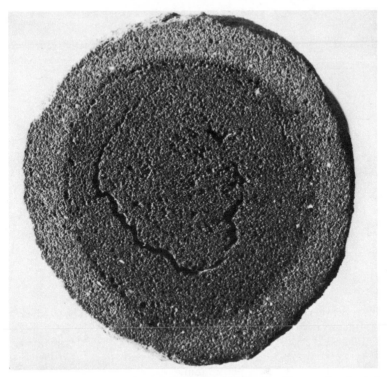

FIG. 8.11   The cross-section of a pulverised-fuel ash pellet, much enlarged.

reducing the production of furnace clinker, hitherto the principal lightweight aggregate, which is the product of chain-grates and similar types of stokers, and it is appropriate that a major outlet for pulverised-fuel ash should be the production of lightweight aggregate. The sintered aggregate is shown in Fig. 8.12.

The first description of a process employed for making aggregate from pulverised-fuel ash appears to be that given by Leftwich in 1946. This process however employed a mixture of clinker, slag, and pulverised-fuel ash as the raw feed. Reference to experiments in America was given by Whitaker[11] in 1953, and the Annual Report of the Building Research Board for 1952[12] showed that work had already been done in the UK at the Building Research Station on the sintering of this ash, work which was continued in the following years, as reported in later publications.[13,14] A paper by Hobbs[15] shows however that others were working independently on this, and subsequently plants were built in the USA and Japan, as well as in the UK.

FIG. 8.12 Sintered pulverised-fuel ash aggregate.

In recent years sintered pulverised-fuel ash aggregate has been advertised from time to time as being available in several parts of the USA, but it is questionable if any of these plants are still in operation. Meanwhile in the UK Lytag continues to be produced after 15 years or so, and the current production is 300 000 tons per annum.

Sintering of pulverised-fuel ash may be effected in several ways. The methods which have received most attention so far are those employing the sintering-strand and the vertical shaft kiln, although some experimental work has been done on rotary kilns. Experience has shown however that of these the sinter-strand method is the only one suitable for the firing of pulverised-fuel ash.

Before the ash can be sintered, it must first be made into pellets or nodules in order to give a permeable fire-bed. This can be done by simply feeding the ash into a tilted rotating pan under a fine spray of water. The rotary motion of the pan causes the material to cascade and with this pellets are formed, which are robust enough to withstand subsequent handling.

Although sintered pulverised-fuel ash is a coal residue and has the same basic mineral composition as furnace clinker, it differs from the latter in important respects:

(1) The fuel content of sintered pulverised-fuel ash is negligible (whatever it might have been in the raw ash), whereas the fuel remaining in clinker may be very high, and sometimes of a chemically unstable character.

(2)   Because of the fineness of pulverised-fuel ash, minerals such as pyrites and lime, which are potentially injurious substances, cannot, as in clinker, be present in high local concentrations, but are uniformly distributed and thus harmless. Moreover, because of the fineness, any unstable minerals, if they were present, would be very reactive, and by quickly reaching their ultimate state would obviate such troubles as 'lime-popping' and rust staining which could otherwise arise from delayed reaction.

Concrete made from sintered pulverised-fuel ash aggregate is extensively used for structural reinforced and prestressed work and many examples of its use in this way are to be seen throughout the UK. Other uses for sintered pulverised-fuel ash aggregate include lightweight concrete blocks, roof and floor screeding.

The thermal conductivity (k-value) of concrete made from sintered pulverised-fuel ash aggregate lies in the range 0·22–0·50 W/m/°C (1.52–3.46 Btu in/ft²/h/°F).

Sintered pulverised-fuel ash has an advantage over some other lightweight aggregates in that it is generally produced in or near to populous areas where it is required as an aggregate. For example, the large populations of Merseyside and Lancashire, the industrial Midlands and Greater London and Thames-side, each have about 16 power stations. Pulverised-fuel ash thus avoids the high haulage costs incurred by aggregates which depend on regionalised industries or on distant natural deposits.

Concrete made from sintered pulverised-fuel ash has a high strength/density ratio. Typical properties of the aggregate are shown in Table 8.11.

TABLE 8.11

PHYSICAL PROPERTIES OF CONCRETE MADE FROM SINTERED PULVERISED-FUEL ASH

Mix proportions cement:aggregate (by volume)	*Dry density of concrete*		*Compressive strength*		*Drying shrinkage[b] (per cent)*
	(kg/m³)	*(pcf)*	*(MPa)*	*(psi)*	
1:6	1 490	93	30·0	4 350	0·03
1:4·5	1 520	95	37·5	5 440	0·03
1:3·5	1 635	96	45·0	6 530	0·04
1:6·5[a]	1 660	104	30·0	4 350	0·03
1:5[a]	1 695	106	37·5	5 440	0·03
1:4[a]	1 745	109	45·0	6 530	0·03

[a] Using fine sand
[b] Measured according to BS 1881.

RAW PULVERISED-FUEL ASH

Apart from its use in the sintered form as lightweight aggregate, raw pulverised-fuel ash has been used to a limited extent as an aggregate, and since it can produce a concrete block of density less than $1600 \, kg/m^3$ (100 pcf) it may be regarded as a lightweight aggregate. When used as a partial replacement for more conventional aggregates, for example, in place of the finer sand-size portion of the grading, it improves the workability of the mix and because of its possible pozzolanic activity it may increase the strength of the product. However, the use of pulverised-fuel ash as the complete aggregate leads to certain difficulties. For example, in the British Isles, pulverised-fuel ash has, as a national average, 1·5 per cent by weight of sulphur trioxide, and it may be as high as 2·5 per cent as the average for one station. Because of reaction between sulphate and Portland cement the British Standard for aggregate does not permit the sulphur trioxide content to exceed 1 per cent. Where, however, pulverised-fuel ash is used as the whole aggregate or filler in aerated concrete, the sulphur content is not so important, since the weight of aggregate is normally small in relation to the cement content and to the volume of the concrete produced. Moreover, in aerated concrete, because of its mode of manufacture, the effect of sulphur on the cement is not a matter of interest to the user of the product and would concern only the manufacturer.

FURNACE BOTTOM ASH

As explained earlier, pulverised-fuel ash is the residue produced by the combustion of powdered coal, the fuel now used very largely in power-generating stations. This ash is a very fine powder and most of it is suspended in the flue gases, being removed from the gas stream by electrostatic precipitation, cyclone separation or other similar means. In the high temperature of the furnace, however, some melting of the particles takes place and as the molten particles coalesce, they become heavy enough to fall to the bottom of the furnace, from which they are periodically removed.

Analyses carried out from different parts of the country show that the acid-soluble sulphate may vary from 'undetectable' to 3 per cent by weight, while the combustible matter (loss-on-ignition) varies from nil to 25 per cent.

The production of furnace bottom ash in the UK now approaches 3 million tons per annum, so that the useful application of this waste material is a matter of some importance.

Screen analysis shows that the size fraction above 5 mm ($\frac{3}{16}$ in.) ranges from 45–65 per cent, and tests made at the Building Research Establishment indicate that block mixes of 1:9: (cement:ash) are likely to produce units meeting the requirements of the British Standard 2028.[16]

Already some block manufacturers are using furnace bottom ash mixed with other lightweight aggregates, and a few are using it as the whole aggregate.

PUMICE AND SCORIA

These are common rocks of volcanic origin which occur in many parts of the world and which are light enough and generally strong enough to be used as lightweight aggregate. Their lightness is due to their being spongy lavas, the cells having been formed by gases expanding with release of pressure when the material was still plastic; indeed they have been very aptly called 'solid froth'.

Pumice is usually light coloured or nearly white and has a fairly even texture of small interconnected cells, while scoria is usually of dark colour and contains larger and more irregularly-shaped cells, which are not connected.

The principal sources of pumice in Europe are Sicily, Greece, and until recent years, the Rhineland area of Germany, while in the USA it is quarried in California, Oregon, Nevada and New Mexico. Large deposits also occur in New Zealand and certain parts of Africa.

Pumice is the oldest known lightweight aggregate and from about 100 BC onwards was commonly used as an aggregate in the concrete roofs and walls of Roman buildings, notably baths and temples, the best-known surviving example being the Pantheon in Rome, in the dome of which pumice concrete was used. In the mid-nineteenth century pumice as an aggregate was revived in Germany, where there were large deposits of the rock, and its use subsequently spread to other parts of Europe. Its employment in Britain, which was never very large, was interrupted by the last war and it is only in recent years that its use has been revived. Most of the pumice used in Britain comes from the vicinity of Sicily. Mediterranean pumice today is shipped to many countries of Europe, as well as to the eastern seaboard of the USA.

Considering its mode of formation, it is not surprising that pumice varies in quality in different localities, and that it is not all equally suitable as aggregate. The Sicilian and Greek pumice is tough and remarkably free from contaminants; that found in New Zealand is friable.

Whilst the strength of the pumice aggregate is an important factor in the achievements of strength in concrete produced from it, the particle grading and the degree of compaction attainable under different manufacturing conditions influence the density and strength of the concrete. This is

TABLE 8.12
PROPERTIES OF PUMICE CONCRETE

Mix proportions cement: aggregate (by volume)	Dry density of concrete		Compressive strength at 28 days		Drying shrinkage (per cent)	Thermal conductivity, k-value	
	(kg/m³)	(pcf)	(MPa)	(psi)		(W/m °C)	(Btu in/ ft h °F)
Group A							
1:6	770	48	3·8	550 ⎫	0·05	0·17	1·2
1:10	655	41	2·1	300 ⎭			
Group B							
1:8 ⎫	1 185–		12·5	1 810	0·07	0·14	1·0
1:10 ⎬		74–78	9·2	1 340	0·07	0·14	1·0
1:12 ⎭	1 250⎮		7·9	1 150	0·06	0·14	1·0

illustrated by groups A and B in Table 8.12, which are examples of pumice concrete blocks made by different producers.

DIATOMITE

This is essentially a hydrated amorphous silica derived from the skeleton remains of microscopic aquatic plants called diatoms. It is also known as 'kieselguhr'. When pure, diatomite has an average density of 448 kg/m³ (28 pcf), but due to impurities such as sand and clay, it may be much heavier than this. It is mined in many parts of the world. In North America it is obtained from Arizona, Nevada, and Washington State, as well as from

TABLE 8.13
PROPERTIES OF DIATOMITE CONCRETE

Mix proportions cement: aggregate (by volume)	Dry density of concrete		Compressive strength at 28 days		Drying shrinkage (per cent)	Thermal conductivity, k-value	
	(kg/m³)	(pcf)	(MPa)	(psi)		(W/m °C)	(Btu in/ ft² h °F)
1:9·0	688	43	2·2	320	0·26	0·17	1·16
1:6·0	768	48	4·5	655	0·26	0·18	1·27
1:3·7	928	58	8·3	1 200	0·26	0·22	1·56
1:2·4	992	62	11·2	1 625	0·35	0·26	1·80

British Columbia in Canada. In Britain it was until recently mined in the Isle of Skye.

Diatomite has many uses, for example, as a filtering aid in sugar refining, and as a workability aid in concrete. It has also been used as the basis of a lightweight concrete aggregate. In the USA, such an aggregate is Sil-O-cel, which is used for concrete for the insulation of high-temperature furnaces. Also the USA, low-grade diatomite and diatomaceous earths are sintered in rotary kilns at about 1100 °C to produce lightweight aggregates, such as Diacrete, Raylite and Airox.

Table 8.13 shows the properties to be expected from sintered diatomite concrete, according to the US National Bureau of Standards.[17]

ORGANIC AGGREGATES

A survey of lightweight concrete aggregates would not be complete without some reference to organic aggregates. Natural organic materials which have been used as aggregates include crop wastes of various kinds, notably rice husks, but by far the most important vegetable product to be used in this way is sawdust. Sawdust has been used as an aggregate for many years, having been studied at the Building Research Station as far back as 1924. A concise but informative account of the use of sawdust as an aggregate was given by Parker in 1947.[18] Sawdust bonded with cement is for some reason known not as concrete but as 'sawdust cement'. The mixes vary from 1:1 to 1:4 cement:sawdust, by volume, according to the purpose for which the product is required.

Although sawdust consists largely of cellulose, it also contains soluble sugars, acids, resins, oils and waxes and other organic substances in varying degree, according to the nature of the timber from which it was derived. Some of these have an inhibiting effect on the setting and hardening of the cement. At best, this leads to uncertainty of the properties of the product; at worst, it may lead to properties so poor as to be virtually useless. For this reason, many patents have been registered over the years on methods of pre-treating sawdust in order to avoid these troubles. Parker lists forms of treatment which have been proposed to deal with the uncertain character of sawdust. These may be itemised as follows:

(1)   Treatments involving partial oxidation of the wood (including partial charring).

(2)   Treatments designed to waterproof the sawdust and thus prevent solvent action.

(3)   Treatments designed to neutralise with alkali, to precipitate tannates, or to treat with sulphates.

(4)   As an adjunct to any of the above, treatment of the cement to

accelerate setting, i.e. to cause the mechanism of setting to begin before solution of harmful ingredients in the timber has reached a stage at which the cement would be affected.

Most of the softwood sawdusts are rendered compatible with the cement if a mixture of lime and cement is used as the binder, and this treatment is often used in practice.

Parker gives the approximate values to be expected from mixed softwood sawdust, in varying proportions with cement when a lime pre-treatment combined with calcium chloride addition has been used. These

TABLE 8.14
PROPERTIES OF SAWDUST CEMENT

Mix proportions (by volume)	Dry density of concrete		Compressive strength at 28 days		Drying shrinkage (per cent)	Thermal conductivity, k-value	
	(kg/m^3)	(pcf)	(MPa)	(psi)		$(W/m\ °C)$	$(Btu\ in/ ft^2\ h\ °F)$
1:1	1 600	100	34·5	5 000	0·25	—	
1:2	1 200	75	12·1	1 750	0·35	0·3	approx. 2
1:3	880	55	4·8	700	0·5	0·3	approx. 2
1:4	640	40	1·7	250	0·5	0·2	approx. 1·4

results are shown in Table 8.14. This table shows that the strength obtainable from sawdust cement is not high in relation to the richness of mix but the thermal conductivity, though not as low as in some other concretes of comparable density, is nevertheless very satisfactory. The drying shrinkage, however, is very high, almost 10 times as great as in most other lightweight concretes, and thus greatly limits the usefulness of this material.

Sawdust cement has been used for jointless floor finishes and precast floor tiles and its use in wall and roof units has been successful in designs where freedom of movement is possible, such as in pier-and-panel structures.

A much more important application of wood particles is in the production of building blocks. For 30 years or more such blocks have been produced in the UK under the name Lignacite, and today seven factories serve a large area of the country. As explained above with reference to sawdust cement flooring material, wood particles require chemical treatment in order to stabilise them both chemically and physically. The organic aggregate as used in Lignacite is 'mineralised' to meet this requirement. Moreover, to control what would otherwise be a high drying shrinkage and at the same time to attain the compressive strength required

TABLE 8.15
PROPERTIES OF WOOD PARTICLE–CEMENT BUILDING BLOCKS (LIGNACITE)

Properties of blocks	*Accepted values*	
Block density, solid	$1360 \, \text{kg/m}^3$	(85 pcf)
Block density, hollow	$880–1120 \, \text{kg/m}^3$	(55–70 pcf)
Compressive strength, hollow and solid	$3·45 \, \text{MPa}$	(500 psi)
Drying shrinkage	$0·06\%$	
Thermal conductivity, k-value	approx. $0·3 \, \text{W/m} \, °\text{C}$	($2·1 \, \text{Btu in/ft}^2 \, \text{h} \, °\text{F}$)

of blocks, the concrete mix incorporates a proportion of sand. Lignacite blocks satisfy the British Standard 2028.1364:1968, 'Precast concrete blocks'. The basic data for Lignacite are given in Table 8.15. 'Lignacite' blocks have good fire resistance.

For nearly 30 years Durisol has been available not only in Switzerland, where it originated, but in a number of other countries in Europe and elsewhere. Like Lignacite, it is basically a wood particle–cement product available in a number of forms, but mainly as building blocks and walling panels.

Unlike Lignacite, Durisol does not contain sand and this is reflected in its lightness, $575 \, \text{kg/m}^3$ (36 pcf), and correspondingly low thermal conductivity, but the compressive strength at $1·17–2·27 \, \text{MPa}$ (170–330 psi) would not meet the BS 2028 requirements for loadbearing blocks.

SCREEDS

Lightweight aggregate concrete is frequently used as a screed on flat roofs and floors, since it can easily be laid in thicknesses such as will provide falls for drainage or to carry services without increasing the weight unduly. Advantage can also be taken of its thermal insulation. The screed is often given a topping of 1:4 cement and washed sand or other fine aggregate on which to lay the roof covering or floor finish.

The screed should never be less than 35 mm ($1\frac{1}{2}$ in.) thick, but on roofs where it is intended to provide thermal insulation, (thus minimising thermal movements in and heat loss from the structural roof), greater thicknesses will usually be required. To demonstrate this point, Table 8.16 compares three types of lightweight concrete used at specified densities and shows the thickness of screed required in each case, to produce a U-value of 0·22 in a roof of specified construction. The thickness needed for other materials, densities, or U-values may be calculated from published data on thermal conductivity.

TABLE 8.16

THERMAL INSULATION OF LIGHTWEIGHT CONCRETE SCREEDS[a]

Insulating material	Density		Thermal conductivity		Fall of screed (Average thickness)	
	(kg/m^3)	(pcf)	$(W/m\ °C)$	$(Btu\ in/ft^2\ h\ °F)$	(mm)	$(in.)$
Foamed slag	1 120	70	0·23	1·6	150–100	6–4
Aerated concrete	640	40	0·144	1·0	100–50	4–2
Vermiculite	640	40	0·144	1·0	100–50	4–2

[a] All three screeds described have a U-value of 0·22.

High strength is not usually required in a roof screed; probably the roughest treatment which it will receive is from workmen carrying out the next operation on the roof. Foamed slag, sintered pulverised-fuel ash and expanded clay, are suitable aggregates. For producing screeds with a density of about $1120\ kg/m^3$ (70 pcf), mixes of $1:8–1:10$ are recommended. For screeds of density lower than $650\ kg/m^3$ (40 pcf), exfoliated vermiculite or expanded perlite can be employed, in which case the mix proportions should be about $1:5$. Aerated concrete in this density range can also be used.

Porous aggregate absorbs water in the mixing process and high water contents are required to obtain workable mixes. A lightweight concrete screed usually contains a large amount of water when first laid and such screeds take a long time to dry out. On roofs, the screed is usually given two or more weeks to dry out, but if it is not protected from rain it may gain rather than lose moisture. If the roof covering when laid contains substantial amounts of water, serious troubles may ensue. This difficulty, and some ways of dealing with it are discussed in *Building Research Digest No. 8* (Second Series).

In a recent proprietary development, relating particularly to asphalt coverings, bitumen is used in place of cement as the binder for the lightweight aggregate, and the asphalt is bonded directly to the screed, thus avoiding the use of water.

Since floors are subject to much heavier traffic and greater loads than roofs, the design of a lightweight floor screed must take into account the characteristics of the floor finish to be applied. Flexible floor finishes that are incapable of spreading point loading, for example, linoleum, rubber, sheet vinyl, require a topping of at least $12\ mm$ ($\frac{1}{2}$ in.) of $1:4$ cement and sand. Topping requirements are not so stringent where rigid finishes such as wood blocks are used.

FIG. 8.13   Laying a floor screed in sintered pulverised-fuel ash aggregate.

Many finishes (or adhesives used to fix them), are susceptible to moisture, so that it is important to allow the screed to dry out before the finish is applied, and to take the usual precautions against rising ground moisture.

REFERENCES

1. Lea, F. M. (1929). 'Investigations on Breeze and Clinker Aggregates', Building Research Technical Paper No. 7, HMSO.
2. British Standard, BS 3681: 1973. 'Methods for Sampling and Testing of Lightweight Aggregates for Concrete', British Standards Institution.
3. Lea, F. M. (1936). 'The properties of Breeze and Clinker Aggregates and Methods of Testing their Soundness', Building Research Bulletin No. 5, HMSO.
4. Uranovsky, B. (1960). 'The Unsoundness of some Breeze and Clinker Aggregates', CSIR Research Report No. 165, Pretoria, South Africa.
5. Gutt, W., Kinniburgh, W. and Newman, A. J. (1967). 'Blast-furnace Slag as Aggregate for Concrete', *Mag. Concr. Res.*, **19**(59).
6. Parker, T. W. Building Research Station, Private Communication.
7. Jackson, T. E. (1903). Discussion of the paper 'Changes in Colour of Clays on Ignition in Clayware Kilns', by A. Hopwood, *Trans. Ceram. Soc.*, p. 43.
8. Riley, C. M. (1951). 'Relation of Chemical Properties to the Bloating of Clays', *J. Amer. Ceram. Soc.*, **34**(4).

9. Anon. (1919). 'History and Properties of Lightweight Aggregates', *Eng. News Record*, **82**(17).

10. Coleman, E. H. (1935). 'A Lightweight Aggregate from Slate Waste', *Concrete and Constructional Engineering*, **31**(1).

11. Whitaker, T. (1953). 'Lightweight Concrete in America', National Building Studies, Special Report No. 13, HMSO.

12. Building Research Board Annual Report for 1952, HMSO.

13. Kinniburgh, W. (1955). 'Sintered Pulverised-fuel Ash as a Lightweight Aggregate'. *Arch. Jour.*, July 7.

14. Kinniburgh, W. (1956). 'Lightweight Aggregate from Pulverised-fuel Ash', *Concrete and Constructional Engineering*, **51**(12).

15. Hobbs, C. (1959). 'Building Materials from Pulverised-fuel Ash', *Brit. Chem. Engng.*, **4**(4).

16. British Standard, BS 2028.1364:1968. 'Precast Concrete Blocks', British Standards Institution.

17. US Housing and Home Finance Agency (1949). 'Lightweight Aggregate Concretes', US Govt. Printing Office, Washington DC.

18. Parker, T. W. (1947). 'Sawdust–Cement and other Sawdust Building Products', *Chemistry and Industry*, 593–6.

CHAPTER NINE

Lightweight Aggregate Concrete Construction

SUMMARY

The main factors which affect the increasing use of structural lightweight aggregate concrete are discussed, followed by a description of some lightweight aggregates that are suitable for reinforced concrete.

The Regulations and Codes governing the use of reinforced and prestressed lightweight concrete in various countries are reviewed. Past and current research is listed.

GENERAL

For many years lightweight aggregate concrete was considered as a porous, non-compacted material and its use was confined to the construction of walls, mainly of masonry block type. Indeed, until after the war, walls made with lightweight concrete were taken to be mere non-loadbearing partitions in design. It was only in the early 1950s that the use of lightweight concrete blocks ('clinker blocks') was accepted in the UK for loadbearing inner leaf of cavity walls. Soon thereafter the development and production of new types of artificial lightweight aggregates made it possible to introduce lightweight concrete of high strength, suitable for structural work. These advances encouraged the structural use of lightweight aggregate concrete, particularly where the need to reduce weight in a structure was an important consideration for design or for economy.

A further reason for the increase in the structural use of artificial aggregate concretes in the UK as well as in the USA and Western and Eastern Europe was the great increase in general building activity and civil engineering construction, particularly in the field of reinforced concrete and road building, and the consequent spectacular increase in the consumption of natural gravel and crushed rock aggregates. The high rate of exploitation of available reserves has already led to some local shortages of natural aggregates suitable for reinforced concrete construction. In some areas this shortage is caused by actual lack of suitable materials and could only be remedied by the importation of aggregates from other areas at increased cost due to high transport charges. Elsewhere, as in the London area, quarrying of great alluvial sand and gravel deposits is thought to be prejudicial in many cases to existing residential, industrial, or agricultural interests and is therefore generally opposed on those grounds.

It would seem natural then that industry in general, and the building and civil engineering industries in particular, should be increasingly forced to consider the possibility of utilising the vast, unsightly and idle accumulations of waste material left behind by industrial activities.[1] Increasingly, too, the extended use of lightweight aggregates for reinforced concrete has been aided by a realisation among engineers, architects, and building owners, that with modern multi-story buildings a sizeable reduction of their total weight could have considerable practical advantages. There is a direct financial benefit, capable of fairly close assessment, in lower steel consumption and reduced self weight, leading to savings in the design of the foundations and of the loadbearing structure and to better anti-seismic properties. There is also enhanced freedom for the planning architect and engineer with larger column spacings and floor spans. There are however other benefits not at present easily quantifiable: for example, a reduction in weight is followed by savings in transport and greater ease of operation on the site; there is less human fatigue and at the same time greater incentive towards mechanisation of work processes. Together these factors lead to greater speed of erection and hence to a reduction in funding costs, a powerful spur to put new buildings to useful and profitable employment as early as possible. In the more competitive ambience of construction activities in the USA, allied with a generally more favourable attitude towards innovation, these influences led to a rapid development of the structural use of lightweight concrete in that country.

The advantages of reinforced lightweight concrete should be balanced, however, against its disadvantages when the designing engineer and architect and the building owner are faced with a choice of aggregates for a particular undertaking. One disadvantage is that most lightweight aggregates are harsher in texture than gravel-and-sand. Unless workability aids are used, concrete mixes made with them are therefore less workable than gravel concrete. For the same reason, if for no other, they generally need more cement to attain a required strength. Some of the more recently developed sintered aggregates on the other hand are more rounded and less harsh and manufacturers claim that the cement requirements needed to attain the same concrete strength are no higher than for gravel concrete. In the case of sintered pulverised-fuel ash aggregates in particular, it has also been found that, owing to the pozzolanic properties of the fine aggregates themselves, the strength of the concrete increases with age to a greater extent than with gravel aggregate concrete; this in turn may lead to lower cement consumption.

A second disadvantage is that lightweight aggregates are usually more expensive ex-works than gravel or crushed rock aggregates, although this difference may be offset in some cases by lower haulage costs. Moreover, the cost of the aggregate itself is only a relatively small proportion of the total cost of a multi-storey structure.

Finally, greater care in design and more stringent supervision at the site or in the works will be needed, compared with the more conventional reinforced gravel concrete construction. On balance, however, if enforced throughout the concrete industry, this could only rebound to the considerable longer term advantage of the general public as well as of the construction industry.

In the face of considerable initial difficulties, significant advances have taken place and much practical experience has been gathered in the use of lightweight concrete for concrete buildings of importance in many countries, particularly in the USA, Germany and the USSR, as well as in the UK. Before discussing these developments in detail, it may be useful to consider again briefly the regulation and codification of lightweight concrete construction and the nature and properties of the aggregates that are suitable for use with reinforced concrete construction (see also Chapter 8).

REGULATION OF THE ADMISSION AND USE OF STRUCTURAL LIGHTWEIGHT AGGREGATES AND CONCRETES

Aggregate used for reinforced concrete work must produce concrete that is adequately strong and is capable of satisfactory compaction; it must be durable and free from harmful ingredients. The presence of steel reinforcement in the concrete imposes certain restrictions on the choice of aggregate which in general need not apply to mass concrete or porous concretes used for the construction of block masonry walls or for cast-*in-situ* unreinforced wall panels.[2] Thus, boiler clinker is known to contain quantities of sulphur, which may vary; clinker should not be used for reinforced concrete. Organic aggregates are also unsuitable for reinforced concrete work because they may lack adequate dimensional stability, i.e. they shrink or swell excessively with changes in moisture content, and in many cases their durability is uncertain.

According to the British Standard Codes of Practice for reinforced concrete (CP 114:1957[3] as amended in February 1966, CP 116:1966[4]), the following dense and lightweight—natural as well as artificial—aggregates are deemed to be admissable for reinforced concrete construction, including principal as well as subsidiary members: gravel and crushed rock aggregates complying with the requirements of BS 882;[5] air-cooled blast-furnace slag complying with the requirements of BS 1047;[6] foamed blast-furnace slag complying with the requirements of BS 877;[7] expanded clay, slate, shale or slag, and sintered pulverised-fuel ash, and other types of aggregate, provided that they are suitable for reinforced concrete having regard to the properties of concrete made with them, such as strength, density, shrinkage and durability. The grading and the requirements such aggregates should satisfy are given in BS 3797 : 1964.[8]

The unified British Standard Code of Practice for the structural use of concrete, CP 100:1972,[9] places no explicit limitations on the admissibility of lightweight aggregates for use in structural work, but in principle similar restrictions to those outlined in the corresponding preceding codes would appear to apply. It admits expressly, however, aggregates complying with BS 882,[5] BS1047,[6] BS 877,[7] BS 3797,[8] BS 1201[10] and BS 4619.[11] Similar restrictions apply, in some cases by implication only, in the CEB–FIP Recommendations[12] and Codes,[13] as well as in the relevant *CEB–FIP Manual*.[14]

In the USA, generally applicable federal or even state building regulations and codes do not yet exist in practice; however, the AC1 Building Code Requirements for Reinforced Concrete (AC1 318)[15] are fairly widely accepted as applicable by most control authorities throughout the country. The ASTM C 330 specifications for lightweight aggregates for structural concrete[16] governs the admissibility of lightweight aggregates but under AC1 318 even those aggregates that do not comply with C 330 but which 'by special test or actual service' have been shown to produce concrete of adequate strength and durability, may be used, subject to being authorised by the appropriate control authority. ASTM C 330 admits aggregates that are comprised predominantly of lightweight cellular or granular inorganic materials; these include artificial aggregates produced by expanding, calcining and sintering materials such as blast-furnace slag, clay, diatomite, fly ash, shale or slate and also aggregates selected from materials that occur in nature such as pumice, scoria, lava or tuff. In the end, however, more than in any other industrially advanced country, the Engineer in the USA is recognised as the professional person who is expected to shoulder the ultimate burden of technical responsibility for admitting or refusing to admit the use of a particular material on his job. The function of codes of practice in most Western and Northern European countries, other than France, is to provide a 'deemed-to-satisfy' reference for design and construction which can be used in varying degrees for the purposes of mandatory and enforceable building regulations, or can be imposed as contractual obligations between building owner, designer and contractor, adopted as mandatory regulations and enforced accordingly in the civil and criminal courts as well as by arbitration.

In France, *Règlements*[17] issued by several ministries contain both building regulations and codes; they have the force of law and the detailed technical and functional requirements contained in them are regarded as schedules to the law. Non-mandatory French standard codes of practice do not exist in the construction field, for such documents would risk being regarded as interfering with the established functions of the State. Some professional non-mandatory advice for design and construction is provided from time to time with official approval by the appropriate scientific, professional and industrial organisations, by the Agrément authorities and in individual cases by the insurance organisations (e.g. Socotec or Veritas) which provide cover for the construction industry.

In Germany, the code of practice for reinforced concrete construction, DIN 1045,[18] expressly permits the use of crushed brickwork, air-cooled or foamed blast-furnace slag, tufa and pumice as aggregates for reinforced concrete but does not prohibit the use of other types of material.

In the USSR, the use of lightweight concrete and the admissibility for structural work of different materials are governed by a comprehensive system of standards and codes. Some of the latter, taken together with the Soviet Building Regulations, represent concepts which were at times way ahead of contemporary thought in other countries. For example, the Soviet Codes, which are in the nature of textbooks with mandatory validity, were the first to introduce limit state design methods in practice. The Soviet Codes[19] provide rules for lightweight concrete design and construction.

A new legally somewhat confusing feature of the trend towards the international harmonisation, and even the eventual unification of building regulations and standards, is the attempt by the Commission of the European Communities to establish a common market for the construction industries of member countries. Their Directive,[20] which was approved by all Community institutions, including the Council of Ministers, obliges each member country to introduce legislation for the abolition of existing legal, technical or administrative barriers against competition by contractors and/or designers for public works contracts or commissions exceeding 1 million 'units of account' (about £400 000) in value. All these must now be advertised for public competition throughout the member countries of the Community, and it was especially provided in the Directive that where a design or tender submitted was prepared in accordance with 'methods of calculation' (i.e. codes and building regulations) valid in one country but not with those of the country where the public works were to be constructed, then this discrepancy was not to be regarded as sufficient reason for disqualifying the tender or design submitted. Although the Directive became operative in August 1972, none of the High Contracting Parties have been able to pass appropriate legislation fully as required by the Directive, thus leaving its interpretation somewhat uncertain. This must necessarily continue, for whatever the interpretation that will be placed eventually on the text of the Directive by the Community Court in Luxembourg, it is evident that an effective 'common market' for the construction industries of the EEC cannot be formed even in the limited field of public works until the countries of the Community adopt a common system of technical rules, codes and standards. Such an international system of codes of practice is being prepared by the Euro-International Committee for Concrete (CEB) together with associated international sister organisations for the safety of structures and all the major civil engineering and building methods of construction and materials, including lightweight concrete.

LIGHTWEIGHT AGGREGATES SUITABLE FOR STRUCTURAL REINFORCED CONCRETE

Pumice is used for reinforced concrete roof slabs,[21] mainly for industrial roofs in Germany, where these components must comply with the German Standard Specification DIN 4028.[22] Pumice concrete is not generally considered to be suitable for cast-*in-situ* work because of the tendency for this aggregate to float to the surface, leading to segregation of the mixture. This notwithstanding, however, pumice has been used successfully for cast-*in-situ* work in Kenya and Italy.

In its natural state pumice may contain impurities and if used with reinforcement it should be washed before mixing.

In some tropical countries corals—calcareous aggregates of marine origin—are widely used for reinforced concrete construction. The principal difficulty that has been experienced with this type of material seems to have been its salt content. Not much information is at present available on its strength, density, and other properties but it is known that a good deal of work has been done by the US Navy and Army on the use of coral concrete for naval and military bases in the Pacific.

Foamed slag[23] was the first lightweight aggregate suitable for reinforced concrete that was produced in large quantities[24] in the UK. In Germany its main use was for *Schüttbeton*, or cast-*in-situ* loadbearing wall construction,[25] as well as for blocks. In Great Britain and in the USA its use for reinforced concrete is not very common, but in Eastern Europe, particularly in the USSR,[26] the ČSSR, the GDR and Rumania,[27] foamed slag is being widely used for reinforced concrete cast-*in-situ* construction and also for precast large panel structures for houses and multi-storey structures.

Expanded clays and shales produce high quality concrete[28,29] capable of achieving sufficiently high strength for prestressed concrete.[30] In the UK their use for the construction of structural units, both precast and cast-*in-situ*, is now well established under the trade names of Aglite and Leca for high- and low-strength concretes, respectively.[31] In the USA,[32] similar aggregates are marketed under a variety of trade names, e.g. Haydite, Rocklite, Gravelite, Aglite etc. In Eastern Europe, particularly in the USSR, considerable use is made of Keramzit for reinforced concrete work.[33] In Denmark, where Leca originated, this is the principal artificial aggregate available for precast reinforced concrete units; it is made in rotary kilns. In Western Germany, Switzerland and the Netherlands expanded clay concretes, under trade names such as Leca, Leca lade and Korlin, are used for many structural applications such as bridges, prestressed structures and buildings on a fairly large scale.

Waste slate, when subjected to heat, expands and forms a resistant and chemically inert aggregate, suitable for reinforced concrete. It has been used for this purpose in the USA and in Eastern Germany, as well as in the UK where it is known under the trade name Solite.

Sintered pulverised-fuel ash aggregate is being used in the UK for a variety of structural purposes and is being marketed under the trade name Lytag. This material is suitable for both reinforced and prestressed concrete.[31]

RESEARCH ON REINFORCED LIGHTWEIGHT CONCRETE

The interchange between scientific research and practical experience is the necessary foundation for sound and rapid advance in engineering development and industrial practice. In the case of reinforced lightweight concrete, technical advance and impetus for research have come about mainly as a result of the intiative of engineers in the field collaborating with research workers. The results of their researches then found their way into the various Codes of Practice for concrete construction. For some time, detailed and accurate knowledge was not available about the material itself and about its behaviour in actual structures but this must be seen in perspective. The statement can apply equally even to well-known and tried methods of construction in some cases. It is known, for example, that for some aspects of reinforced concrete construction code of practice rules have been drawn up on the basis of informed intuition, relying—in the absence of experimental evidence or much practical experience—on the judgement of experienced reinforced concrete designers and construction engineers. This tends to lead, however, to rules of design that are often cumbersome and conservative, so that sufficient allowance can be made for unknown factors; significantly but less frequently the rules adopted may not turn out to be adequately safe.

For sensible and economical utilisation of new materials and methods of construction, a planned scientific investigation of their properties was obviously desirable. Much of this work has already been accomplished, but some still remains to be done and further practical developments will no doubt occur in the future in the fields of both material technology and structural design.

In the UK, research on structural lightweight concrete has been mainly centred at the Building Research Station, Watford.[34-36] Its work has been mainly concentrated on reinforced and unreinforced concrete,[31] leaving prestressed lightweight concrete aside for the time being, and dealing with problems such as bond strength, shearing strength and durability, as well as with mix design and the behaviour of flexural members and walls. Important research on the properties of expanded clay and sintered pulverised-fuel ash concretes suitable for reinforced and prestressed concrete work has been done at the University of Leeds, mainly on creep and bond strength,[37] and on the behaviour of flexural members and on mix design methods at the Cement and Concrete Association Laboratories at Wexham Springs.[38,39]

In Germany, the Research Institute for Blast-furnace Slag at Rheinhausen, Duisburg, an organisation financed by the iron and steel industry, was concerned mainly with the physical properties of slag aggregates, and of concrete made with them, particularly of *Schüttbeton*, the porous no-fines type of concrete suitable for cast-*in-situ* loadbearing wall construction[40] The structural properties of foamed slag and other types of lightweight concrete are the subject of investigations at the Research Institute of the Cement Industry at Düsseldorf, especially on the strength and deformation of all types of concrete under sustained loading. The leading German universities have also promoted a number of important research programmes on lightweight concrete, notably at Stuttgart, Darmstadt, and Aachen.[41-43]

In the USA, research on sintered lightweight aggregate concretes was initiated by the National Bureau of Standards, by the aggregate producers and by the cement industry. The Housing and Home Finance Agency was responsible for a thorough survey of the available sources of lightweight aggregate[44] and of the properties of concrete made with these aggregates. Work on the structural properties of lightweight concrete and on mix design has been carried out for the cement industry at the laboratories of the Portland Cement Association at Chicago[30] and for the aggregate manufacturers at the Universities of Oregon[29] and Illinois.[28] This work led to a great increase in the use of lightweight concrete for structural purposes.

Research of importance is also in progress in many other countries on the properties and application of structural lightweight concrete. In particular, the research laboratories of the building and civil engineering industries of the USSR with the Central Building Research Institute for Concrete in Moscow (NIIZhB–Gosstroy) are engaged on work concerned mainly with expanded clays, pulverised-fuel ash aggregates and foamed slag and are investigating problems of structural design and durability.[45] Under the guidance of Professors Michalov and Gvozdev its contribution to Soviet and international codification has been considerable. Research of economic and technical importance is also in progress mainly on the properties and application of natural lightweight aggregates in the Caucasus at the Research Institutions of Armenia and Georgia.[46]

REFERENCES

1. Gutt, W., Nixon P. J. *et al.* (1974). 'A Survey of the Locations Disposal and Prospective Uses of the Major Industrial By-products and Waste Materials', Building Research Establishment Current Paper CP 19/74, HMSO.
2. Scott, W. L., Glanville, W. H. and Thomas, F. G. (1965). *Explanatory Handbook on the British Standard Code of Practice for Reinforced Concrete* (114:1957) Concrete Publications, London.
3. British Standard Code of Practice 114:1957. 'The Structural Use of Reinforced Concrete in Buildings', British Standards Institution.
4. British Standard Code of Practice 116:1966. 'The Structural Use of Precast Concrete', British Standards Institution.
5. British Standard 882:1965 'Coarse and Fine Aggregates from Natural Sources for Concrete', British Standards Institution.
6. British Standard 1047:1952. 'Air-cooled Blast-Furnace Slag Coarse Aggregate for Concrete', British Standards Institution.
7. British Standard 877:1967. 'Foamed or expanded Blast-Furnace Slag Lightweight Aggregate for Concrete', British Standards Institution.
8. British Standard 3797:1964. 'Lightweight Aggregates for Concrete', British Standards Institution.
9. British Standard Code of Practice 110:1972. The Structural Use of Concrete', British Standards Institution.
10. British Standard 1201:1965. 'Aggregates for Granolithic Concrete Floor Finishes', British Standards Institution.
11. British Standard 4619:1970. 'Heavy Aggregates for Concrete and Gypsum Plaster', British Standards Institution.
12. CEB–FIP International Recommendations for Concrete Construction (1970), Comité Euro-International du Béton (CEB), Paris.
13. International System of Codes of Practice for Civil Engineering, Vol. 2, 'Model Code for Concrete Construction' Draft, 1977. Comité Euro-International du Béton, (CEB), Paris.
14. CEB–FIP (1977). *Technology of Lightweight Concrete Structures*, Construction Press, Hornby, Lancaster, UK.
15. American Concrete Institute Standard ACI 318:1971. 'Building Code Requirements for Reinforced Concrete', ACI, Detroit.
16. American Society for Testing Materials Specification No. C330, 'Lightweight Aggregates for Structural Concrete', ASTM, Chicago.
17. Rule CC BA 68, 'Règles Techniques de Conception et de Calcul des Ouvrages et Constructions en Béton Armé' (Technical Regulations for the Design and calculation of Reinforced Concrete Structures), Société de Diffusion des Techniques du Bâtiment et des Travaux Publics, Paris.
18. German Standards DIN 1044 and 1045, 'Bestimmungen für Ausführung von Bauwerken aus Stahlbeton', (Code of Practice for the Use of Reinforced Concrete in Buildings), Deutschen Ausschuss für Stahlbeton.
19. NIIZhB SSSR (1970). 'Recommendations for the Design of Lightweight Concrete Structures' Moscow.
20. Direction du Conseil des Ministres (1971). No. 71/304/CEE 'Concernant la Suppression des Restrictions à la Libre des Services dans le domain des Marchées Publics de Travaux Publics', 26 July 1971, Paris

21. Köhne, L. and Glöckner, H. (1957). 'Notes on the Economy of Different Types of Roof Covering', *Der Bau und die Bauindustrie*, **10**(9).
22. German Standard DIN 4028. 'Stahlbeton—hohldielen, Bestimmungen für Herstellung und Verlegung', (Regulations for the manufacture and Use of Precast Reinforced Concrete Hollow Slabs), Deutschen Ausschuss für Stahlbeton.
23. Parker, T. W. (1937). 'Foamed Blast-furnace Slag', Special Report No. 19, Iron and Steel Institute, London.
24. Gallai-Hatchard, M. (1954). 'History of the Developments in Foamed Slag Production in Great Britain to Date', *Silicates Industriels*, **20**(1).
25. Bramann, K. (1957). 'Foamed Slag', *Das Baugewerbe* (5) and (6).
26. Buzhevich, G. A. (1970). 'Lightweight Concrete made with Porous Aggregates', Stroyizdat, Moscow.
27. Cireseanu, P. and Pascanu, V. (1959). 'Low-cost Building Construction using Lightweight Aggregates', *Revista Constructiilor si a Materialelor de Constructii*, **11**, 1.
28. Richaot, F. E. and Jensen, V. P. (1931). 'Test of Plain and Reinforced Concrete made of Haydite Aggregates', University of Illinois Engineering Experiment Station, Urbana, Illinois.
29. Ritchie, D. D. and Graf, S. H. (1951). 'Expanded Shale Aggregate in Structural Concrete', Oregon Engineering Experiment Station, Oregon.
30. Shideler, J. J. (1957). 'Lightweight Aggregate Concrete for Structural Use', *Amer. Concr. Inst. J.*, **29**(4).
31. Short, A. (1959). 'The Use of Lightweight Concrete for Reinforced Concrete Construction', *Reinforced Concrete Review*, **5**(6).
32. Whitaker, T. (1953). 'Lightweight Concrete in America', National Building Studies Special Report No. 13, HMSO.
33. Ashrabov, A. B. (1958). 'The Use of Keramzit Concrete in Industrial Building Construction', Gosstroy, Moscow, USSR.
34. Nurse, R. W. (1956). 'The Utilisation of Fly-ash for Building Material', *J. Inst. Fuel*, **29**(181).
35. Parker, T. W. (1950). 'Blastfurnace Slag Building Materials', Institute of Engineers and Shipbuilders in Scotland (December).
36. Parker, T. W. and Newman, A. J. 'Foamed Slag Concrete' Note A 73, Building Research Station, Garston, Watford.
37. Evans, R. H. and Hardwick, J. R. (1960). 'Lightweight Concrete with Sintered Clay Aggregate', *Reinforced Concrete Review*, **5**(6).
38. Owens, P. L. (1973). 'Basic Mix Method. Selection of Proportions for Medium Strength Concretes', Basic Mix Series No. 1, Cement and Concrete Association, London.
39. Spratt, B. H. (1975). *An Introduction to Lightweight Concrete*, Cement and Concrete Association, London.
40. Kramer, W. and Vinkeloe, R. (1960). 'The influence of the Added Fines on the Compressive Strength and Thermal Insulation Properties of Foamed Slag Concrete', *Die Bauwirtschaft*, (30).
41. Wesche, K. (1957). 'Material Basis for the Design of Lightweight Concrete Structures, *Beton und Stahlbetonbau*, **62**(11).
42. Weigler, H. and Reissman, K. (1965). 'Research on Structural Lightweight

Concretes', *Betonstein-Zeitung*, **1965**, 31, 11, pp. 615/29 and Mitteilungen aus dem Institut für Massivbau on de T. H. Darmstadt, Heft 8.

43. Weigler, H. and Karl, S. (1969). 'Creep of Lightweight Concrete under Early Loading', *Betonstein-Zeitung*, **35**(10).
44. US Housing and Home Finance Agency (1949). 'Lightweight Aggregate Concrete', US Government Printing Office, Washington DC.
45. Buzhevich, G. A. (Ed.) (1971). 'Technology and Properties of New Types of Lightweight Concrete made with Porous Aggregates', (NIIZhB Proceedings), Stroyizdat, Moscow.
46. Piradov, A. B. (1973). '*Structural Properties of Plain and Reinforced Lightweight Concrete*', Stroyizdat, Moscow.

CHAPTER TEN

The Properties of Structural Lightweight Aggregate Concrete

SUMMARY

The following properties of compacted lightweight aggregate concrete intended for use as a structural material are considered: the relationship between compressive strength and density, tensile strength and modulus of rupture, the effects of the water–cement ratio used, the effects of the admixture of sand to the mix, and the creep properties.

DENSITY AND COMPRESSIVE STRENGTH

The dry density of compacted concrete made with different lightweight aggregates varies from about 800–2100 kg/m³ (50–130 pcf) for cube strengths ranging from about 7–50 MPa (1000–7000 psi).[1,2] Structural lightweight concrete is defined in most codes of practice and by RILEM in a more restricted way by limiting the density of lightweight concrete to between 1200 and 2000 kg/m³ (75–125 pcf).[3] The actual relationship between the density and cube strength of lightweight concrete varies considerably, however, for different types of aggregate[4] (Fig. 10.1).

For sand and gravel concrete the measured dry density ranges from about 2200 kg/m³ (139 pcf) for a 28 day cube strength of about 7 MPa (1000 psi) to about 2300 kg/m³ (144 pcf) for a cube strength of about 28 MPa (4000 psi). For the same average 28-day cube strengths the dry density of compacted foamed slag concrete ranges from about 1700–1900 kg/m³ (105–120 pcf) when the mix contains only lightweight aggregate; when the fines consist of sand and lightweight material in equal parts, then the corresponding densities vary between 1800 and 2000 kg/m³ (115 and 125 pcf).

The dry density of concrete made with expanded clay and with sintered pulverised-fuel ash aggregate varies from about 1400–1600 kg/m³ (85–100 pcf) when made without sand and from 1600–1800 kg/m³ (100–110 pcf) when the fines include sand, for the same range of 28-day cube crushing strengths.

Thus, while for the same crushing strengths the density of expanded clay and pulverised-fuel ash aggregate concrete containing only lightweight aggregate is 60–70 per cent of the density of gravel concrete, the density of

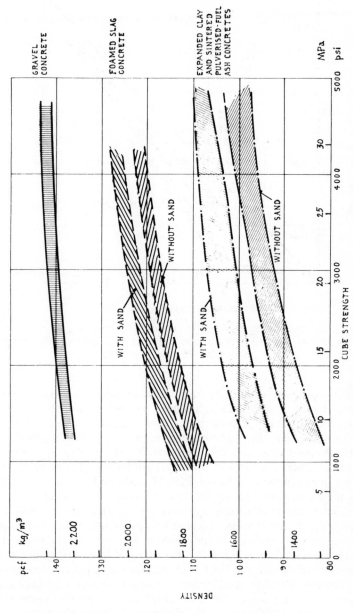

FIG. 10.1 Relationship between the cube crushing strength and dry density of various types of concrete at 28 days.

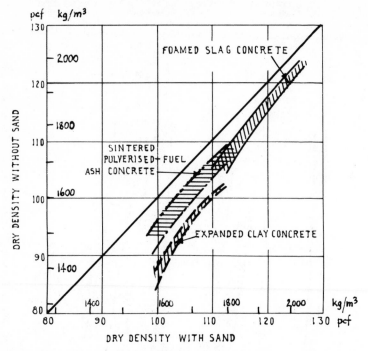

FIG. 10.2   The effect on the dry density of lightweight concretes of replacing one-half of the fine lightweight aggregate by sand, for the same cube strength, ranging from about 7–30 MPa (1000–4500 psi).

foamed slag concrete is about 80–85 per cent of the corresponding gravel concrete. If sand is added to lightweight concrete mixes, their density increases somewhat; the effect of the addition of sand on density is less for foamed slag concrete than for concretes made with sintered aggregate.

Although compacted concrete made with foamed slag aggregate is heavier than concrete made with other types of lightweight aggregate, this difference in weight tends to be considerably reduced for non-compacted, porous mixes. It is also found that for the same compressive strength, heavier and harder foamed slag aggregate produces a lighter concrete.

In part, the greater density of foamed slag concrete is ascribed to the greater bulk density and also to the higher specific gravity of foamed slag aggregate compared with those of other types of lightweight aggregate. More important, however, is the fact that foamed slag has an open-pored surface texture. Although usually care is taken to saturate the aggregate with water before use, some cement will accumulate in the open pores, thus increasing the weight of the concrete. Owing to the brittle character of the material the grading of the aggregate may change during mixing and compaction, since the coarse aggregate is abraded and broken up and is thus reduced in size. This may reduce the yield for the compacted concrete.

By adding sand to compacted lightweight concrete mixes, both density and compressive strength are increased considerably. The effect of the addition of sand on the relationship between compressive strength and density is shown in Fig. 10.2. For foamed slag concrete of high strength and density the addition of sand has little effect on either property. For the expanded clay and pulverised-fuel ash aggregates, however, the density of the concrete is increased considerably and is often of greater importance than any increase in compressive strength achieved by the addition of sand to the mix. For example, whereas for foamed slag concrete the increase in density owing to the addition of sand might vary from $3\frac{1}{2}$ per cent for low strengths to less than 1 per cent for higher strength concretes, the corresponding increases in density for sintered clay and pulverised-fuel ash concretes may be 10–12 per cent. The effect of the addition of sand to foamed slag concrete has been the subject of a detailed study by Parker and Newman.[5]

The density of typical lightweight concrete mixes is given in Table 14.1 in relation to their cement content.

TENSILE STRENGTH AND MODULUS OF RUPTURE

The strength of concrete is difficult to determine because standard tests are necessarily subject to the influence of a large number of variables either unknown or not capable of control. Standard cube and cylinder tests serve to determine an index, rather than an absolute measure of the crushing strength of concrete. Various methods have been tried also to obtain a similar index for the tensile strength of concrete but none proved entirely suitable. For example, the modulus of rupture represents the tensile stress at which a standard $10 \times 10 \times 40$ cm (about $4 \times 4 \times 16$ in.) concrete prism breaks when subjected to a bending test. Although a useful indication of tensile strength, the modulus of rupture is generally higher than the latter, since the modulus of rupture test includes the effect of creep of the concrete under tensile stresses before failure occurs, even when subjected to short duration loading tests. The bending moments which cause failure are thus somewhat higher than the bending moment which would have been resisted by the prism, had the failure occurred at the real tensile strength of the concrete. The cylinder splitting test (or 'Brazilian test') is also commonly used as a measure of the tensile strength. With this test a standard concrete cylinder 15 cm (6 in.) base diameter and 30 cm (12 in.) high, is subjected to compression along its side (Figs. 10.3 and 10.4). The direct tensile strength test is now not used for concrete except in special cases.

FIG. 10.3 Test arrangements for the cylinder splitting test.

FIG. 10.4 Lightweight concrete cylinder after the cylinder splitting test.

Results obtained in the UK from modulus of rupture and cylinder splitting tests with various lightweight aggregates and concrete mixes have been compared with the performance of gravel concrete. These results indicate that in general the modulus of rupture[2,4,6] and the splitting strength[2,7,8] of lightweight concretes tend to be of the same order as, or slightly higher than, that obtained with gravel concrete having the same compressive strength. Comparing a broader range of aggregates, however,

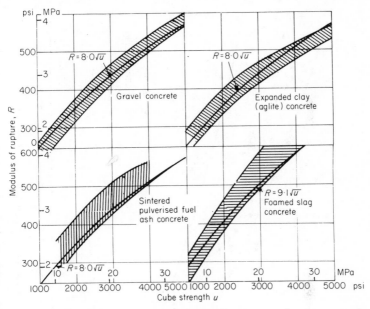

FIG. 10.5 Relationships between modulus of rupture and cube strength for different types of concrete.

of British, German and Dutch origin, considerable variations were found to occur for the splitting strength of concrete made with different aggregates[1] and for most lightweight concretes the tensile strength is less than that of gravel concrete of the same compressive strength. The modulus of rupture obtained for concretes made with different types of aggregate is shown in Fig. 10.5 in relation to the compressive strength. For compressive strengths ranging from 7 to about 35 MPa (1000–5000 psi), the moduli of rupture tend to vary from about 1·7–3·9 MPa (250–550 psi).

The relationship between modulus of rupture and density varies considerably for different types of concrete and a consistent relationship is difficult to establish. The approximate correlation of compressive strength and modulus of rupture for both gravel concrete and lightweight aggregate

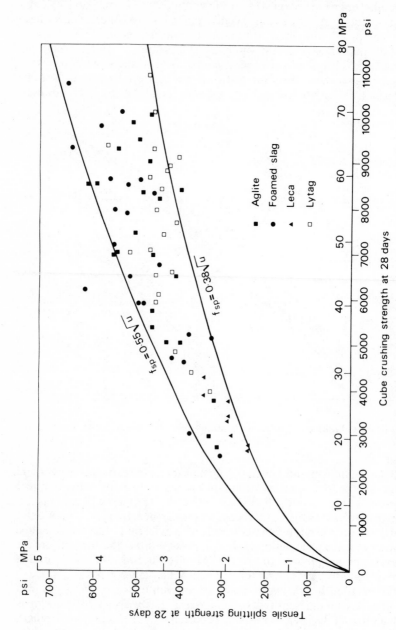

Fig. 10.6   Relationship between tensile splitting strength and cube strength of lightweight concretes.

concrete was found to be best represented by a parabolic equation of this form:

$$f_{cr} = 0.67 f_c^{1/2}, \text{MPa} \qquad (f_{cr} = 8.0 f_c^{1/2}, \text{psi})$$

where f_{cr} denotes the modulus of rupture and f_c denotes the cube strength—with the exception of foamed slag concrete for which the approximate parabolic expression assumed the following form to fit the experimental results:

$$f_{cr} = 0.76 f_c^{1/2}, \text{MPa} \qquad (f_{cr} = 9.1 f_c^{1/2}, \text{psi})$$

Thus, for low compressive strengths the ratio of modulus of rupture and compressive strength is larger than for higher compressive strengths. Other research workers confirm these conclusions. Evans and Hardwick[6] obtained approximately the following relation:

$$f_{cr} = 0.67 f_c^{1/2}, \text{MPa} \qquad (f_{cr} = 8.0 f_c^{1/2}, \text{psi})$$

for sintered clay (Aglite) concrete with cube strengths ranging from 32–53 MPa (4500–7500 psi). The relationship of the cylinder splitting strengths to cube strengths obtained from tests at the Building Research Station (Fig. 10.6) can be expressed approximately by the following equation:[2]

$$f_{ct} = K f_c^{1/2}$$

for all types of concrete, where f_{ct} is the cylinder splitting strength and f_c the cube strength. For units of MPa, the coefficient K was found to vary from about 0.37–0.5, the average value being about 0.42. The corresponding K values for units in psi are 4.5–6.0 and 5.0, respectively.

The results of split cylinder tests made by Hanson,[8] indicate that the split cylinder strength of saturated lightweight concrete is equal to or lower than that of gravel concrete of equal cylinder crushing strength for a wide range of compressive strengths. These findings may not conflict seriously with the results obtained at the Building Research Station, since the cube strengths which form the basis of the design of the concrete used for the latter do not necessarily form a constant relationship with the cylinder strength of the same lightweight concrete.

It appears that the two types of test, i.e. modulus of rupture and cylinder splitting tests, do not represent the same property of the concrete although both may serve as an indication of the tensile strength. In general, the cylinder splitting strength is about 60 per cent of the modulus of rupture. The modulus of rupture is greatly influenced by the diffused moisture distribution in the test specimen as it dries out.[2]

Hanson's tests[8] indicate that the tensile strength of concrete is greatly affected by its moisture content. The split cylinder tensile strength of saturated lightweight concrete is considerably higher than the average tensile strength of the same concrete tested in an air-dry state. The results obtained in a saturated state moreover are more uniform. On the other hand for denser gravel aggregate concrete the tensile strength was found to be slightly higher for the dry than for the saturated material. The tensile strength is an important criterion of the liability to cracking. Since concrete is such a heterogeneous material, its tensile strength tends to vary considerably and its composition will affect not only the tensile stress at which cracking occurs but also the mechanism of the process itself. In gravel concrete, for example, the strength and stiffness of the aggregate itself are usually very great compared with those of the cement matrix, both in compression and in tension. Failure in tension will therefore very rarely occur as a result of fracture of the aggregate but almost invariably because of breakdown of the bond between the matrix and the surface of the aggregate or fracture of the matrix itself.

The aggregate particles themselves are not very compressible, and are not in general subject to appreciable shrinkage. The tensile stresses induced in the matrix through shrinkage due to loss of moisture are therefore all the more important and increase the liability of the matrix to cracking.

The appearance of the cracks in lightweight concrete is quite different from that in gravel concrete and indicates, by its more regular, linear form that fracture is caused by tensile stresses in the aggregate particles themselves, as well as by fracture of the matrix, since the tensile strength of the aggregate is usually less than that of the hardened matrix. In the absence of external restraints shrinkage causes lower tensile stresses in the matrix of lightweight aggregate concrete than in gravel concrete because the resistance of lightweight aggregate particles against local deformation is less. The tensile strength of different types of dense and lightweight aggregate and their liability to cracking is thus likely to vary considerably for different materials and mixes.

The tensile strength of lightweight concrete is subject to considerable fluctuation, particularly in the early stages of its life. Owing to its higher initial water content and faster rate of desiccation of the outer layers of concrete, drying shrinkage takes place at differing rates throughout the concrete with varying diffusion rates of moisture in it. This leads to secondary stresses in the material causing early internal cracking and lower tensile strength in early life. Later as a result of healing of cracks and creep, this trend is reversed and increase of strength with aging is usually resumed.

MODULUS OF DEFORMATION

For the same compressive strength, the modulus of deformation of lightweight concrete is in general considerably lower than that of dense, gravel concrete.[1] The *E*-value of lightweight concrete ranges between one-

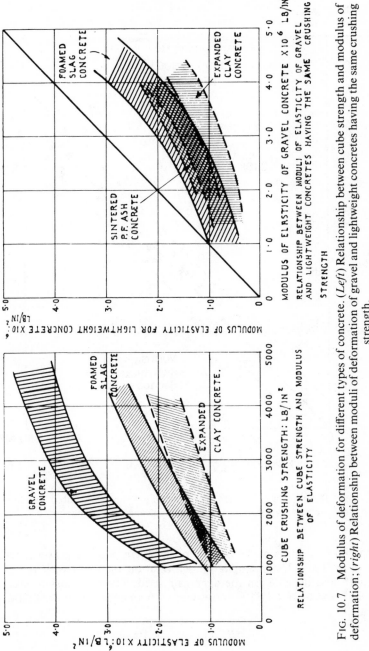

FIG. 10.7 Modulus of deformation for different types of concrete. (*Left*) Relationship between cube strength and modulus of deformation; (*right*) Relationship between moduli of deformation of gravel and lightweight concretes having the same crushing strength.

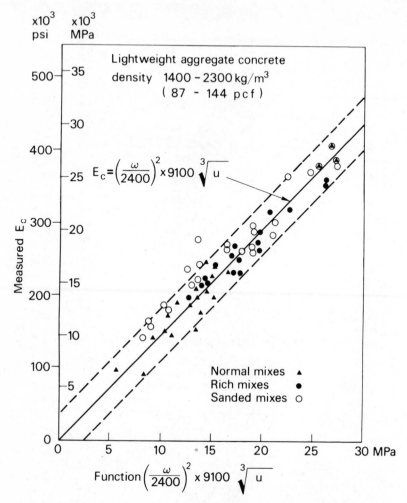

FIG. 10.8 Relationship between the calculated and measured moduli of deformation for various lightweight aggregate concretes.

third and two-thirds of the *E*-value of the corresponding gravel concrete mix (Fig. 10.7) The modulus of deformation increases with the cube strength and depends on the aggregate used. The relationship given in Tables 1 and 64 of CP 110[9] agrees well with an equation of the following form:

$$E_c = k(f_c)^{1/3}, \text{MPa}$$

where for the mean value, $k = 9100$. This form of equation has been adopted by CEB.[3] The modulus of deformation increases with the density (ω) of lightweight concrete. This can be allowed for by applying a correction factor for the density of the concrete thus:

$$E_c = \left(\frac{\omega}{2400}\right)^2 \times 9100u^{1/3}, \text{MPa}$$

The relationship between the E-value calculated with this equation and measured values obtained at the Building Research Station[2] is shown in Fig. 10.8 which indicates that the E-values for lightweight concrete range from about 10×10^3 to 30×10^3 MPa for different strengths and aggregates under short-term loading. The formula given here appears to provide a prediction of the E to within about ± 2500 MPa of the measured values.

For dense aggregates of volcanic origin the formulae given above do not apply; these aggregates are rather softer than usual and concretes made with them do not differ greatly in their deformability from typical lightweight aggregate concretes. Such is the case, for example, for the Andesite aggregate used in Mexico City.

The modulus of deformation is of special importance for structural lightweight concrete construction because of its effect on the deflections of flexural members, on the distribution of internal forces in the cross-section of compression members and on the critical load in the case of members liable to failure due to elastic instability, where the lower E-value of lightweight concrete has an unfavourable influence. On the other hand, the resistance of lightweight concrete members to impact loads may be enhanced by their lower modulus of deformation.

EFFECT OF THE WATER/CEMENT RATIO

The design curves correlating the cube strength and water/cement ratio of dense gravel concrete do not apply to lightweight aggregate concrete. Owing to their porosity and in some cases inferior workability, lightweight concretes generally need more water to attain the same strength.

The effect of the water/cement ratio on the workability and on the crushing strength of lightweight concrete has been considered in some detail in Chapter 3. It has been shown that a broad relationship exists between cube strength and water/cement ratio (Fig. 3.3) but that this relationship is different for every type of lightweight aggregate and has to be considered separately.

Tests made at the Building Research Station[4] indicate that a linear

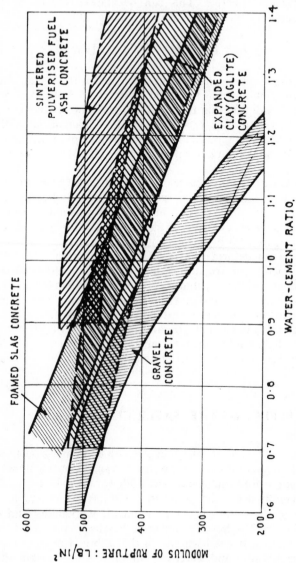

FIG. 10.9   Relationship between water/cement ratio and modulus of rupture for different types of cements.

relationship can be deduced for the water/cement ratio and the modulus of rupture for fully compacted concrete mixes (Fig. 10.9).

EFFECT OF THE ADMIXTURE OF SAND

It is common practice to replace a part of the fine lightweight aggregate with quartz river sand in lightweight concrete mixes, so as to increase the compressive strength and bond strength of the resulting concrete, to improve its durability and the protection against corrosion it can afford to embedded steel, to improve its workability and to reduce the cement requirements and the shrinkage of the concrete. Since it has been shown that the addition of sand also increases the density of the concrete, the question arises as to the degree to which this disadvantage can be balanced in practice by the advantages of adding sand to the mix. The increase in density is less serious with foamed slag concrete, but is relatively more important for the lighter, sintered aggregates (Fig. 10.2).

The effect of the addition of sand on the bond strength of lightweight concrete is not very great, except in so far as the bond strength tends to increase with the compressive strength. For the same compressive strength, however, the presence of sand in the mix does not cause a substantial change in bond strength. This may not be generally the case however for every sintered type of aggregate and the ACI Code 318-1971, for example, allows a substantial reduction of the required development length if the mix is sanded. Nor is its effect on durability very noticeable. The shrinkage of lightweight concrete is reduced by the addition of sand, which acts as a stabilising element in the structure of the matrix.

For the same workability and compressive strength the sand replaces some proportion of the cement in the binder and may reduce the cement requirement for some types of lightweight aggregate (Fig. 10.10). Tests made at the Building Research Station show that for various types of lightweight concretes and various mixes, the cement requirements were reduced by 13–25 per cent by weight, if half of the lightweight fines by volume was replaced by river sand. The greatest economy in cement owing to the addition of sand was obtained with foamed slag concretes; the cement consumption of concrete made with the sintered types of aggregate was less affected.

It appears that in the case of foamed slag concrete a substantial part of the cement that would otherwise have found its way into the open pores of the coarse foamed slag aggregate during mixing and would have hardened there, making little contribution to the strength of the concrete, was replaced by the sand. Thus the addition of sand has the effect of improving the properties of the concrete substantially, with less cement and without very greatly increasing the weight of the material. By contrast, the lightweight

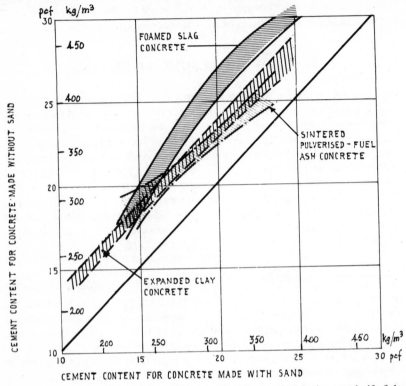

FIG. 10.10 The effect on the required cement content of replacing one-half of the fine lightweight aggregate by sand, for lightweight concrete mixes, to obtain the same cube strength, ranging from about 7–30 MPa (1000–4500 psi).

foamed slag fines cannot penetrate into the open pores because they themselves consist of harsh particles of a porous nature, although the pores are much smaller than in the larger, coarse aggregate. Sand particles are frequently much less harsh and are capable of entering the open pores. For the same reason, workability is generally improved to a greater extent with foamed slag than with other types of aggregate if sand is added to the mix. Improved workability in turn leads to a reduction in the time required to mix the concrete properly, thus preserving the grading of this brittle type of aggregate. Better workability also results in better compaction and higher strength for the same density.

In the case of the sintered aggregates the open, broken pores on the surface are generally smaller than in foamed slag and they therefore tend to absorb less of the binder paste. As a rule, therefore, the addition of sand to lightweight concrete mixes, other than for foamed slag concrete, is less advantageous, except in special circumstances where it is necessary to increase the compressive strength of lightweight concrete for a particular structural component or whole structure even if this leads to an increase in density.

The percentage increase in density as well as the reduction in cement consumption which can result from the addition of sand to a lightweight concrete mix, tend to become less important as the compressive strength of the concrete increases. In general, weak mixes are more sensitive to the addition of sand or of other materials. Particularly for cast-*in-situ* loadbearing wall construction (*Schüttbeton*),[10] crushed granulated slag has been used successfully with proprietary mixes (Thermocrete construction). Since granulated slag has marked pozzolanic properties, its presence in the mix instead of sand may lead not only to saving in weight and of cement as well as to improvement in workability, but also to improved characteristics. It also improves the thermal insulation of the concrete walls appreciably.

CREEP

Concrete is not a dimensionally stable material, even when changes in temperature do not occur. It is subject to time-dependent deformations. Owing to loss of moisture it is liable to shrinkage and moisture movements.If wetted it tends to expand. Concrete deforms—or creeps— when subjected to sustained compressive or tensile stresses. Although moisture movement and creep differ fundamentally in nature, they affect each other[11] and are both affected by a variety of circumstances, such as the type of exposure to which the concrete is subjected, the mix used, the type of aggregate used, the dimensions of the member and other factors. The creep of structural lightweight concrete has been the subject of investigations by Shideler,[12] Evans,[6] the Research Institute for the Cement Industry in Düsseldorf, the Universities of Munich, Aachen, and Delft, the Otto Graf Institute, Stuttgart, and others. For a comprehensive assessment of the creep properties of concrete the work of Neville, Rüsch, Chiorino, Bazant and others is of great importance. At the Building Research Station research on creep has been concerned with the behaviour of reinforced concrete flexural members (Fig. 10.11) subjected to loading under controlled conditions of temperature and humidity, no attempt being made to measure shrinkage and creep deformations separately. Most of the tests made by other workers were made on concrete cylinders subjected to axial loading, or in a few cases, to eccentric loading.

The effect of creep on the behaviour of concrete structures can be both favourable and unfavourable. On the one hand, creep leads to increased deflections and greatly increased losses of prestress in prestressed concrete structures owing to the deformation of the material. On the other hand,

FIG. 10.11   Sustained laboratory loading tests on flexural members made with different types of concrete.

creep tends to balance secondary stresses due to shrinkage and thermal stresses and to uneven moisture diffusion in the material in the early stages of its life. This particularly affects the behaviour of lightweight concrete since these factors—moisture movements, moisture diffusion—are usually more important than for normal aggregate concrete.

Creep normally increases with the hardened cement paste content and is reduced with the strength and compaction of the concrete. It also varies with the type of lightweight aggregate used. Since creep is proportional to the applied stress up to about 60 per cent of the strength of the concrete, a useful comparison of different materials can be based on the specific creep which is the creep strain per unit stress. Typical values of specific creep vary between $6 \cdot 5 \times 10^{-5}$ and 9×10^{-5} 1/MPa (46–63×10^{-6} 1/psi).

For the same compressive strength, both the absolute shrinkage and creep of most lightweight concretes are generally larger than of gravel concrete. The results of the creep tests on gravel and lightweight aggregate concrete having a cube strength of 20–35 MPa (3000–5000 psi) at 28 days indicate that for less than one year's duration of loading some expanded clay, shale, and slate aggregates can have lower creep than gravel concrete. With increasing duration of loading, however, the creep of the lightweight concrete specimens tended to increase at a greater rate than that of gravel concrete. The estimated ultimate creep was found to be higher for lightweight than for gravel aggregate concrete, the difference varying between 20 and 60 per cent of the creep for the latter. The ultimate creep can be calculated from a hyperbolic equation which was found to be reasonably applicable to the test results.[12]

$$e_c = \frac{m_c ts}{n_c + t}$$

where e_c is the creep strain at time t; m_c is the ultimate creep strain; t is the time under load (days); s is the stress (psi); and n_c is the time in days, when $e_c = m_c/2$.

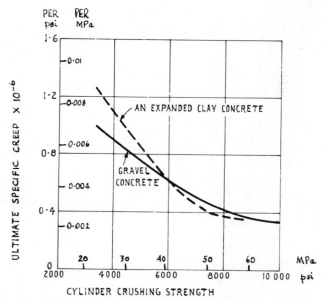

FIG. 10.12   The effect of the crushing strength on the ultimate creep of concrete made with gravel and lightweight aggregates, the specimens being loaded at the age of seven days—Shideler's tests.[12]

For concrete having a high compressive strength (50–63 MPa, or 7000–9000 psi) the creep measured is usually lower, for every type of aggregate, than for weaker concretes (Fig. 10.12), but the reduction is generally somewhat greater for lightweight concretes than for gravel concrete. The creep of lightweight concrete having such high compressive strengths is of the same order as for corresponding gravel concrete (Fig. 10.13). For compressive strengths of 21–25 MPa (3000–4000 psi) the creep of lightweight concretes made with different aggregates tends to vary considerably.[3] It was found at the Building Research Station that the permanent deformation of beams made with foamed slag aggregate

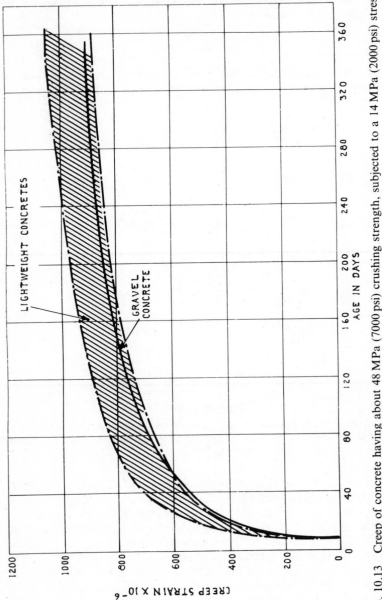

Fig. 10.13 Creep of concrete having about 48 MPa (7000 psi) crushing strength, subjected to a 14 MPa (2000 psi) stress—Shideler's tests.[12]

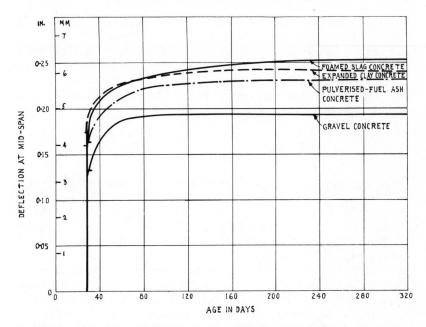

FIG. 10.14   Deformation of beams made with different types of aggregate, subjected to twice the design load, Span = 3·65 m (12ft), Span/depth = 29.

concrete under loading is somewhat higher than that of concrete made with other types of lightweight aggregate (Fig. 10.14) and that the permanent deflection of gravel concrete members is least. Similar results were obtained by other workers.[13]

For sintered pulverised-fuel ash concrete the initial rate of creep is considerably greater than for other types of lightweight concrete but this slows down considerably later and final creep for the same imposed stress is of the same order for most types of lightweight concrete.

Initial creep for concrete loaded at an early age before it has reached about two-thirds of its final strength is also greater. Final creep values are normally reached at an age of 2–3 years.

The fundamental physical nature of creep phenomena is complex. Total creep movement can be assumed to consist of two parts: the delayed plastic deformation and the viscous flow.[1] Of these, flow produces a permanent deformation. The delayed elastic deformation is irreversible since it is essentially due to potential energy, stored in the aggregate particles.[1,15] That potential energy will be smaller with larger elastic deformability of the aggregate, i.e. a lower resistance to deformation. Thus, whereas for normal aggregate concrete the delayed elastic deformation represents about 40 per cent of the total creep, for most lightweight aggregate concretes the corresponding proportion was found to be 20–30 per cent only.[15]

For most lightweight aggregates it has been assumed that creep will be higher than for normal aggregate (gravel) concrete. From results obtained for some high grade expanded clay and shale aggregates this appears to be doubtful; some lightweight aggregates can have equal or even less creep than gravel concrete.[16]

SHRINKAGE

Time-dependent deformation due to changes in the moisture balance in the material is a phenomenon peculiarly inherent in the nature and propensities of concrete with a cement-bound matrix. It normally takes the form of shrinkage, but temporarily and in thicker scantlings of lightweight concrete, it can result in appreciable local expansion due to the diffusion of moisture from the aggregate particles into the cement matrix.

Normally the development of moisture movement depends mainly on the type of aggregate used, and on the amount and quality of the cement paste in the concrete. The latter factors are themselves largely dependent on the type of aggregate used because different aggregates require the inclusion of different proportions of cement paste for the achievement of the necessary workability. That will govern the strength of the concrete along with the quality of the cement matrix. For the same strength of concrete, however, aggregate particle strength and rigidity—as in the case of most lightweight aggregates—will demand a cement paste with a higher cement content and strength. Rougher, open textured aggregate shapes and surfaces will also demand more water and cement for reasonable workability and consequently for the attainment of a given strength. For these reasons many lightweight aggregate concretes have a distinct propensity for greater moisture movement than ordinary gravel concrete of the same strength. This becomes more pronounced for concretes of higher strength and sometimes with members having more massive cross-sections.

For structural concretes of 30–50 MPa (4200–7000 psi) compressive strength made with high grade expanded clay or sintered pulverised-fuel ash lightweight aggregates, at a temperature of about 20 °C and at a relative ambient humidity of about 65 per cent, the final shrinkage obtained was 400×10^{-6} to 600×10^{-6}, not greatly different from that for some gravel aggregate concretes in similar circumstances.[1]

For concretes made with other types of lightweight aggregate having an open textured, irregular surface the final shrinkage strain may rise to 1000×10^{-6}.[12]

For larger elements with massive cross-sections the moisture diffusion within the mass of concrete, as between the porous aggregate particles and the absorptive cement–sand matrix will be uneven in different parts of the member. This may lead to differential secondary stresses and internal cracking in the material until a reasonable moisture balance has been reached. Depending on the thickness of the cross-section, this process may take several years. The apparent moisture movement however, may be relatively small, no greater than for gravel concrete in such cases, owing to the self-imposed internal restraints in the material.

In design, the moisture movement of lightweight concrete will assume importance for some structures, e.g. for the calculation of losses of pre-stress in prestressed concrete or for dimensional stability in large structures, such as tall buildings with suspended floor systems. For such cases it has been regarded as good practice to assume that the time-dependent deformations of lightweight concrete will be twice as high than those for ordinary concrete of the same compressive strength. This may well be on the safe side for simple and small structures. A more thorough investigation of the factors involved may well be worthwhile for larger structures where the use of lightweight concrete may then lead to considerable savings.[17]

REFERENCES

1. CEB–FIP (1977). Manual On the Technology and Design of Lightweight Concrete Structures, CEB, Paris.
2. Teychenné, D. C. (1967). 'Structural Concrete made with Lightweight Aggregates'. *Concrete*, **1**, April 1967. (Also Building Research Establishment Engineering Paper No. 48, Building Research Station, Garston, Watford.)
3. International Standard Code of Practice, Vol. 2, 'Model Code for Concrete Construction', Draft 1977, Comité Euro-International du Béton (CEB), Paris.
4. Short, A. and Lewis, R. I. (1962). 'Some Design Considerations', Symposium on Structural Lightweight Concrete, Reinforced Concrete Association, Brighton.
5. Parker, T. W. and Newman, A. J. 'Foamed Slag Concrete', Note No. A73, Building Research Station, Garston, Watford.
6. Evans, R. H. and Hardwick, T. R. (1960). 'Lightweight Concrete with Sintered Clay Aggregate', *Reinforced Concrete Review*, **5**(6).
7. Brewer, R. (1962). Contribution to discussion of paper by J. A. Hanson, *Amer. Concr. Inst. J.*, **34**(1).
8. Hanson, J. A. (1961). 'Tensile Strength and Diagonal Tension Resistance of Structural Lightweight Concrete', *American Concrete Inst. J.* **34**(1).
9. British Standard Code of Practice 110:1972. 'The Structural Use of Concrete', British Standards Institution.
10. Ott, K. F. (1959). 'The "Thermocrete" Method of Construction', *Baurundschau*, **49**, 268.
11. Lea, F. M. and Lee, C. R. (1946). 'Shrinkage and Creep in Concrete', Symposium on 'Shrinkage and Cracking of Cementive Materials', Society of Chemical Industry, London.

12. Shideler, J. J. (1957). 'Lightweight Aggregate Concrete for Structural Use', *Amer. Concrete Inst. J.*, **29,** 4.
13. Ross, A. D. (1937). 'Concrete Creep Data', *The Structural Engineer*, **15,** 8.
14. Tertea, I. and Mirsu, O. (1959). 'Some Observations on the Permanent Deformation of Lightweight Concretes (Expanded Clay and Foamed Slag)' *Lucrari Stientifice*, Inst. Politecnic, Cluj, Romania.
15. Róstasy, F. S. *et al.* (1972). 'Shrinkage and Creep of Lightweight Concrete made of Aggregates having Different Moisture Contents', Report of Otto-Graf Institute, Technical University, Stuttgart.
16. Karl, S. and Bomhard, H. (1976). Private communication.
17. Weigler, H. and Karl, S. (1972). 'Reinforced Lightweight Concrete', Bauverlag, Wiesbaden.

CHAPTER ELEVEN

Protection against Deterioration of Lightweight Aggregate Concrete

SUMMARY

The factors that mainly affect the corrosion of steel reinforcement embedded in concrete are discussed, viz., cement content, carbonation, concrete cover and exposure. Various investigations on the protection afforded by lightweight concrete against corrosion of the reinforcement are described and conclusions are drawn. The resistance against deterioration of actual structures made with different kinds of lightweight aggregate is considered with examples. Where properly designed and made, reinforced lightweight concrete is as safe against deterioration due to corrosion of the reinforcement or attack on the concrete, as other types of concrete containing steel reinforcement.

GENERAL

Perhaps the greatest obstacle to a more widespread and bolder use of lightweight aggregate concrete for reinforced concrete construction in the past has been the anxiety of reinforced concrete engineers that this type of porous material would be more permeable by water or water vapours than dense gravel concrete and that it might therefore prove to be more vulnerable to corrosion of the reinforcement embedded in it.

In view of the misconceptions that still prevail, it seems necessary to emphasise that well-compacted structural grade lightweight concrete made with a chemically inert aggregate is no less resistant to deterioration of both steel and concrete than well-compacted gravel aggregate concrete. In fact the quality of the concrete has a far greater influence on its performance and durability than the type of aggregate with which it is made.

How can 'quality' of concrete be characterised? A number of factors can be defined which influence it. Of these, cement content is one of the most important and will be discussed later. Among other important factors are water content, compaction, aggregate particle size gradients and the curing procedures used. Nearly all these are closely interrelated.

It is known that corrosion of the reinforcement can, and indeed frequently does, occur with dense gravel or crushed rock aggregate concrete,[1] where the material is lean in cement, poorly compacted and easily permeable, where the cover is inadequate or where the structure is exposed to severe industrial pollution of the surrounding atmosphere, or where additives are used which may attack the cement matrix or the steel reinforcement; although the use of calcium chloride for reinforced and prestressed concrete has now been discontinued, there are many existing buildings where it has been used to encourage earlier setting and hardening. Extensive repairs have become necessary in many such cases. The increasing use of thin cladding slabs with inadequate cover over the reinforcement may also encourage corrosion and deterioration.

Corrosion requires moisture and free oxygen to combine with the iron, but the presence of corrosive substances such as sulphur compounds and chlorides will accelerate deterioration. It is important to bear in mind that in some parts of the UK and of other industrialised countries the atmosphere is not only very humid during much of the year but is also polluted. However, concrete with an adequate cement content surrounding the reinforcement is an alkaline material and, if well compacted, provides powerful protection against corrosion of embedded steel bars. Provided that this protection does not diminish by a reduction of the alkalinity of the concrete, reinforced concrete structures show considerable resistance to this type of deterioration, even under severe conditions of weathering.

CORROSION OF EMBEDDED REINFORCEMENT

Reliable evidence on the protection afforded by lightweight concrete, or indeed of any type of concrete, against the corrosion of the embedded reinforcement is not plentiful. Information is available on the behaviour of gravel concrete exposed to the action of sea-water obtained by means of scientifically planned experiments and from experience, but until recently little information was available on the performance of various types of lightweight concrete.

The first in this field was Krüger, whose investigations[2] on the comparative behaviour of gravel and foamed slag concretes were prompted in 1941 by the need to examine the conflicting claims of the producers of natural pumice and of foamed slag aggregates in Germany. In the course of this investigation gravel and foamed slag concrete specimens containing steel bars with concrete covers ranging from 20–50 mm ($\frac{3}{4}$–2 in.) in thickness were subjected to identical conditions of exposure after curing. Some specimens of both types of concrete were left out in the open while the remainder was placed alternately under water and then in a room in normal atmospheric conditions. Some of the bars were coated with cement slurry before embedment, but most of the steel bars embedded in the concrete were not subjected to any preliminary treatment.

After exposure periods ranging from three months to three years, the specimens were broken open and the embedded bars were inspected. Their condition was found to vary considerably, although some rusting was noted on most bars. The results of these tests led to the conclusion that for the rich mixes used, both the type of aggregate and the type of exposure to which the concrete is subjected may well be of secondary importance only. It appears, however, that for such mixes protection against corrosion is greatly enhanced by increasing the thickness of the concrete cover and by coating the reinforcement with cement slurry before embedment. Anything that might facilitate penetration of water to the steel and tends to eliminate the alkaline substances contained in the concrete would therefore necessarily increase the danger of corrosion of the embedded reinforcement.

Because of its limitations, comprehensive conclusions cannot be drawn from Krüger's work. Only one mix, which was rich in cement and therefore highly alkaline, was tested for each of the two aggregates used, namely gravel and foamed slag. Moreover, details of the test specimens and the conditions of test are not known with certainty.

Exposure tests of a more comprehensive nature than have been made hitherto on the corrosion-resisting properties of various kinds of dense and lightweight aggregate concretes were therefore made by the Building Research Station in England. The results of these tests indicate that prolonged and detailed exposure tests made under natural conditions are necessary to obtain a reliable assessment of the performance of each type of concrete. Once the rate of corrosion is known and the criteria that govern it are determined, then the probable durability, and corrosion resistance of various types of concrete can be determined with accelerated tests in the laboratory.

Most of these tests were made under severe conditions of exposure in East London.[3] Although such conditions may well occur in severely polluted industrial environments and are not, therefore, to be regarded as accelerated test conditions, there was a high SO_2 content in the air which was probably produced by a nearby gasworks and a sulphuric acid plant. The exposure site on which the test specimens were placed was located on the leeward side of these sources of pollution.

The test specimens used were prisms containing bright mild steel bars (Fig. 11.1), standing upright on concrete slabs placed on the ground. The types of aggregate and the mix proportions are given in Table 11.1. In addition to gravel, five different types of lightweight aggregate were used in these tests. The concrete cover for the embedded bars was 25 mm, 37 mm and 50 mm (1 in., $1\frac{1}{2}$ in. and 2 in.) respectively. One of the two bars embedded in each prism, with a cover of $1\frac{1}{2}$ in., was coated with cement slurry before embedment. In continental practice this additional protection through cement slurry treatment is regarded as adequate for exposed

TABLE 11.1

PROPERTIES OF SOME LIGHTWEIGHT AND SAND AND GRAVEL CONCRETES USED FOR THE INVESTIGATION OF THE PROTECTION AGAINST CORROSION AFFORDED TO EMBEDDED STEEL REINFORCEMENT

Aggregate	Mix by volume					Water–cement ratio	Average cube strength at 28 days		Average dry density	
	Cement	Sand	Gravel	Lightweight aggregate Fine	Medium		(MPa)	(psi)	(kg/m³)	(pcf)
1	2	3	4	5	6	7	8	9	10	11
Foamed slag	1	—		4·5	4·5	1·35	7·4	1070	1760	110
	1	1·8		2·5	2·5	0·73	20·8	3020	1940	121
	1	—		2·7	4·5	1·30	9·0	1300	1870	117
	1	1·25		1·25	2·5	0·70	23·2	3380	1990	124
Expanded clay	1	—		4·5	4·5	1·40	7·2	1050	1330	83
	1	1·8		2·5	2·5	0·80	22·3	3230	1540	96
	1	—		2·7	4·5	1·35	13·5	1960	1620	101
	1	1·25		1·25	2·5	0·80	29·3	4250	1750	109
Sintered pulverised-fuel ash	1	—		4·5	4·5	1·42	18·2	2630	1540	96
	1	—		2·5	2·5	0·90	27·1	3930	1630	102
	1	1·35		3·15	4·5	1·35	21·9	3170	1650	103
	1	1·25	—	1·25	2·5	0·85	30·6	4450	1760	110
Sand and gravel	1	4·5	4·5	—		0·95	14·9	2160	2210	138
	1	2·5	2·5			0·60	30·6	4430	2280	142

FIG. 11.1 Exposure specimen.

members. When the specimens were broken open for inspection it was found that the actual position of the bars rarely deviated from the prescribed one by more than 3 mm ($\frac{1}{8}$ in.).

Bright mild steel bars were used in preference to plain black reinforcing steel because the surface texture of the bright bars is more uniform and their weight could therefore be determined more accurately. It was also easier to ensure that no rust was present on the surface of any of the bars when casting the specimens. It was found from tests, however, that the propensity to corrode and the rate at which rusting took place was not influenced greatly by the type of bar used.

To assess the effects of exposure on the concrete and on the embedded bars, specimens were removed from the exposure site and broken open after various periods of exposure. The steel bars they contained were then removed for inspection and weighing. Before being broken up, the surface of the specimens was examined for dust formation, exposure of the coarse aggregate, crazing cracks and the formation of algae. The depth of carbonation in the concrete was also measured on freshly broken concrete surfaces by spraying them with phenolphthalein, carbonation of the concrete being indicated by the absence of the characteristic pink colour.

The steel bars were then extracted and the rust and concrete adhering to the surface of the steel bars were removed by immersing them in a solution of hydrochloric acid ('Clarke's Solution'). Inevitably a small quantity of steel was also removed along with the rust, but this was taken into

Fig. 11.2   Beams exposed to the weather at Garston and subjected to sustained loading test.

consideration in assessing the corrosion resulting from exposure. That loss was assessed by comparing the measured weight of each steel bar before it was embedded in the concrete, with the weight of the same bar obtained after removal from the broken specimen and after freeing the surface of rust products.

The conditions of exposure were determined by continuous observation of the atmospheric conditions at the exposure site. Measurements were made of the air temperature, rainfall, and of the sulphur content of the atmosphere.

Tests were also made with reinforced concrete beams using gravel and various types of lightweight aggregate; these beams were exposed to the weather in a cracked condition and subjected to loading at Garston (Fig.

11.2), where atmospheric conditions were much less severe than in East London.

A number of conclusions can be reached from this work and from investigations carried out elsewhere on gravel concrete exposed under different conditions. Perhaps the most important conclusion is that there is a relationship between the propensity of embedded steel bars to corrode and the carbonation of the concrete. It was found that carbonation of the

FIG. 11.3   Broken exposure specimens showing the depth of carbonation in well-compacted and poorly compacted lightweight concrete.

alkaline materials contained in the concrete and the rate at which carbonation spreads inwards from the surface depends, to a much greater extent on the quality of the concrete, i.e. its grading, compaction and cement content, than on the type of aggregate used.

For well-compacted gravel concrete of structural quality the carbonated outer layer gradually attains a maximum thickness of about $1 \cdot 5$ mm ($\frac{1}{16}$ in.) after about three years exposure (Fig. 11.3). For lightweight concrete having a similar compressive strength and quality, the depth of the carbonated layer of concrete varies somewhat for different aggregates, but is in general greater than that obtained for gravel concrete and may reach about $2 \cdot 5$ mm ($\frac{1}{10}$ in.). In the case of sintered pulverised-fuel ash aggregates the thickness of the carbonated concrete is generally no greater than for gravel concrete. After reaching these depths further carbonation then ceases for most types of concrete in the absence of cracking and thus the risk of corrosion of the reinforcement also diminishes.

With weak, poorly compacted, lean concrete, however, the rate at which carbonation proceeds is always faster than with well-compacted material. Such concrete of low quality may be sufficiently deprived of free alkaline material to a depth of up to 25 mm (1 in.) after about two years, that it becomes incapable of providing protection to embedded steel bars against corrosion. This is especially obvious where the cement content of the concrete varies, e.g. as a result of 'cement gain' at the division between successive lifts of concrete. Where steel is partly in contact with carbonated material and partly with concrete that is still alkaline, then it has a tendency to corrode in the former and to remain sound in the latter (Fig. 11.4).

FIG. 11.4   Broken exposure specimen showing the corrosion of embedded steel bars where in contact with carbonated lightweight concrete.

The chemical and electrochemical processes involved are not as yet clearly understood but they may be described in general terms. It is known that the surface of the steel bar is covered with a protective film of oxides. This protective film can be destroyed or penetrated, however, in a corrosive environment. It appears that the concrete, being alkaline, provides an anti-corrosive environment which reduces the vulnerability of the steel reinforcement to corrosion. The alkaline substances in the concrete, mainly the free lime produced from the cement during setting, may disappear, however, either as a result of leaching out from the concrete by moisture or by combining with the carbon dioxide carried into the concrete from the surrounding atmosphere, to form calcium carbonate. If this occurs, the concrete becomes less alkaline and can no longer protect the steel adequately by maintaining the oxide film intact. In the presence of moisture a combination of the iron with the oxygen occurs, leading to corrosion of the steel; this is facilitated by electrolytic processes in the presence of dissimilar materials. Carbonation can occur more readily in the external layers of concrete since there is greater concentration of CO_2 in the external layers than in the interior; with increasing depth, therefore, the rate at which carbonation proceeds from the surface towards the interior of the concrete diminishes considerably.

This reduction of the rate of carbonation with depth may be influenced, however, by cracking of the concrete, which permits the ingress of CO_2 and thus encourages the carbonation of the adjacent layers of concrete. Crazing cracks are specially likely to occur on exposed surfaces of concrete made with lightweight aggregates if the grading of the aggregate includes too large a proportion of very fine, dusty particles. Certain types of pulverised-fuel ash aggregate concrete are particularly prone to this. The width of the cracks is generally too small at first to affect the rate of carbonation in the interior of the concrete at all. With the passing of the years, however, exposed surfaces of this type tend to develop interconnected systems of fairly deep cracks which cannot be without effect on the likelihood of corrosion of the embedded reinforcement if the carbonation reaches the steel. In some cases cracks may extend and become deeper, but Snowdon[4] has shown that the cracks may tend to seal and to close up. More information is needed on the effect of cracking on carbonation of the concrete and the factors which affect the autogenous healing of lightweight concrete. Carbonation will spread inwards along the crack paths, but will tend to stop if the crack width is small, e.g. less than $0\cdot127$ mm ($0\cdot005$ in.).

Exposure to the weather does not necessarily lead to the conditions that are most favourable to carbonation of the concrete, for the presence of liquid water in saturated concrete physically hinders the chemical combination of the free lime with CO_2. The combination of circumstances that is likely to be most conducive to carbonation of the concrete would appear to be storage under cover, in a moist atmosphere rich in CO_2. On the other hand, once the concrete has carbonated, rusting of the embedded steel becomes rapid and severe if reinforced concrete is exposed to the weather in a polluted atmosphere.

Surface deterioration of the concrete has been found to occur with any type of concrete, especially if it is not adequately compacted. Exposure of the coarse aggregate, crazing and dust formation on the surface are normal occurrences, particularly on smooth concrete surfaces exposed to the weather, whatever the aggregate used. Pitting of the surface, owing to erosion of the matrix, is more likely with lean mixes, particularly where they consist entirely of lightweight aggregates, i.e. if the fines do not contain quartz sand, but it appears that the degree of pitting is not affected greatly by the type of aggregate used. On the other hand, the formation of dust on the surface of the concrete as a result of weathering is greatly affected by the aggregate, sintered pulverised-fuel ash aggregates being more liable to this than other types of aggregate.

RESISTANCE OF REINFORCED LIGHTWEIGHT CONCRETE
STRUCTURES AGAINST DETERIORATION

Considerable evidence has been obtained on the performance of reinforced concrete structures made with different kinds of lightweight aggregate concrete in continental climatic conditions in Europe and in America, and in general this evidence is favourable. In the industrial conurbations of Great Britain, however, the atmosphere is at times more humid and may be more polluted than in heavily industrialised areas elsewhere. Experience abroad may not therefore necessarily apply to the UK. Nevertheless, such experience is of considerable importance when assessing the behaviour of lightweight concrete structures observed over a period in Great Britain.

Most of the earlier lightweight concrete structures in Western Europe and in the UK are made of foamed slag concrete. On housing estates built by Local Authorities at Chesterfield[5] and Glasgow, for example, reinforced foamed slag concrete cast *in situ* and precast elements were used for the construction of 2-storey buildings, in the form of lintels, wall plates, frames and wall panels. After 20 years, corrosion has not occurred in these structures and the concrete itself has not deteriorated, although in some of the buildings conditions were favourable to deterioration owing to the penetration of driving rain. At the cast-*in-situ* wall plates and lintels, cases of faulty workmanship occurred, however; for example, the upper surfaces of some of these members were sloping inwards, leading to rain penetration.

Parts of the Mulberry Harbour scheme constructed during the Second World War were also made with foamed slag concrete. Abandoned in the storms that broke after D-Day, some of these pontoons eventually found their way to the south coast of England (Fig. 11.5). Where the battering of the waves and of the shingle on the shore broke up the concrete covering, the bare bars were badly corroded but where the concrete continued to adhere to and protect the bars, corrosion was not found to have occurred after about two years in the sea. Information on the mix proportions used is no longer available but the mix is said to have been rich, and probably contained sand.

Several private houses and industrial buildings containing reinforced foamed slag concrete that were built some 30 years ago in Southern England, some near the coast, are in existence and show no damage due to corrosion of the steel or deterioration of the concrete.

In Germany, under conditions of fairly severe industrial pollution and humidity, a number of structures of considerable importance and size built with reinforced foamed slag concrete have shown no signs of damage due to corrosion after 10 to 25 years' life.

In the coal mines of the Ruhr valley, because of the danger of fire, the use of foamed slag concrete has become established for precast reinforced concrete 'lagging slabs', supported by steel arches to replace timber lagging in the main drifts and galleries. The slabs are 1 m long, about 0·3 m wide and 50–75 mm thick, reinforced with a welded cage which is dipped in cement slurry before being placed in the mould where the concrete is vibrated to a high degree of compaction. The mix used is fairly rich, containing crushed air-cooled or granulated slag for fine aggregate. Gravel or sand is not used for these slabs in view of the tendency of the quartz to shatter at high temperatures. There is no evidence of corrosion of the

FIG. 11.5   Wreck of foamed slag concrete floating harbour section (Mulberry Harbour).

embedded bars, even where these were in contact with corrosive effluents in the mines. Rusting was only observed where, owing to inadequate structural design of the slabs or excessive pressure at faults in the rock, the slabs failed and the steel bars were exposed.

The use of natural pumice was introduced in the UK before the war, mainly for block making and it is being imported into the UK and USA from Greece and the Lipari Islands of Italy. In Germany, pumice concrete was also used for manufacturing precast reinforced roof slabs on a large scale (Fig. 16.4) since the early 1920s and, as a result, extensive experience is available on the durability of this type of building element in practice. Pumice concrete members were found to be adequately durable under normal conditions of usage in roofs and framed structures in industry and domestic buildings.[6] In humid and industrially polluted conditions, however—e.g. if used for roofing steelworks or foundries—it has been reported that in some instances failures have taken place after about 10 years' use.

These lightweight precast concrete hollow slabs made with both pumice and foamed slag concretes are standard building products in Germany.

With the exhaustion of the reserves of the pumice deposits in the Rhine Valley, German and Dutch block and slab makers now use the underlying layers of old lava. This material produces heavier concrete than pumice. The slabs must comply with the appropriate standard specification (DIN 4028)[7] which demands that the reinforcement should be embedded in 'dense concrete'. In practice this requirement is deemed to be adequately fulfilled by pouring cement slurry on the reinforcing bars when placing them in the mould. Owing to this treatment and as a result of vibration near the reinforcement, the density of the concrete is considerably greater in the tension zone than in the compression zone, where only handling reinforcement is placed in the form of $\frac{1}{8}$ in. wires to resist damage during transport and erection; these frequently corrode in practice but, because of their small diameter, rarely cause damage due to expansion of the corrosion products. Whereas foamed slag is frequently used for *in situ* work, pumice concrete has rarely been so used because of its tendency, mentioned above, to 'float' to the surface, i.e. for the aggregate to segregate from the cement matrix. It has been successfully used for cast-*in-situ* reinforced slabs in Kenya.

Expanded clay and shale aggregate concrete is used more than other types of lightweight concrete for reinforced lightweight concrete construction both in the USA and the USSR. In the UK it has been used successfully in multi-storey construction as well as for the construction of ships' hulls during the war.[8] Some of these ships are still afloat and none perished as a result of corrosion of the embedded reinforcement, under conditions of great severity, in sea-water. Similar evidence has been obtained in America.[9] Expanded clay concrete has also been used for the construction of bridge decks under severely exposed conditions without damage to the concrete or the reinforcement.[10]

In the absence of an effective protective coating on the embedded steel bars, corrosion of the reinforcement is likely where the aggregate, the cement or the water contain corrosive substances. Fortunately all lightweight aggregates available in the UK, except furnace clinker, are chemically inert towards steel and present no inherent danger of corrosion.

When crushed, foamed slag tends to show traces of a smell of sulphur. This is caused by the presence of sulphide gases in the discrete pores of the material or generation of such gases by the combination of moisture with certain sulphides; these have no deleterious effect on any embedded steel. Some artificial lightweight aggregates may contain a small, usually variable percentage of unburnt carbon. Carbon has no effect either on the concrete or on the steel if present only in small quantities, but it may reduce strength.

To summarise, the causes and mechanism of corrosion of steel embedded in concrete are not yet known with precision. The likelihood of corrosion cannot be predicted therefore at present with certainty. Both research and experience tend to indicate, however, that in the absence of chemically aggressive substances in the aggregate used, the nature of the latter—i.e. whether it is dense or lightweight, natural or artificial—has much less influence on the resistance of the concrete against corrosion of the embedded reinforcement than other factors, such as the thickness of the concrete cover, the conditions to which the concrete is later exposed in practice, and the factors governing the quality of the concrete, such as workability, cement content, aggregate grading and compaction. Although concrete made with lightweight aggregates tends to carbonate somewhat faster than concrete made with dense aggregates, careful compaction and adequate cement content will reduce the depth of the concrete that is carbonated within a given period of time, at a given depth of cover, for any type of concrete.

Since carbonated concrete cannot afford adequate protection to steel reinforcement that is not adequately protected by other means—e.g. by coating the bars with a waterproof material, it is important to delay and, if possible, to prevent the spread of carbonation to the level of the steel reinforcement embedded in the concrete. In every structure therefore the steel must always be covered with an adequate thickness of alkaline concrete. To ensure an adequate cover in lightweight concrete exposed to the weather, it would seem advisable that in design the minimum concrete cover required for normal aggregate concrete in the BS Code of Practice CP 114:1957[11] should be increased by about 12 mm ($\frac{1}{2}$ in.) where lightweight aggregate concrete is used externally. For example, for exposed concrete surfaces, the British Codes recommend a minimum concrete cover of 38 mm ($1\frac{1}{2}$ in.). Where lightweight concrete is used the cover given should not be less than 50 mm (2 in.). In addition, the maximum size of the coarse aggregate used for reinforced lightweight concrete structures should not exceed 12 mm ($\frac{1}{2}$ in.) to ensure that an adequately thick barrier of cement matrix is present always, to prevent the penetration of carbon dioxide in the moisture from outside. In the later British Standard Code, CP 110:1972,[12] no increase for the lightweight concrete cover is prescribed above that for gravel concrete, for internal, non-corrosive conditions. For any other ambience, for lightweight concrete the concrete cover must be increased by 10 mm (0·4 in.) over that of gravel concrete. Moreover for lightweight concrete which has a 28-day cube strength of less than 20 MPa (2900 psi), the cover must be not less than 25 mm (1 in.) thick, even for internal, non-corrosive conditions. No special increase in the cover is required by the ACI Code[13] for lightweight concretes but the cover must be increased if the concrete is porous.

The requirements with regard to concrete cover in the German Code of Practice for reinforced lightweight concrete[7] are much less stringent than in the UK; in some cases the permissible cover, even for exposed members, is less than 12 mm ($\frac{1}{2}$ in.). This appears to be insufficient for humid, polluted conditions. With the more stringent British requirements it is found that the number of structures where the reinforcement shows obvious signs of corrosion is much smaller than on the continent of Europe.

Experience thus shows that with adequate cover and provided that reasonable care is used in design, mixing and placing, lightweight aggregate concrete is capable of providing as good a protection against corrosion of the reinforcement and is as resistant against deterioration as dense gravel concrete. Where the conditions of use are exceptionally severe—for example, in the case of reinforced concrete permanently exposed to corrosive, damp conditions or to aggressive waters underground—special measures are necessary for dense as well as for lightweight aggregate concrete, to provide adequate protection against deterioration. In such cases a concrete cover of 76 mm (3 in.) or even more may well be desirable.

The CEB–FIP International Recommendations[14] also provide for increased concrete cover, related to the maximum aggregate diameter and in any case to a minimum cover which is greater than that for ordinary concrete. The *Draft International Code* (Volume II, Concrete)[15] requires that the cover should be not less than 15 mm (about $\frac{5}{8}$ in.) or alternatively equal to the bar diameter or—in aggressive conditions—equal to the maximum aggregate size plus 5 mm (0·2 in.) whichever is the greater. Such cover can be increased where necessary to take account of the severity of the exposure of the components. These minimum requirements are considered to be adequate for ordinary structural concretes, but normally the cover for lightweight concrete should be increased by 5 mm.

On balance, with increasing experience and greater knowledge of the long-term behaviour of lightweight concrete structures in service, special precautions for lightweight concrete are shown to have been generally superfluous or at any rate no more desirable than in the case of normal-weight concrete.

For all types of concrete, whatever type of aggregate is used, a decisive factor which largely determines its resistance to chemical attack and the protection it can provide for the embedded steel reinforcement against corrosive influences, must be considered to be the cement content, allied with the effective distribution of the Portland cement throughout the fabric of the concrete and the fullest possible hydration of the cement and any pozzolanic materials in the concrete. There are a number of reasons for the critical influence of the cement content of concrete on its durability. Resistance against the penetration of liquids or gases into the concrete is one. To attain a suitably low permeability it is necessary to ensure that the concrete is well compacted, that there is sufficient cement in the mix, that the cement is sufficiently hydrated by proper curing and that the water/cement ratio in the concrete when cast is as low as possible, consistent with adequate workability for good compaction. There are pronounced interrelations between these properties. An adequate cement content will provide sufficient alkalinity for the protection of the embedded reinforcement and a low permeability will prevent the combination of the alkalis with CO_2 and water, which would lead to carbonation.

In some codes and standards relating to concrete a minimum cement content has been specified to safeguard durability and long-term serviceability, for with modern techniques of mixing and placing and careful workmanship, required strengths can be obtained with a relatively low cement content, but in exposed conditions this could later result in serious damage to the building and losses for both owner and user. Although the imposition of minimum cement content requirements may lead to a slight increase in inital costs, they are likely to be accepted eventually as a necessary safeguard for concrete producers as well as for designers and building owners, provided that those requirements are not unnecessarily onerous. It would seem superfluous and extravagant and it would not encourage optimum efficiency, for example, if concrete kept in dry, non-corrosive conditions inside buildings were to be required to have the same minimum cement content as concrete used for parts of the building exposed to the weather or to severely corrosive conditions of service. Where conditions of exposure are mild—as in the inside of dwellings—a lower cement content might be acceptable therefore if the required strength can be attained without too great a degree of variability. It should be remembered, however, that in developed industrial societies the type of user in large buildings is apt to change as much as nine times in the course of their useful life. A seemingly innocuous occupancy may thus give way to one of a highly corrosive nature. Low cement content may then give rise to insufficient resistance to chemical attack. It follows that proof of adequate compressive or tensile strength through standard tests alone cannot be regarded as a sufficient criterion for adequate concrete quality. There are, however, fairly reliable methods and equipment for the measurement of the cement content of wet mixes and in the foreseeable future such measurements may well be preferred to cube or cylinder compression and splitting tests as a criterion of acceptability in a concrete structure. In addition to their greater technical relevance they have the advantage of immediacy and help to avoid subsequent disputes or litigation or indeed the need to cut out concrete that turns out eventually to have insufficient strength. Most codes of practice, however, avoid the issue by omitting to establish minimum cement content requirements. Recently the matter has received more serious consideration. CP 110:1072[12] has established fairly precise rules, the required minimum Portland cement content per unit volume of finished concrete varying from 200–410 kg/m³ (12–25 pcf), depending on the nominal maximum aggregate size, on the type of exposure—ranging from 'mild' to 'severe'—on the degree of control exercised on the water–cement ratio and on whether the material is used for plain, reinforced or prestressed concrete. Separate rules apply to concrete exposed to sulphate attack, depending also on the type of cement used, viz.

Portland, sulphate-resisting Portland or Supersulphated. (High alumina cements should no longer be used for structural work.)

The *Draft CEB–FIP International*[14] Code asks for a minimum cement content ranging from 250–300 kg/m^3 (15–18 pcf), depending on conditions of use. These rules apply to lightweight as well as to normal weight concretes.

REFERENCES

1. Hamilton, S. B. (1956). 'The Durability of Reinforced Concrete in Buildings'. National Building Studies, Spec. Rep. No. 25, HMSO.
2. Krüger, L. (1941). 'The Properties and Use of Foamed Slag', *Archiv für das Eisenhüttenwesen*, **15**(2).
3. Short, A. (1959). 'The Use of Lightweight Concrete for Reinforced Concrete Construction', *Reinforced Concrete Review*, **5**(3).
4. Snowdon, L. C. (1961). 'The Moisture Movement of Natural Aggregates and its Effect on Concrete'. RILEM Symposium on the Durability of Concrete. Prague.
5. Wikeley, J. B. (1950). 'The Engineer and House Construction'. Public Works Congress, London.
6. Müller, H. E. (1957). 'Safety against Corrosion in Reinforced Pumice Concrete Hollow Slabs', *Der Bau und die Bauindustrie*, **10**(9).
7. German Standard DIN 4028: 'Stahlbetonhohldielen, Bestimmungen für Herstellung und Verlegung' ('Regulations for the Manufacture and Use of Precast Reinforced Concrete Hollow Slabs'). Deutscher Ausschuss für Stahlbeton.
8. 'Concrete-steel Barges' (1943), *The Engineer*, **176**(4581).
9. Wilson, C. (1954). 'Concrete Ship Resists Seawater for 34 Years', *Concrete*, **62**(1).
10. Woodruff, G. B. (1938). 'Lightweight Concrete Pavement on the San Francisco–Oakland Bay Bridge', *Amer. Concr. Inst. J.*, **9**(3).
11. British Standard Code of Practice, 114:1957. 'The Structural Use of Reinforced Concrete in Buildings', British Standards Institution.
12. British Standard Code of Practice, CP 110:1972. 'The Structural Use of Concrete', British Standards Institution.
13. American Concrete Institute Standard ACI 318: 'Building Code Requirements for Reinforced Concrete', ACI, Detroit.
14. CEB–FIP International Recommendations for Concrete Construction (1970). Comité Européen du Béton, Paris.
15. International Standard Code of Practice, Vol. 2, 'Model Code for Concrete Construction', Draft 1977, Comité Euro-International du Béton (CEB), Paris.

CHAPTER TWELVE

Bond Strength of Reinforced Lightweight Aggregate Concrete

SUMMARY

The interaction between steel and concrete through bond and anchorage forces is discussed and the results of bond tests made with lightweight aggregate concrete beams and pull-out specimens using different types of steel—round or deformed bars—are interpreted. The effect of some important factors on the bond strength of lightweight concrete is described, viz. the effect of different bar diameters, embedment lengths, the type of bar surface, 'cavitation', the type of aggregate used, and others.

For ordinary round bars placed horizontally, the bond strength of lightweight concrete is considerably lower than that of gravel concrete. For deformed bars the ultimate bond strength is sensibly the same for both gravel and lightweight aggregate concretes, but for the latter the same slip occurs at a lower load.

GENERAL

Composite methods of construction, such as reinforced concrete, are dependent for their safety and stiffness on the transmission of the internal forces between the constituent materials which make up a cross-section. The transfer of the internal forces and the composite character of the construction are maintained either by bond resistance or through anchorage forces.

Although it is of such importance, the fundamental physical nature of the bond between steel and concrete in reinforced concrete construction is not yet fully understood. It seems, however, that at least three distinct elements may affect the bond performance of reinforced concrete: colloidal adhesion, i.e. glueyness; shrinkage of the concrete around the reinforcement; and frictional forces at the interfaces of the steel and concrete.

The existence of colloidal adhesion between steel and concrete is apparently supported by the results of experiments made with flat, very smooth steel plates on which concrete has been cast without any additional bonding or anchorage.[1] Although there was no friction present, some resistance could be measured against forces tending to move the two

189

Lightweight Concrete

surfaces in relation to each other; however, this may have been the result of interlocking through micro-indentations in the surface of the steel.[2] Valid chemical evidence for colloidal adhesion could not be found, and even if such adhesion existed it could only contribute slightly to the total resistance in the cross-section. Moreover, adhesion, if it is caused by micro-indentations, must disappear if the initial slip between the steel bars and the concrete equals the width of the micro-indentations.

The greater part of the bond between steel and concrete is probably caused by frictional forces. These are governed mainly by the surface characteristics at the interfaces. Friction and bond resistance are therefore increased by rusting, provided the surface of the bars does not flake. Shrinkage due to the drying out of the concrete tends to produce compressive forces bearing against the surface of the embedded bar, thereby increasing frictional resistance and hence bond strength. Frictional resistance can also increase as a result of other types of radial strain.

The internal forces which occur in a member under loading are transmitted through bond stresses. Increasing bond stresses under load, however, lead to slip between the steel and the concrete. On releasing the load, some reversal of movement is bound to take place and it has been suggested that this induces the formation of small wedging elements, consisting of crushed particles of matrix and fine aggregate, between the steel and the concrete (dilatancy).[2] When subjected to repeated loading this wedging action would inhibit any increase of slip and thus would increase the bond resistance. In lightweight concrete the broken aggregate particles are relatively soft and friable compared with quartz sand. Unless it contains sand or other hard fine aggregate such as crushed air-cooled or granulated slag, lightweight concrete is not likely, as a result of dilatancy, to maintain its ultimate bond strength under repeated loading.

The bond resistance of reinforced concrete members can be maintained partly because steel and concrete expand and contract at a very similar rate under changing thermal conditions. Were this not so, recurring thermal stresses would occur which might lead to failure in bond.

In the absence of adequate bond resistance, composite action can be ensured by providing suitable anchorage for the reinforcing bars in the concrete. This is achieved by means of end anchorage fittings, such as welded anchorage plates or—more usually—by the provision of hooks at the ends of the bars. Alternatively, a mechanical anchorage effect can be induced along the reinforcing bars through ribs or other types of surface deformation produced on the embedded bars. These in turn will form corresponding impressions in the surrounding concrete and the resulting mutually complementary undulations ensure that the internal forces are transmitted through bearing pressures along the length of the bars.

When failure takes place as a result of crushing of the concrete at the anchorages, the bearing stresses between the deformed steel surfaces and the surrounding concrete are considerably higher than the compressible strength of the concrete, owing to the complicated triaxial stress conditions which develop at the interfaces. Indeed, where deformed bars are used, bursting of the concrete along the reinforcement is a frequent form of failure in the laboratory; this is a result of the tensile stresses set up in the concrete if the thickness of the concrete cover is insufficient to distribute the bursting forces, or where the stirrups provided are not adequate for this purpose.

Where the conditions of exposure are severe and the concrete cover is not sufficient by itself to provide a reliable safeguard, then it may be deemed necessary to provide the reinforcing bars with a special coating of cement slurry before or during casting, to protect the bars against corrosion; alternatively, some other protective treatment or coating may be used. More frequently, however, the reinforcing bars are placed without any preliminary treatment, just as they are delivered at the site or at the precasting works. The surface treatment of the bars may influence the bond properties and its effect on the bond strength must be taken into account.

In the UK ordinary round mild steel bars have been the most frequently used type of reinforcement with gravel aggregate concrete, in the past and it seems likely that for some time such reinforcement will be in general use in practice for reinforced lightweight concrete also. The use of deformed bars has become more widespread however, because of its technical and economic advantages, associated with the higher permissible stresses allowed by the BS Code of Practice CP 114:1957[3] and by CP 110:1972[4] for bars having a guaranteed yield point stress. In the USA this development has progressed so far that ordinary round reinforcing bars are now little used in practice and deformed bars of various types and qualities are generally preferred for both dense and lightweight concrete structures. This trend has spread to Western Europe.

BOND TESTS

Much careful research has been carried out by workers in many countries on the bond strength of concrete made with different aggregates and with different types of steel reinforcement and with different surface protection treatments applied to the bars.[5−7] Most of this experimental research was concerned mainly with the detailed practical problems of bond, related to the materials used and the type of structure; fundamental aspects were not treated.[8] A variety of experimental methods and standards were adopted for the tests so that in retrospect it is now difficult to induce a valid comparison between the results obtained by different research workers in their experiments; it is equally difficult to compare the experimental laboratory conditions with practice. Pull-out and push-out tests and variations of these were at first mainly used to assess the behaviour of various types of steel and concrete. Later, following the initiative of American research workers,[9] specially designed bond beams have been introduced to compare the bond and anchorage stresses and slip for different types of bar embedded in concrete.

None of these methods can reproduce accurately the stresses and deformations that are likely to be present in flexural members under loading in a structure. It seems likely, nevertheless, that the results of carefully conducted tests on the specially designed bond beams will give a more relevant picture of the bond performance of flexural members than any of the other bond tests, which are rather more artificial and small-scale. The design of the beams will, however, affect the answer and also the comparative performance of different types of concrete or steel. They are also much more expensive to produce and to test than pull-out specimens which, *faute de mieux*, are more generally employed.

Because of this uncertainty about their meaning and significance, bond tests seem to have made relatively little impact on design. Their main object was to enlarge the understanding of the stress and cracking processes in flexural members and so eventually to enable designers to design more safely and economically. But Codes of Practice do not attempt to govern the permissible design stresses in bond by reference to some experimental bond strength obtained with standard acceptance tests, or in any other way. Permissible stresses in bond are generally laid down in relation to the 28-day compressive strength of the concrete or its 'characteristic strength' derived from the latter, obtained either by means of cube-crushing tests or with tests on cylinders on prisms. Bond tests, where they were adopted as a standard test in the form of pull-out tests in the United Kingdom,[3] and as beam tests in the USA, are used as an efficiency index for the various types of high tensile or deformed steel bars tested. In this way the bond characteristics of deformed bars can be compared in a standard way with those of ordinary round mild steel bars to ensure that the former qualify for the increase in permissible stress allowed for deformed bars by the various Codes. These tests are made with a standard gravel concrete to ensure uniform and comparable test conditions for the steel.

In examining the bond strength of lightweight concrete there is therefore no absolute standard on which to fall back as a criterion for establishing a safe and reasonable bond stress to be used for design with the accepted methods of engineering theory. The only comparison that can usefully be made is a comparison of the bond properties of lightweight concrete specimens with those of the corresponding gravel concrete ones. If the results obtained do not differ greatly to the disadvantage of the former, then the permissible stress generally admitted for various types of steel and various qualities of gravel concrete might also be considered safe for use with lightweight aggregate concrete. Where this is not so, and the bond strength of lightweight concrete is substantially lower than that of gravel concrete, then the permissible stresses for the former would probably have to be reduced for safe design. In making such a comparison it should be borne in mind that the gravel aggregate used in making the test specimens is usually of excellent quality. In comparing the bond performance of lightweight concrete with that of gravel concrete, it should also be taken into account that much of the reinforced concrete work carried out in practice is made with dense aggregate that may be inferior in many respects, including bond, to the gravel aggregate used for the test specimens, and thus to most structural lightweight concretes.

Since the bond strength of lightweight concrete structural members cannot be determined *a priori*, but only by comparison with the actual behaviour of similar reinforced concrete members made with gravel aggregate concrete, an investigation was carried out by the Building Research Station[8] to compare the bond strength of lightweight and gravel aggregate concretes of the same compressive strength, following investigations carried out mainly in the USA on pull-out specimens.[7] The principal variable factors which are found to affect the bond performance of steel bars embedded in concrete are:[10]

(1) The surface texture of steel bars (roughness, round smooth or deformed cross-section).
(2) The strength of the concrete.
(3) The compaction of the concrete near the reinforcing bars.
(4) The quality of the matrix.
(5) The resistance of the aggregate particles against deformation and crushing at the ribs on the bar surface.
(6) The modulus of deformation (*E*-value) of the concrete.
(7) The position of the bars in the section.
(8) The diameter of the bars.

For the tests made at the Building Research Station both pull-out specimens (Fig. 12.1) and specially designed bond beams were used. The pull-out specimens were made with different aggregates, bar diameters, types of bar and embedment lengths. The variables chosen for the tests made with bond beams were the type of aggregate used, the type of bar and the embedment length. Foamed slag, expanded clay, and sintered pulverised-fuel ash aggregates were used in addition to sand and gravel. Four types of bar were tested, namely bright mild steel bars, ordinary round mild steel reinforcing bars, 'square-twisted' cold-worked mild steel bars, and ribbed cold-worked mild steel bars. The two latter types of bar are regarded as high-tensile deformed steel bars. For the pull-out tests, the diameter of the round bright or ordinary mild steel reinforcing bars varied from 6–25 mm ($\frac{1}{4}$–1 in.). The embedment length varied from 150–300 mm

FIG. 12.1 Pull-out test arrangement.

(6–12 in.) for the pull-out specimens and from 230–840 mm (9–33 in.) for the beams.

The bond beams were 1·50 m (5 ft) and 2·29 m (7 ft 6 in.) long. The reinforcement was placed in the middle of the width of the beam, with a cover of 25 mm (1 in.) from the bottom. At a distance equal to the desired embedment length from each end of the beam, the reinforcing bar was laid bare and at these points the strain was measured on the steel, the load being placed directly above these points. Stirrups were placed in the beams to prevent shear failure near the ends. The measured strains in the steel bar gave an indication of the magnitude, of the internal forces resisted by bond or anchorage along the bars but not of their distribution. The slip of the bars at the ends was also measured.

Thus, the end sections of the bond beams extending from the cored cavity where the strains were measured to the ends of the beams, were similar to pull-out units. In principle, such beam end sections differ from pull-out specimens, however, in that the stress conditions in both steel and concrete are similar to those that would obtain in an ordinary flexural member, since both the concrete and the steel reinforcement are subjected to tensile stresses. The stress conditions in ordinary pull-out specimens on the other hand are essentially different: while the steel bar is subjected to tension, the stress distribution in the concrete is somewhat confused. Near the shoulder, where the platen of the testing machine impinges upon the concrete, compressive stresses are developed, but the stress conditions inside the specimen are not known.

The results obtained with both pull-out and beam specimens display considerable scatter particularly for lightweight concretes. Nevertheless, some conclusions of value to the development of lightweight concrete structural design could be reached from the results of the experimental work carried out at the Building Research Station and elsewhere. In comparing the performance of dense, gravel aggregate concrete with that of different types of lightweight concrete, however, the interpretation of these conclusions varied somewhat. Shideler considers[11] that the bond strength of structural lightweight aggregate concrete is normally high and that at equal compressive strengths, comparable bond strengths should be expected, although the bond strength would be lower for horizontal bars, with a considerable depth of concrete beneath them. Similar conclusions were reached by other American workers. The tests on which these conclusions are based were made with deformed bars. Similar views are held by some lightweight aggregate manufacturers in the UK.

PLAIN ROUND BARS

Work carried out in the UK extended to both plain round mild steel bars and to deformed reinforcing bars.[8] For plain round bars the bond strength measured with pull-out tests is generally somewhat lower for lightweight than for the particular dense aggregate concrete used, but for some types of aggregate, for example expanded clay, the ratio is higher and may even approach unity (Fig. 12.2).

On the other hand, for special bond beams with plain round bars the effect of using different types of aggregate was found to be much greater. The ratio of the ultimate bond strengths obtained with lightweight aggregate concrete and dense gravel aggregate concrete of the same compressive strength ranges from 0·5–0·7, the average value being rather lower than 0·6 (Fig. 12.3). In some exceptional cases, however, particularly for higher compressive strengths and especially for sintered pulverised-fuel ash aggregates, high bond strengths, reaching those obtained with dense aggregate concrete, have been recorded.

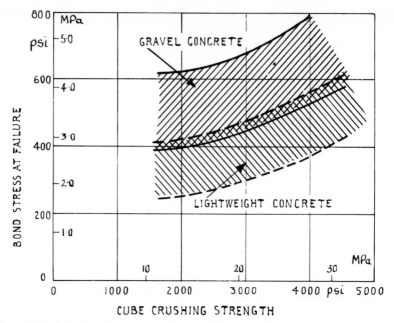

FIG. 12.2   Relationship between cube crushing strength and bond stress at failure
of pull-out specimens of plain, round mild steel bars.

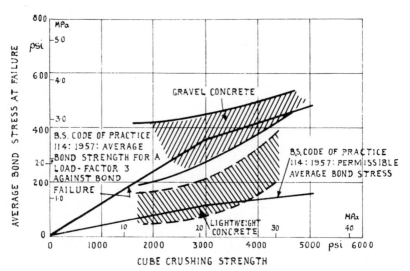

FIG. 12.3   Relationship between cube crushing strength and the average bond
stress at failure for beams with a plain, round mild steel reinforcing bar.

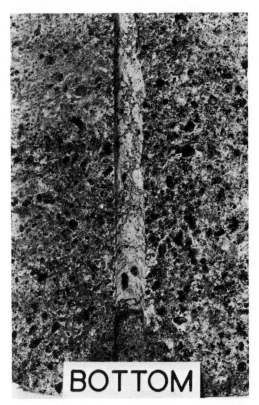

BOTTOM

FIG. 12.4   Cavitation under horizontal bars embedded in lightweight concrete.

For most concretes, but particularly with lightweight concrete, the position of the embedded bars at the time of casting has considerable influence. Where the bars are held horizontally, as in most flexural members, the bond strength is lower than for bars held vertically. This also holds in varying degrees for pull-out specimens where the bars are held horizontally during casting. The formation of irregular cavities beneath horizontal bars is not uncommon, even with dense concrete members and this form of 'cavitation' (Fig. 12.4) occurs regularly in the case of lightweight concrete, particularly around the bars near the top of a cross-section. Cavitation is probably caused by a greater tendency for the fresh lightweight concrete to bleed, particularly with harsh mixes. The formation of such very shallow cavities and the consequent loss of contact at the bottom of horizontal bars between the embedded steel and the concrete causes a reduction in bond strength; this does not occur with vertical bars. The extent to which the bond strength of concrete is affected by this tendency to bleed may vary for different aggregates and mixes. It does not affect the bond strength in columns where the bars are held vertically during casting. The manufacturers of some of the newer, less harsh aggregates, claim that when properly mixed their material is much less prone to bleed.

Attempts to remedy this tendency by re-vibration of the concrete have not led to any very great improvement. It has also been suggested that the reinforcing bars should be allowed to sink with the concrete instead of being held rigidly in the shuttering. This is not a very practical procedure either on the site or in the factory.

In assessing bond performance, it is necessary to have regard not only to the ultimate static load at which failure in bond takes place but also to the development of the relative movement between the steel and the concrete, i.e. slip. For the same bond stress the slip that occurs in beams at the ends of plain round bars embedded in lightweight concrete is generally greater than with dense concrete, but the commencement of slip occurs within a range of 40–80 per cent of the ultimate load for all types of aggregate. A slip of 0·025 mm (0·001 in.), sometimes regarded as a criterion of failure in bond, occurs at 70–90 per cent of the ultimate load for all aggregates, but since the failing load in bond tends to be lower for lightweight concrete, the critical bond stress for a given slip is also correspondingly lower. There appears to be, therefore, no fundamental qualitative difference between the bond stress/slip relationship for dense and lightweight aggregate concretes in the case of mild steel plain round bars, but a considerable quantitative difference.

For plain round bars their diameter has been held to have some influence upon the bond strength of dense concrete; a reduction in bar diameter generally increases bond strength. For lightweight concrete the effect of the bar diameter on the bond strength of plain round bars was found not to be very great. In some instances, if the diameter of the embedded bars is reduced to about 6 mm ($\frac{1}{4}$ in.) or less, the bond resistance tends to diminish with some types of lean lightweight aggregate concrete mixes, particularly with foamed slag used without an admixture of sand.

The effect of the length of embedment on the bond stress at failure for plain round bars is only of importance in the case of short lengths of embedment. Where the embedment length does not exceed about 20 times the bar diameter, the bond stress at failure tends to become smaller with increasing embedment length (Fig. 12.5), but the reduction is much less for lightweight than for dense concrete. For longer embedment the bond stress at failure tends to remain sensibly constant, but for lightweight concrete a slight increase may occur for embedment lengths exceeding 40 times the bar diameter. This slight increase may be caused by a variable distribution of 'cavitation' underneath the bars.

The correlation between the crushing strength and the bond strength of concrete has been noted by several research workers both for dense gravel

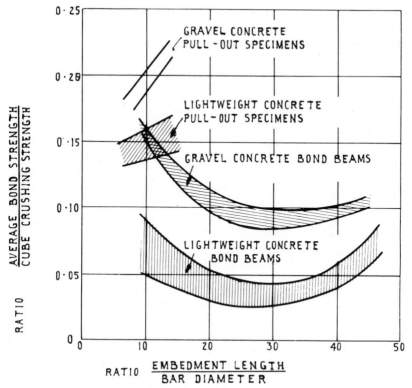

FIG. 12.5   Relationship between bond strength and embedment length.

and lightweight aggregate concretes. For both types of concrete there is a tendency for the bond strength to increase with increasing compressive strength but, although the scatter of the test results is considerable, the correlation is not linear in either case (Figs. 12.2 and 12.3).

Often lightweight aggregates are used in combination with natural sand. The addition of sand to a lightweight concrete mix increases both the density and the crushing strength of the resulting concrete ('sanded lightweight concrete'). At the same time the bond strength is also increased. In addition, for concretes of comparable crushing strength, the slip of the embedded bars under load tends to become somewhat smaller with mixes containing sand.

DEFORMED BARS

The increasing use that is being made of deformed bars in reinforced concrete construction is based in the main on the higher bond strength and better crack distribution which is claimed for such bars. This is of special importance for high-tensile steel bars where the highest permissible tensile stresses generally allowed in design must also be followed in general by higher bond stresses and greater crack widths or reduced crack spacing. In addition to bond, which is obviously present as in the case of plain round bars, deformed bars also grip the concrete by well-distributed mechanical anchorages along their length. For simplicity, this combined bond-anchorage property of deformed bars will be described as 'bond'.

There are variations in the effectiveness of different types of deformed bar surface; ribbed bars, for example, are more effective in increasing bond strength and in reducing crack widths than other types of cross-section. The available test results indicate, however, that for the same crushing strength, the ultimate bond strengths obtained with deformed bars embedded in gravel concrete and lightweight concrete are of the same order of magnitude. The mode of failure can hardly be described, however, as a bond failure in the manner of plain round bars, i.e. a cessation of the adherence of the steel to the concrete surfaces, for this must break down before the mechanical anchorage, which is essential for the effectiveness of deformed bars, can become operative. Failure in the case of deformed bars is probably caused by crushing of the concrete at the pressure interfaces between steel and concrete, at the surface of the extruding ribs, followed by direct shearing of the concrete parallel to the bar. In some cases failure occurs by bursting of the concrete owing to tensile stresses near the bearing surfaces, developed as a result of tri-axial stress conditions.

With any kind of concrete some slight movement (slip) must take place between steel and concrete before the surface extrusions on the deformed bars can grip the concrete surfaces sufficiently to transmit internal forces. For lightweight concrete, this initial displacement has to be greater than for gravel concrete, largely because of its much lower modulus of deformation (E-value), the greater initial drying shrinkage and the bleeding which increases the minute gap between steel and concrete surfaces. This lag in the action of deformed bars in lightweight concrete is shown by a comparison of the slip measured in bond beams made with dense and lightweight concrete. Test results indicate that the load for a given recorded slip is generally lower for lightweight aggregate concrete than for gravel concretes of comparable strength[10] (Fig. 12.6).

The mode of action of the deformed bars in flexural members is such as to allow very large relative displacements between steel and concrete before the failing load is reached. It is obvious, however, that from the user's point of view failure due to loss of servicibility must be deemed to have occurred owing to excessive deflections partly induced by the large slip between the two materials, before the ultimate collapse load is reached.

Tests under repeated loading lead to similar conclusions. Repeated loading introduces many variable, arbitrary conditions. Nevertheless, it

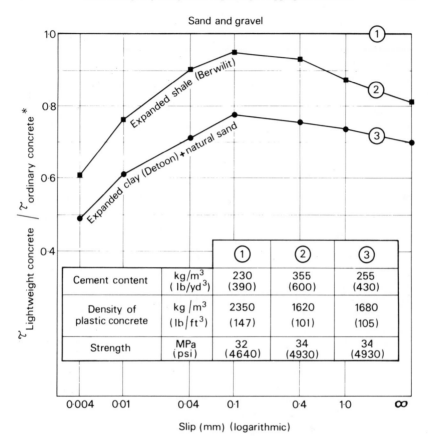

Sand and gravel

* converted to a concrete strength of 33 MPa (4790 psi)

FIG. 12.6 A comparison of slip measured in bond beams for lightweight and dense concretes.

seems reasonable to expect that a degree of slip will be harmless if a large number of repetitions of the static load that causes it does not lead to failure in bond. On the other hand, a slip might be regarded as critical if the load causing it leads to bond failure after less than one million repetitions. The bond resistance of beams reinforced with deformed bars and subjected to repeated loading has been shown to be unaffected where the initial slip due to loading was less than 0·0025 mm (0·0001 in.). Where the load was such as to cause an initial slip of 0·025 mm (0·001 in.) or more, however, failure followed in some cases during the repeated loading tests, whatever aggregate was used. A slip of 0·025 mm (0·001 in.) under static loading may therefore be regarded as a convenient criterion of failure. On the basis of this criterion, the functional failing load in bond for both deformed bars and plain round bars appears to be lower for lightweight concrete than for gravel concrete.

Tests made with deformed bars embedded in pull-out specimens generally gave bond strengths that were 20–30 per cent higher than those obtained with the beams, although primary failure in the pull-out specimens did not occur as a result of slip of the bar, but because of splitting caused by bursting forces in the concrete, even for specimens containing spiral reinforcement.

The test results almost invariably indicate this important conclusion: for normal flexural members the ultimate collapse load reached as a result of possible bond failure, i.e. the final reserve of strength, is significantly enhanced as a result of using deformed bars, whatever type of aggregate is used for the concrete. For deformed bars the ultimate bond stress is likely to be of the same order for dense and lightweight concretes if their compressive strength is of the same order.

The crushing strength of concrete generally increases with age, largely as a result of the continuing slow hydration of the cement in the matrix. The increasing strength of the concrete can be taken into account in design.[12] Lightweight concrete, in common with gravel aggregate concrete, also increases its strength, but apparently at a somewhat lower rate than dense aggregate concrete. This difference may be partly ascribed to the nature of the crushing test in which collapse is caused by a combination of load effects, largely by shear. On the other hand, the bond strength of lightweight concrete appears to increase at a rate that is higher than that of the compressive strength and higher than that allowed for in the Code. It seems likely, on the balance of the evidence, that the actual increase of the compressive strength with age, for well-compacted lightweight concrete placed in flexural members, is not less than that of corresponding dense concrete.

With some lightweight aggregates, such as sintered pulverised-fuel ash aggregates, the increase in strength, including bond strength, with age is very marked. It can be more than for ordinary gravel concrete, particularly in the higher strength ranges where gravel concrete tends not to increase appreciably in strength. On the other hand, with most clay-based lightweight aggregates an increase of strength with age cannot be relied upon. In such cases, therefore, the manufacturer of the aggregate should provide evidence on the effect of aging on the behaviour of concrete made with his product.

To summarise, as indicated in the *CEB–FIP Manual on Lightweight Concrete*,[10] the bond anchorage properties of lightweight concrete are not simply a function of its compressive strength but will depend on a number of circumstances, including the type of bar surface, strength, compaction of the concrete, the quality and composition of the matrix, the modulus of deformation of the concrete, in addition to the type of aggregate itself.

CODES OF PRACTICE

A possible reduction of the bond-anchorage strength or the slip resistance of lightweight concrete compared with ordinary concrete must be taken into account in the relevant provisions of the codes of practice. In general, most codes of practice, even those which accept semi-probabilistic concepts of design, such as CP 110:1972,[4] the CEB–FIP International Recommendations[13] or the ACI 318–1971 Code[14] tend to adopt for the time being a deterministic design approach to the assessment of bond or anchorage resistance.

For example, the British Code CP 110:1972[4] provides for a reduction of design bond stresses by 50 per cent in the case of mild steel bars and 20 per cent for deformed bars, when used with lightweight aggregate concrete.

The ACI 318–1971 Code dispenses with the concept of bond stress except indirectly and defines bond and anchorage resistance in terms of 'development length.' For lightweight concrete it requires an increase of the development length by 18 per cent for 'sanded lightweight concrete' mixes and by 33 per cent for 'all lightweight concrete' mixes, corresponding to a reduction of 25 per cent in the bond stress relating to deformed bars. This reduction may be abated, however, where the concrete is specified in terms of its splitting tensile strength and the proportioning and quality control of the concrete is of a prescribed high standard.

The CEB–FIP International Recommendations[13] and the subsequent CEB–FIP International Model Code for Concrete[15] accept the view that for vertically placed bars, viz. in columns, walls and vertical compression or tension members the bond resistance of lightweight concrete is of the same order as for ordinary gravel aggregate concrete and can be so treated in design. For both lightweight concrete and ordinary concrete flexural members, however, where the fresh concrete is placed at an angle to the direction of the reinforcement, a distinction is made between 'good' and 'bad' bond conditions. The design bond stress for bars embedded in bad bond conditions is only 70 per cent of the design bond stress appropriate for bars placed in good bond conditions, for gravel concretes. The corresponding reduced percentage in the design bond stress for lightweight concrete is 50 per cent. Good bond conditions are assumed to exist for all reinforcing bars which are inclined by 45–90° to the horizontal. Where the bars are horizontal or are inclined by less than 45° to the horizontal, good bond conditions are taken to exist only for those bars which are placed in the lower half of the cross-section or at a distance of not less than 30 cm (12 in.) from the upper face of the member or below a construction joint.

For lightweight concrete the same rules apply but the critical distance from the top is raised to 45 cm (18 in.). All other reinforcing bars are assumed to operate in bad bond conditions.

Justification for this measure, which has been adopted in modified forms by various Codes of Practice, e.g. by the ACI Code, lies with the consistent test results discussed above.

REFERENCES

1. Glanville, W. H. (1930). 'Studies in Reinforced Concrete: Bond Resistance', Building Research Technical Paper No. 10, HMSO.
2. Evans, R. H. and Robinson, G. W. (1955). 'Bond Stresses in Prestressed Concrete from X-ray Photographs', *Proc. Inst., Civ., Eng*, **4**(3).
3. British Standard Code of Practice 114:1957: 'The Structural Use of Reinforced Concrete in Buildings', British Standards Institution.
4. British Standard Code of Practice 110:1972. 'The Structural Use of Concrete', British Standards Institution.
5. Richart, F. E. and Jensen, V. P. (1931). 'Tests of Plain and Reinforced Concrete made with Haydite Aggregates', Bulletin No. 237, Engineering Experiment Station, University of Illinois, Urbana, Illinois.
6. Ritchie, D. D. and Graf, S. H. (1951). 'Expanded Shale Aggregate in Structural Concrete', Bulletin No. 30, Engineering Experiment Station, Oregon.
7. Shideler, J. J. (1957). 'Lightweight Aggregate Concrete for Structural Use', *Amer. Concr. Inst. J.*, **29**(4).
8. Short, A. 'The Use of Lightweight Concrete for Reinforced Concrete Construction', *Reinforced Concrete Review*, **5**(3).
9. Clark, A. P. (1949). 'Bond of Concrete Reinforcing Bars', *Amer. Concr. Inst. J.*, **21**(3).
10. Euro–International Committee for Concrete (CEB–FIP) (1977) *Manual for the Technology and Design of Lightweight Concrete*, Construction Press, Hornby, Lancaster, UK.
11. Shideler, J. J. (1961). 'Manufacture and Use of Lightweight Aggregates for Structural Concrete', Bulletin D. 40, Portland Cement Association Research and Development Laboratories, Illinois.
12. Scott, W. L., Glanville, W. H. and Thomas, F. G. (1965). *Handbook on the British Code of Practice for Reinforced Concrete* 114:1957, Concrete Publications, London.
13. CEB–FIP International Recommendations for Concrete Construction (1970). Comité Européen du Beton, Paris.
14. Building Code Requirements for Reinforced Concrete ACI 318–1971, ACI, Detroit.
15. International System of Standard Codes of Practice for Civil Engineering: Vol. 2, 'Model Code for Concrete', Draft, (1977), CEB, Paris.

CHAPTER THIRTEEN

Shear Resistance of Lightweight Aggregate Concrete Flexural Members

SUMMARY

The shear strength of reinforced concrete beams that do not contain shear reinforcement is examined. American and British tests and ultimate load theories are compared.

The shear strength of lightweight aggregate concrete beams is somewhat lower than that of corresponding gravel concrete ones. This is probably attributable to the typical mode of cracking which usually occurs with the two different types of concrete.

GENERAL

The precise nature of diagonal shear failure in reinforced concrete flexural members has not yet been fully elucidated and methods of design used in different countries vary somewhat in their approach to this problem. It has been accepted for example that where the shear stress in the concrete, as calculated with conventional elastic design methods, exceeds a certain proportion of the cube strength, then additional transverse reinforcement must be used, either in the form of stirrups or bent-up longitudinal bars to resist shearing forces. In the UK, the whole of the internal shear force in a cross-section must be resisted by the shear reinforcement,[1] if the permissible shear stress in the concrete is exceeded, according to the British Standard Code of Practice CP 114:1957. Thus, it is assumed that neither the concrete—which is taken as having been cracked and therefore inoperative—nor dowel-action by the longitudinal reinforcement, can be relied upon to assist materially in resisting shear. The later British Code, CP 110:1972, however, makes allowance for the help obtained from dowel-action of the longitudinal bars by increasing the allowable shear stress in the concrete with increasing steel percentage in beams made with gravel aggregate concrete. Similar provisions apply, albeit with a reduced allowance for dowel-action of the longitudinal bars for beams made with lightweight aggregate concrete. Moreover, in most cases a minimum link reinforcement must be provided. In any event, where special shear reinforcement is provided in the form of links or bent-up longitudinal bars, the whole of the nominal ultimate shear across the section must be resisted by that reinforcement in lightweight concrete members. For lightweight concrete slabs the design must comply with the same requirements as for gravel concrete. The American ACI Code[3] requires that the additional shear reinforcement should be capable of resisting the excess shear above the prescribed permissible stress. The nominal shearing stress below which no special shear reinforcement need be provided is reduced by 15 per cent for 'sand-lightweight' concrete and by 25 per cent for 'all-lightweight' concrete. The Soviet Code of Practice NTU-3-49 used to take account of the contribution to shear resistance made by the tension reinforcement. This contribution was assumed to be 20–40 per cent of the total, provided that the bars continued for 15–30 bar diameters beyond the supports and that they were anchored with hooks. Later, the Soviet Code of Practice was revised and the new code appears to take account of the tensile reinforcement in calculating shear resistance. In the International Model Code[4] the proposed shear recommendations are based on the tensile strength of the concrete but in essence its concepts derive from the classic lattice concept of shear. The reduced shearing resistance of lightweight concrete beams is taken into account by the lower tensile strength of lightweight concrete.

In view of a number of failures in shear that occurred after the war, particularly in America, attention was directed to this difficult question and much research work followed. It was found that for *beams without shear reinforcement* the ultimate loadbearing capacity can be taken as identical with the diagonal cracking load and that the latter is greatly influenced by the strength of the concrete, the percentage and type of the tension reinforcement, the dimensions of the beam, the applied bending moment and the resistance moment of the cross-section.

The results of experimental investigations on the shear performance of reinforced concrete beams made with dense gravel aggregate led to empirical formulae.

In the USA, a solution of the shear problem has been attempted by a Committee set up by the American Concrete Institute, relying on an empirical formula obtained from the ultimate design theory. This work is based on tests and the design equation derived by Bower and Viest[5] is:

$$\frac{Q}{bd_1 f_c'^{1/2}} = 1 \cdot 9 + 2500 \frac{pd}{(M/Q)f_c'^{1/2}} \le 3 \cdot 5,$$

where Q is the total internal shear; f_c' is the cylinder crushing strength of the concrete; b is the width of the cross-section; d is the effective depth of the cross-section; p is the reinforcement proportion; M/Q is the ratio of moment to shear.

This formula starts from the principal tensile stress at a point. It is assumed that the principal stress is comparable to the tensile strength of the concrete which, in turn, is taken as being proportional to the square root of the crushing strength of the concrete. To compare the theoretical values with those obtained by experiment, the tensile strength of the concrete has been determined with the cylinder splitting test.

Both the American tests[6,7] and tests made by Taylor at the Building Research Station[8] on beams containing no shear reinforcement indicate considerable scatter in the behaviour of such beams. For beams in which

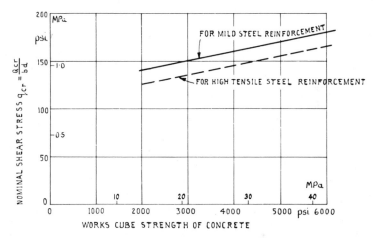

FIG. 13.1 Relationship between the diagonal cracking stress and the cube crushing strength, as determined by Taylor for gravel concrete.

the maximum applied bending moment is equal to the resistance moment of the section, Taylor therefore proposes the following simpler equation:

$$Q = q_{cr}bd_1,$$

where Q is the shear force at the formation of the diagonal crack; b is the width of the beam; d_1 is the effective depth of the section; q_{cr} is the nominal shear stress at the formation of the diagonal crack.

The values of q_{cr} for permissible tensile stresses of 138 MPa (20 000 psi) and 207 MPa (30 000 psi) in the block, respectively, are given in Fig. 13.1 in relation to the crushing strength of the concrete.

At sections where the maximum applied bending moment is less than the calculated ultimate resistance moment of the cross-section, the shear force required to cause diagonal cracking is somewhat greater. The appropriate values for q_{cr} can be obtained from Fig. 13.2.

The diagonal cracking load predicted with this formula for 69 beams was checked and was found to be within $\pm$ 19 per cent of the actual diagonal

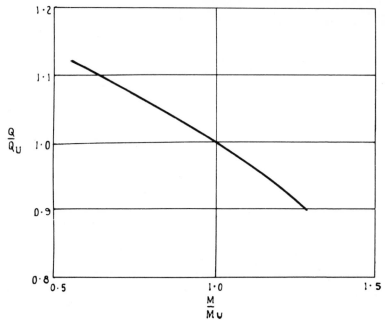

Fɪɢ. 13.2　Increase of the load at which diagonal cracking occurs with reduction of the bending moment, i.e. of the shear span, according to Taylor. (Q denotes the load at which cracking occurs for a bending moment M; Q_u denotes the load at which diagonal cracking occurs for the calculated ultimate resistance moment $M = M_u$.)

cracking load. The average value of the ratios of theoretical to experimental cracking load was 0·99 and the coefficient of variation was 8·8 per cent.

The present elastic method of design[1,3] has been found to lead at times to inadequate shear strength for beams without shear reinforcement.

TESTS ON LIGHTWEIGHT CONCRETE BEAMS

Evidence on the shear strength of lightweight concrete beams is much less plentiful than for gravel concrete. Hanson's work[6] on 10 different lightweight aggregates, comprising expanded shale, clay and slate, sintered shale and foamed slag, as well as ordinary gravel aggregate, is of note. The compressive strength of the concrete used varied from 20 MPa (3000 psi) to about 70 MPa (10 000 psi), the variation of the shear strength of the beams being considerable for different aggregates (Fig. 13.3). Some of the results obtained from these tests and from those made at Texas University by

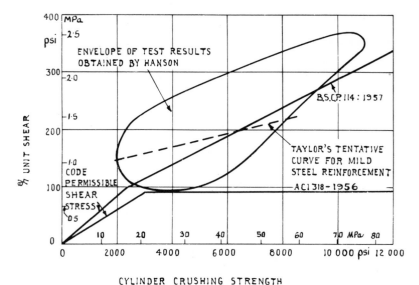

FIG. 13.3   Comparison of the measured unit shear obtained by Hanson with the permissible shear stress laid down in the British and American Codes of Practice for reinforced concrete.

Aguirre *et al.*, are in some respects in agreement with those made at the Building Research Station by Taylor and Brewer on beams made with sintered clay and sintered pulverised-fuel ash aggregate concretes as well as with gravel concrete, ranging in compressive strength from about 24 MPa (3500 psi) to about 38 MPa (5500 psi).

The diagonal cracking load may thus be regarded in most cases, particularly for longer spans, as the ultimate load, whatever the aggregate used in making the beams. It is generally accepted that for comparable compressive strength of the concrete, lightweight concrete beams are likely to have a lower diagonal cracking load than similar dense gravel concrete beams (Fig. 13.4). The unit shear strength of beams made with sintered pulverised-fuel ash aggregate concrete and sintered clay aggregate concrete made in the UK was about 80–90 per cent of the unit shear strength of gravel concrete beams obtained with Taylor's formula. The corresponding diagonal cracking load for American-made lightweight aggregate beams was 60–100 per cent of the cracking load of gravel concrete beams having the same compressive stress. The reason for this difference in the behaviour of dense and lightweight aggregate concretes probably lies in their differing mode of failure in tension, and the somewhat lower tensile strength of lightweight concrete. This is not invariably so, however—the results obtained from split cylinder tests at the Building Research Station indicate

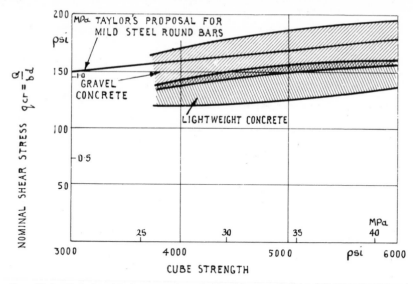

FIG. 13.4   Relationship between the cube crushing strength and the nominal shear stress at which diagonal cracking occurs, for different types of concrete.

that gravel concrete and other lightweight concretes did not differ greatly in their tensile strength for moist curing, but lower tensile strengths have been obtained for dry specimens, particularly for lean mixes, for certain lightweight aggregates, probably owing to induced shrinkage stresses.

Primary tension failure in dense aggregate concrete generally occurs as a result of a breakdown of the bond between the surface of the aggregate and the matrix or, less frequently, owing to failure of the matrix itself in tension. Splitting of an aggregate itself only occurs rarely, except in the case of some of the softer crushed rock aggregates. The crack that is apparent following the tension failure of gravel concrete is therefore almost always a jagged line that follows the outline of the pieces of aggregate—gravel or crushed rock—adjacent to the crack. Thus the diagonal crack may take an appreciable time to develop, due to the resistance in shear as well as in tension, of adjacent, interlocking pieces of aggregate, against displacement relative to each other. Such displacement must occur, however, for failure of the member in shear cannot occur without appreciable vertical movement of the crack faces in relation to each other.

In the case of lightweight aggregate concrete, on the other hand, cracking normally occurs as a result of a fissure through the aggregate itself (Fig. 13.5) because the aggregate particles themselves are softer and weaker than the matrix. Thus, the additional resistance against shear failure due to interaction of strong interlocking aggregate particles cannot be expected and failure occurs earlier. It seems likely that under repeated loading the relative shear strength of lightweight concrete beams is higher when compared with dense concrete beams than under static loading, because under repeated loading the interlocking stones may be gradually loosened. The interlocking action in gravel aggregate concrete is a somewhat variable factor, however, and this appears to be one reason for the considerable scatter in the diagonal cracking strength of gravel concrete shear beams.

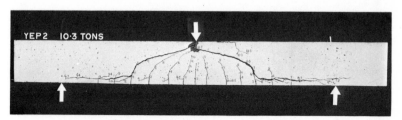

FIG. 13.5   Lightweight concrete beam after failure in shear.

Taylor's and Brewer's tests indicate that the diagonal cracking loads obtained with identical lightweight concrete beams (Fig. 13.4) were more uniform than with dense concrete beams.

For beams where the permissible shear stress in the concrete is exceeded under working loads, additional reinforcement is required. Tests on beams containing shear reinforcement indicate, however, that the shear reinforcement obtained with the usual design rules[1] tends to be unnecessarily heavy in some cases. Taylor's tests at the Building Research Station show that the full bending strength of beams can be developed and failure in shear can be prevented with much less shear reinforcement than that obtained from the conventional theory.

The shear performance of lightweight concrete beams fitted with special shear reinforcement in the form of stirrups or bent-up longitudinal bars is similar to that of concrete elements.

REFERENCES

1. Scott, W. L., Glanville, W. H. and Thomas, F. G. (1957). *Explanatory Handbook on the British Standard Code of Practice for Reinforced Concrete* (114:1957), Concrete Publications, London.
2. British Standard Code of Practice CP 110:1972. 'The Structural Use of Concrete', British Standards Institution.
3. American Concrete Institute Standard, ACI 318–56. Building Code Requirements for Reinforced Concrete, ACI, Detroit.
4. International System of Codes of Practice for Civil Engineering, Vol. 2 'Model Code for Concrete', Draft (1977), CEB, Paris.

5. Bower, J. E. and Viest, I. M. (1960). 'Shear Strength of Restrained Concrete Beams without Web Reinforcement', *Amer. Concr. Inst. J.*, **32**(1).
6. Hanson, J. A. (1959). 'Shear Strength of Lightweight Reinforced Concrete Beams', *Amer. Concr. Inst. J.*, **30**(9).
7. Hanson, J. A. (1961). 'Tensile Strength and Diagonal Tension Resistance of Structural Lightweight Concrete', *Amer. Concr. Inst. J.*, **34**(1).
8. Taylor, R. (1960). 'Some Shear Tests on Reinforced Concrete Beams without Shear Reinforcement', *Mag. Concr. Res.*, **12**(36).

CHAPTER FOURTEEN

Design Considerations for Structural Lightweight Aggregate Concrete

SUMMARY

After a review of the two alternative methods of design for reinforced concrete allowed by Codes of Practice, based on the elastic theory and on ultimate strength respectively, the applicability of these design methods to structural lightweight concrete is considered. Limit state design methods are considered, and examples are given for lightweight concrete.

GENERAL

In the UK, the Code of Practice relevant to the design and construction of ordinary gravel concrete and also for lightweight concrete is CP 110:1972,[1] which applies to reinforced prestressed and precast concretes, including concretes made with gravel or lightweight aggregates and also aerated concrete. CP 110:1972 is based on semi-probabilistic limit state design principles derived from the International Recommendations of the Euro-International Committee for Concrete (CEB)[2] and based on the use of partial safety coefficients. This document forms the foundation of most modern European Codes of Practice including the Draft International System of Civil Engineering Codes of Practice which is the result of close co-operation between the main international technical organisations, in particular CEB, the International Council for Building (CIB), the European Convention for Structural Steelwork (CECM), the International Federation for Prestressing (FIP) and others. It is expected that in due course the International Standardisation Organisation (ISO), the Economic Commission for Europe (ECE), as well as the Commission of the European Communities (EEC) and the Council for Mutual Economic Assistance (CMEA, better known as Comecon) will also adopt international or regional codes and building regulations based on semi-probabilistic limit state design methods pioneered by CEB and originally proposed by Soviet scientists and engineers, in particular Professors Gvozdev and Streletzki.

The development of structural design towards semi-probabilistic methods based on partial coefficients of safety (Level 1) has been progressing steadily since the late '50s. Valuable scientific studies by USSR, US, Mexican, Scandinavian, Portuguese, British, German and Italian research workers tended towards more advanced, fully probabilistic methods of design (Levels 2 and 3), avoiding the necessary approximations of the intermediate, semi-probabilistic method, and based on a more complete understanding and fuller application of scientifically justifiable statistical methods. In fact, however, sufficient data and practical experience are not as yet available in statistically tractable form to enable designers to shed practical approximations and to use such methods without complicated, cumbersome and rough calibration procedures. While fully probabilistic safety calculation methods are therefore likely to remain a fruitful field for research exercises, they can only attain importance for practical design in isolated instances or as a tool for code committees, to help in the determination of partial coefficients of safety. Indeed, for the time being in the UK, as in the USA and most other countries where the new limit state design methods have been introduced in recent codes of practice, the 'traditional' methods based on permissible stresses or ultimate strength and global safety factors for material properties alone, are also admitted by free use of the preceding codes. These continue to be valid according to the building regulations in force in the various countries, together with the new codes.

In the UK, the Codes of Practice that continue to be relevant to the design of concrete structures—including lightweight concrete—parallel with CP 110:1972, are CP 114:1969[3] for reinforced concrete, CP 115:1969[4] for prestressed concrete and CP 116:1969[5] for precast concrete.

In most countries, codes of practice for design and construction are recognised as non-mandatory documents, the result of the knowledge and theoretical insight of the experienced engineers who make up the code drafting committees. These committees normally include official members to represent the views of government. The resulting documents, though not legally binding *ab initio*, become so binding by contract and by professional convention and judgement. They are moreover normally referred to and adopted by statute, through building regulations in which they are 'deemed to satisfy' the relevant legally enforceable requirements. Thus structures which satisfy the relevant codes, are automatically accepted by official control authorities as being in accordance with building regulations. Codes of practice so distinguished are not, however, regarded as having exclusive validity: such a code merely represents one of possibly many different systems which can be used for designing and building structures that can satisfy the requirements established by the State for the protection of the safety of its citizens and their property. Thus, the building regulations, enforced by central and local, federal, state and municipal authorities, as the case may be, contain detailed requirements for the loads which buildings and structures must be designed to resist safely. In some countries, as in France, the building regulations do not refer to separate non-mandatory codes but contain schedules which give detailed instructions on design but in most countries, including the UK, references to 'deemed to satisfy' rules—such as codes of practice—usually suffice. While detailed loading requirements are fundamental to the responsibility of the State for the safety of its citizens, detailed design requirements, including the partial safety coefficients for material properties, used for limit state design methods, are generally left to be decided by the engineering profession on its own judgement and authority.

These are difficult matters: differences of views on the allocation of technical legal and administrative responsibilities between the State and the individual engineer have been highlighted by a number of spectacular structural failures, and perhaps strengthened by fear of a repetition of such failures, since the use of new materials and methods for construction purposes can lead to errors and sometimes to unsuitable uses. In the United States of America a number of different specifications are in force for different states and municipalities, but the building code requirements of the American Concrete Institute (ACI 318-63)[6] are regarded as generally applicable.

Laboratory investigations on the properties of reinforced lightweight concrete elements showed that in general the regulations in force for gravel concrete can be safely applied also to the design and construction of reinforced concrete structures made with lightweight aggregates, although in some respects the behaviour of lightweight concrete can differ from that of ordinary gravel concrete. The use of normal, conventional design methods applicable to gravel aggregate concrete would very rarely result in structures that are unsafe if applied to the design of lightweight concrete structures. Their load factors against excessive deformation or against cracking can be lower in some cases, however, than those generally required for similar dense gravel concrete structures. On the other hand, in some cases, e.g. fire resistance, the codes of practice for normal reinforced and prestressed concrete construction may be too restrictive when applied to lightweight concrete without modification, thus hindering development.

Parts of the codes of practice were, therefore, in need of some reassessment for lightweight concrete, especially in so far as they related to the permissible stresses in the concrete and in the steel, the concrete cover required (see Chapter 11), design for bond and shear, and the stiffness of members. It was obvious, however, that the re-assessment required was of a very limited nature. Present knowledge on the performance of structural lightweight concrete fully supports the view that reinforced or prestressed lightweight concretes are not essentially different materials and do not involve substantially different methods of construction from reinforced or prestressed gravel concrete.

Nevertheless, in the UK, until 1965 when CP 114:1957 was amended and

CP 116:1965 was published, artificial aggregates were at a disadvantage compared with gravel or crushed rock aggregates. Natural aggregates can easily comply with the relevant standard specification BS 882,[7] which relates to such aggregates only, without any need to prove that concrete made with them satisfies any particular performance requirements when used with different types of steel reinforcement. These materials might then be used at a lower effective load factor against failure, when used with nominal mixes, than corresponding lightweight aggregate concretes. Although crushed rock aggregates usually produce excellent structural material, dense concrete made with some types of sandstone and limestone aggregates is known to be inferior to concrete made with good gravel aggregate. Indeed, it may have a lower modulus of deformation, more unfavourable cracking and stiffness characteristics and worse bond and shear properties than lightweight concrete of comparable compressive strength. Being natural aggregates complying with BS 882, however, no objection has in the past been raised to the use of such aggregates in reinforced and prestressed concrete structures. Nor, admittedly does there appear to be any valid reason in most cases why any such objection should be raised. Restrictions have been introduced however in recent years[8,9] to avoid serviceability failures which have occurred with dimensionally unstable shrinking aggregates in general use in Scotland. These are usually dolerites or whinstones and are obtained both from gravel pits and rock quarries. It is worth recalling that none of the artificial aggregates made in the UK, the USA or elsewhere in Europe or in Australia have been found anything but dimensionally stable and chemically inert, resistant to both alkaline and acid environments.

CP 110:1972 also tends to avoid discrimination against high grade lightweight aggregates in the structural use of such materials. For reinforced concrete it allows the use of aggregates covered by the relevant British Standards[10,11] but makes the engineer responsible for specifying or approving the use of other aggregates not covered by standards, provided that there is satisfactory evidence on the properties of concrete made with them. Lightweight concrete below grade 15, i.e. a characteristic strength (or 28-day cube strength) of less than about 15 MPa (1900 psi), is not admitted however except for plain concrete walls. Higher minimum strength requirements apply to prestressed concrete.

CONCRETE MIXES

The philosophy of design for concrete used in reinforced concrete construction has developed in two separate and not always mutually consistent directions. On the one hand, the traditional approach continues to provide for 'nominal mixes' for small jobs, usually specified by volume but preferably by weight in the case of larger structures, for the rapid and simple specification of suitable mixes where the degree of supervision provided is adequate only for this type of concrete. CP 114:1957, as amended later,[3] also provides for the use of lightweight aggregates for nominal mixes, provided that the concrete produced satisfies the strength requirements laid down in the Code (Table 14.1).

Progressive concrete practice should prefer the use of mixtures, as in Clause 209 of CP 114[3] or Clause 107–109 of CP 116,[5] designed specially for the job, on the basis of trial mixes, with a high degree of site or works supervision, and allowing for higher stresses in the concrete than for nominal mixes. For improved practice, moreover, both codes introduced 'standard mixes'. In essence, the standard mixes are mixtures that are known to produce concrete of the specified strengths, assuming a standard deviation of 7–3·5 MPa (1000–500 psi) with the same degree of supervision as that required for designed mixes, thus avoiding the need for trial mixes. This is an aid for the designer and concrete technologist, a convenient supporting measure and should not in any way permit or encourage a reduction in the standard of supervision demanded in the codes of practice for designed mixes. According to CP 114, where this required degree of quality control cannot be provided, standard mixes may still be used as nominal mixes with the appropriate reduction in permissible stress or increase in the calculated load factor.

In the case of lightweight aggregates admitted for use with reinforced concrete structures the standard mixes may be different from those given for gravel aggregate concrete. For such materials the mix proportions recommended by the makers of a particular lightweight aggregate may be accepted as standard, provided that this recommendation is based on the results of suitable tests.

Lightweight aggregates are made under controlled conditions and are frequently more uniform in their physical and concrete-making properties than natural aggregates. The Engineer must be satisfied when specifying a standard mix as recommended by the supplier of a particular material, that the recommended mix does truly apply to the material as manufactured and supplied at the time. The exercising of extra care to ensure that this is so should not be regarded as an additional obligation on the Engineer for it should in fact apply whatever aggregate is being used, whether natural or artificial, heavy or light.

Both CP 116 and CP 114 provide in similar terms for the special treatment of lightweight aggregate concrete used for structural purposes. CP 116 determines the cement content for reinforced or prestressed concrete. While for lightweight aggregate concretes the same lower limits apply as for heavier normal aggregate concretes; for higher strengths the upper limit of 535 kg/m^3 (33 pcf) applicable to normal aggregate concrete may be exceeded for lightweight aggregates provided that the engineer is

TABLE 14.1

EQUIVALENT NOMINAL MIX PROPORTIONS FOR VARIOUS LIGHTWEIGHT CONCRETES CORRESPONDING TO THE NOMINAL MIXES LAID DOWN IN CP 114:1965

Nominal mix using dense aggregates complying with BS 882	Cube crushing strength at 28 days				Equivalent nominal mix proportions by volume using various lightweight aggregates											
	Preliminary test		Works test		Aglite			Foamed slag			Lytag			Leca		
					Cement: fine: medium	Air-dry density 28 days		Cement: sand: coarse	Air-dry density 28 days		Cement: fine: medium	Air-dry density 28 days		Cement: sand: medium	Air-dry density 28 days	
	(MPa)	(psi)	(MPa)	(psi)		(kg/m³)	(pcf)		(kg/m³)	(pcf)		(kg/m³)	(pcf)		(kg/m³)	(pcf)
1:1:2	40	6 000	30	4 500	1:1·5:2	1 680	105	1:1:2	2 000	126	1:1·3:2·6	1 710	106	—	—	—
1:1½:3	34	5 000	25·5	3 750	1:2:2·5	1 630	102	1:1·3:2·6	1 950	122	1:1·8:2·9	1 670	104	—	—	—
1:2:4	28	4 000	21	3 000	1:2·5:3·5	1 570	98	1:1·6:3·2	1 890	118	1:2·6:3·2	1 630	102	—	—	—
—	—	—	15	2 200	—	—	—	—	—	—	—	—	—	1:2:3	1 410	90

satisfied that the concrete produced is suitable in all other respects, such as limitation on drying shrinkage and creep. Similarly, the general strength requirements given for various grades of concrete in CP 116 also apply to lightweight aggregate concretes but nominal mixes are not provided for in CP 116.

With lightweight aggregate concretes a lower minimum specified works cube strength can be used than for normal aggregate concretes, but only under internal, non-corrosive conditions and subject to suitable precautions. The specified works cube strength of fully compacted normal aggregate concretes should not be lower at 28 days than 21 MPa (3000 psi).

TABLE 14.2

PERMISSIBLE STRESSES IN LIGHTWEIGHT AGGREGATE CONCRETE
HAVING A SPECIFIED WORKS CUBE STRENGTH BETWEEN 14–20 MPa
(2 000–2 950 psi)

Specified works cube strength	Permissible stresses				
	Compressive		Shear in slabs only	Bond	
	Direct	Due to bending		Average	Local
u_w	$\dfrac{u_w}{3 \cdot 65}$	$\dfrac{u_w}{2 \cdot 73}$	$\dfrac{u_w}{40}$	$\dfrac{u_w}{50}$	$\dfrac{u_w}{33}$

For lightweight concretes the minimum strength is 14 MPa (2000 psi) and the 7-day strength should be not less than two-thirds of this value, but it is essential that the mix proportions should be such that the concrete is sufficiently workable for full compaction. Moreover, with the special low-strength mixes, where the works cube strength at 28 days lies between 14–20 MPa (2000–2950 psi), special reduced permissible concrete stresses apply (Table 14.2).

For purposes of specifying concrete, CP 110:1972[1] provides for classification according to the constituent components (ordinary and special structural concretes) and according to who bears the burden of responsibility (Designed or Prescribed Mixes). For Designed Mixes the engineer bears responsibility for establishing the required properties of the concrete (strength, workability, minimum cement content for durability) but after that the manufacturer or contractor can select mix proportions to satisfy the engineer's specification. For Prescribed Mixes the engineer will be responsible for specifying mix proportions as well, and he must satisfy himself that with those mix proportions the concrete supplied will have adequate strength and other properties.

The provisions of CP 110 specify grades and uses for concrete (Table 14.3). A controversial measure introduced in CP 110:1972 has been the requirement for a minimum cement content (weight of cement per unit volume of finished concrete), depending on the severity of exposure (mild, moderate, severe and when exposed to salt for de-icing), on the degree of control over the maximum free-water/cement ratio, on the maximum size

TABLE 14.3
GRADES OF CONCRETE

Grade	Characteristic strength (28-day cube strength)		Lowest grade for compliance with appropriate use
	(*MPa*)	(*psi*)	
7	7·0	1 000	Plain concrete
10	10·0	1 450	Plain concrete
15	15·0	2 150	Reinforced concrete with lightweight aggregate
20	20·0	2 900	Reinforced concrete with dense aggregate
25	25·0	3 600	
30	30·0	4 350	Concrete with post-tensioned tendons
40	40·0	5 800	Concrete with pretensioned tendons
50	50·0	7 250	
60	60·0	8 700	

of the aggregate particles used and on the type of use (plain, reinforced or prestressed). Special requirements apply to concrete exposed to sulphate attack. These provisions were included in CP 110:1972 in anticipation of the introduction of a British Standard for concrete. The requirements for the Designed and Prescribed Mixes are laid down in considerable detail including provisions for placing and curing. The use of high-alumina cement and of calcium chloride as an admixture have since been discontinued and the relevant clauses in CP 110 no longer apply. In principle, the provisions of CP 110 relating to the material concrete apply equally to lightweight and dense aggregate concrete.

METHODS OF DESIGN

The conventional method of reinforced concrete design is based on the elastic theory and on certain permissible stresses laid down for steel and concrete. For working loads, under short duration loading, it is possible to obtain a reasonable correlation between theory and actual performance in the laboratory, if certain assumptions are made as to the relationship of the moduli of deformation (*E*-values) of the two materials. The permissible stresses adopted must be such that at working loads the structure possesses a reserve of strength appropriate to its needs. This presumes an established relationship between the stress at which the material is deemed to have failed and the permissible stress. In reinforced concrete that ratio is generally taken to be somewhat higher for concrete in compression than for steel in tension. A higher safety factor for concrete was considered necessary because the properties of concrete are generally less uniform and reliable than those of steel.

The stress at which steel is deemed to fail in a flexural member is the yield point stress or—where a clearly defined yield point does not exist—the proof stress, i.e. the stress at which the permanent deformation of the material is 0·25 per cent. For concrete, the cube strength or the cylinder strength has been used as a criterion of failure. The crushing of concrete cubes is not, however, simply a failure in compression: it is a complex occurrence which is also akin to failure in shear and in which the restraints at the compression faces play an important role. Owing to these secondary effects the cube strength can only represent an approximate index of the actual stress at which compression failure occurs in a flexural member. In fact, the actual strength of the concrete in the compressive zone of a beam or slab is usually lower than the cube-crushing strength and is much closer to the cylinder strength. The relationship between the cube and cylinder strengths is somewhat variable; it has been assumed for practical purposes that the ratio of the cylinder and cube strengths of gravel aggregate concrete ranges between 0·7 and 0·8. Test results indicate that this value also applies to concrete made with lightweight aggregates of intermediate strength, i.e. less that about 35 MPa (5000 psi). It seems doubtful if this value applies equally to higher strength concretes made with lightweight aggregates.

The conventional method of design based on the elastic theory does not always accurately reflect the behaviour of reinforced concrete structures at incipient failure, for under those conditions a linear triangular stress distribution no longer exists. Load factor methods of design based on a consideration of the performance of structures under ultimate loading conditions, at incipient failure, overcame this difficulty since these ultimate strength or load factor methods of design do not work with the modular ratio and provide an indication of the ultimate load-bearing capacity of a structure; this is then divided by an appropriate load factor to obtain the working load.

A concise study of the problems involved with load factor methods of design and in choosing the correct load factor for different conditions has been published by Thomas.[12] His conclusions form the basis of the CEB–FIP International Recommendations for concrete construction.[2]

Both the British Codes CP 114 and CP 116 and the earlier version of the

American Concrete Institute Code ACI 318 allow the use of the conventional method of design based on a modular ratio and also an ultimate strength method. CP 110 and the later version of ACI 318 introduce limit state design. The load factor method adopted in the British Codes is based on the assumption of a uniform stress distribution in the compression zone. It is assumed that at failure this uniform stress is equal to two-thirds of the cube strength (i.e. approximately 90 per cent of the cylinder strength) of the concrete. The depth of beam or slab to which this uniform stress block extends must be such that the total internal compressive force balances the total tension transmitted to the tensile reinforcement in the cross-section, acting at its yield stress. Appropriate allowance must be made for the compression reinforcement where this is provided.

Evidence obtained from a large number of tests indicates that in fact a curved stress distribution occurs across the section.[13] For practical purposes a rectangular stress block based on two-thirds of the cube strength can be adopted in place of the curved stress distribution and if the depth of the block is taken as equal to about 85 per cent of the depth of the neutral axis, it represents the strength of the cross-section adequately for design. The resistance moment of the cross-section so obtained can then be calculated on the basis of a load factor, generally of $2 \cdot 0$, against failure resulting from crushing of the concrete or yielding of the steel. Because of the greater variability of the concrete than of the steel reinforcement, a load factor greater than $2 \cdot 0$ would appear to be necessary where failure is likely to occur by crushing of the concrete. To take account of this, the stress used for the stress block is multiplied by a further reduction factor of $\frac{2}{3}$. Thus the stress in the compression zone at which failure is assumed to take place is $\frac{4}{9}u$. Applying a load factor $2 \cdot 0$ the stress at working load is $\frac{2}{9}u$ and substituting the permissible stress ($u = 3p_c$) in terms of the permissible stress used for design with the elastic theory, the stress block at working load should be $\frac{2}{3}p_c$. The design formulae for the ultimate strength theory in the code thus permit the use of the same permissible stresses as for the conventional theory, but in truth they are no longer permissible stresses but indices relating to the permissible load.

To simplify the design calculations still further, the position of the neutral axis has been assumed to coincide with the depth of the assumed rectangular stress block in the compression zone of the concrete. Owing to this simplification, the calculated strains on the compressive reinforcement are somewhat lower than those obtained with the more accurate theory.

The ultimate strength design adopted by the American Concrete Institute Building Code Requirements[6] requires a minimum load factor of $1 \cdot 8$ for flexural members and does not lay down any particular kind of compressive stress distribution. The diagram of the stress distribution may be assumed rectangular, trapezoidal, parabolic or of any other shape, provided the ultimate strength arrived at is in reasonable agreement with tests.

The results of tests on reinforced lightweight concrete members indicate that the design methods adopted by the Codes are fully applicable to reinforced lightweight concrete, if the properties of the material are taken into account. For the elastic method of design it is necessary to take account of the greater creep and the reduced modulus of deformation (*E*-

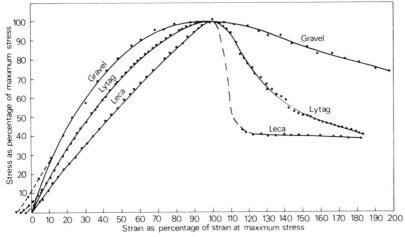

FIG. 14.1 Comparative relation between stress and strain for 6 in. square by 12 in. long prisms of concrete.

value) which is generally about half of that of gravel concrete for the same strength. For CP 114, therefore, an *m*-value of 25–30 would seem to be appropriate.

For the ultimate strength theory it has been concluded in the light of many tests that plane sections remain plane, i.e. that the strains vary linearly across the cross-section and that the ultimate strain in the extreme compressive fibre in gravel concrete reaches approximately 3300×10^{-6} at incipient failure due to crushing of the concrete. The ultimate compressibility of lightweight concrete will be somewhat less.

The actual stress–strain relationship for most lightweight concretes differs from that for normal dense aggregate concrete in two important respects. First, the tangent *E*-value at the origin of the stress–strain or load–deformation curve is less, usually about one-half of gravel concrete. Secondly, while the shape of the ascending branch of the curve is similar for most types of concrete, for lightweight concrete—after reaching maximum stress—rupture often occurs much more rapidly than for gravel concrete in an almost brittle type of failure[14] (Fig. 14.1).[15]

The maximum strain reached by most lightweight concretes lies between $2000-2500 \times 10^{-6}$. For design purposes the International Draft Code[16] prescribes an ultimate compressibility of 2500×10^{-6}.[16]

The different load–deformation relationship and the lower strain at failure to which lightweight concrete is liable has little effect however on the behaviour of normal flexural members at incipient failure. Most such members, slabs or beams, fail in the first instance as a result of failure of the tension reinforcement, not of the concrete. In heavily reinforced members, moreover, where failure might be assumed to occur owing to rupture of the concrete in the compression zone, in practice the internal forces are redistributed with increasing loads and rupture does not occur suddenly as it could in the case of single, isolated members in compression. On balance, therefore, the same limit state design rules and rules for bending–compression design are used for lightweight as for dense aggregate concretes. However, for compression members additional measures may be necessary.

Whatever design method is used, it is necessary to ensure that the structure evolved is not only safe against collapse under vertical loading and stable against overturning forces but that its deformations under load are not excessive. Dimensional limitations and restrictions on permissible steel stresses have been used to ensure that the deformations of reinforced concrete structures do not exceed an acceptable standard. It may be necessary, in addition, to check deflections by means of the elastic theory. In the case of complex statically indeterminate structures this may lead to lengthy calculations and the use of computer programs.

The alternative design methods—elastic or ultimate—permitted in the codes of practice may be used at will. It has been held that for lightweight concrete the limiting M_r/bd^2 value beyond which the ultimate design method becomes more economical is somewhat higher than for dense concrete, due to the difference in the moduli of deformation.

The permissible stresses for reinforced lightweight aggregate concrete in normal strength mixes are the same as those for normal concrete in the case of the compression stresses but special reduced permissible stresses apply to bond and shearing stresses in certain conditions.

As for the permissible stresses in the steel reinforcement, these are identical with those specified for normal concrete but the tensile stress in main bars must not in any case exceed 210 MPa (30 000 psi) and plain high tensile bars must not be used. These latter restrictions were introduced to provide an additional safeguard against excessive deflections which in any case are somewhat higher for lightweight aggregate concretes. Such a restriction seems superfluous since a limitation of the deformation of structures can be achieved in other, simpler ways, without restricting the use of certain types of high strength reinforcement. To safeguard the stiffness of members made of lightweight aggregate concretes both British codes prescribe maximum values for the ratio of span to overall depth for all beams and for slabs having imposed loads exceeding 60 MPa (8750 psi). These ratios are about 85 per cent of those allowed for normal concrete.

The rules established in CP 110:1972,[1] as amended in 1976, apply to reinforced lightweight concrete except for the following:

concrete cover required for durability and for resistance against fire;
increase of strength with age;
shear resistance of beams and slabs, including punching shear;
torsional resistance of beams;
deflection of beams and slabs;
design of short columns and slender columns;
design of short and slender walls;
bond development;
bearing stress inside bends in the reinforcement.

For prestressed concrete the same considerations apply, but in addition CP 110 draws attention to higher losses of prestress for tendons to allow for the time-dependent deformations of lightweight concretes, which tend to be higher than for gravel concrete of high strength. There are, however, considerable variations in the time-dependent deformation of different lightweight concretes, depending on the type of lightweight aggregate they contain, and it is preferable that design of prestressed lightweight concrete should be based on data obtained from dependable experimental evidence. This is frequently available and provided by the manufacturers of lightweight aggregates.

In general, the special requirements established in CP 110:1972 do not differ greatly from those in the Draft International CEB–FIP Model Code for Concrete[16] or in the other modern codes such as the clauses included in successive editions of ACI Code 318,[6] of the earlier British Standard Codes[3–5] and of the Soviet Code for structural lightweight concrete.[17]

Safety principles of limit state design

The general objective of design has been defined[18] in the International Draft Code for Safety as 'the achievement of acceptable probabilities that the structure produced will not become unfit for use during its intended life span'. It follows that the structure must be capable of resisting, with an appropriate degree of safety, all loads and deformations which are liable to occur during construction and normal use in the conditions and environment for which it was intended.

The performance of the structure is conveniently judged in terms of a series of 'limit states'. The design and proportions of the structure must be such that the limit states are not reached, i.e. that the structure does not collapse as a whole or in part and does not become unfit for use. It is statistically impossible in real life to exclude completely the possibility of a limit state being reached and the next best practicable procedure is to ensure that the probability of a limit state being reached is reduced to a level which is deemed to be technically, economically and socially acceptable.

There are a number of limit states which are relevant to any one structure and they should all be considered in design. The usual approach of experienced designers, however, is to select the most critical limit state for the design and then check that the remaining limit state criteria are in fact satisfied by the resulting design. The two principal types of limit state to be considered in design are:

(1) The ultimate limit states corresponding to the ultimate load-carrying capacity;

(2) The serviceability limit states corresponding to normal use and to durability.

Ultimate limit states

In practice, the strength of a structure should be sufficient to prevent any of the ultimate limit states being reached, thus causing failure of the structure. An ultimate limit state can be reached owing to:[18]

(1) Loss of equilibrium of a part or the whole of the structure considered as a rigid body.

(2) Rupture or excessive deformation of critical sections of the structure.

(3) Transformation of the structure into a mechanism.

(4) Buckling due to elastic or plastic instability.

(5) Fatigue.

Other ultimate limit states or similar conditions can occur, particularly in structures intended for special uses. It is essential, for example, to take measures in design to reduce the possibility of 'progressive collapse' where destruction of one member as a result of an extraneous event (explosion, collision with a vehicle or aircraft, or unforeseen accidental loading or even inadequate local design combined with an overload) leads to a degree of damage and destruction which is excessive when taken together with the original cause of the incident. The design should be such that in major structures failure of one or some other stated number of components does not lead to such disproportionate destruction. Consideration of progressive collapse has been recognised as a necessity following the collapse of a substantial part of a multi-storey precast panel structure, the Ronan Point building in London.[19] The investigation carried out by an official tribunal with powers to call for papers and witnesses in evidence reached conclusions which were of considerable interest and importance, although they were not generally accepted as entirely correct or adequate to deal with the difficult technical and administrative problems involved. In fact, some of the conclusions reached seemed to lead to a misinterpretation of the functions of codes of practice and of the responsibilities of designers. The work of the Ronan Point tribunal was valuable however since it set out the relevant facts with great clarity, engendered a continuing discussion of high intellectual and technical standard, and above all demonstrated the most appropriate procedures which might be adopted for the investigation of a major structural failure with the aim of protecting the community, and extending the boundaries of professional knowledge and experience.

Fire resistance is a further limit state which needs careful assessment in the design of structures, all the more so as it does not yet seem capable of treatment by formal methods of calculation. The determination of fire resistance is normally governed more by test results obtained for given structural situations and materials in terms of duration of resistance in building fires.

Durability is another complex structural property which may be regarded as an ultimate limit state in certain conditions. It requires careful consideration of the conditions of use, of the materials and workmanship employed and of the regime of inspection, maintenance and repairs which it is practicable to enforce in particular cases.

Serviceability limit states

Reaching the serviceability limit states can be as damaging to a structure as the reaching of any of the ultimate limit states, for it can necessitate replacement of the structure owing to grave breaches of statutory (e.g. Building Regulations relating to both structural and functional requirements for safety and health) or contractual obligations on the part of those taking part in the building operations—albeit usually without the loss of life which is unfortunately so often a corollary of an unforeseen and sudden structural collapse or fire. The principal types of serviceability limit state are as follows.

Deformation limit states. These are reached where the deflections or local deformations of the structure or any part of it become so large that its efficient functioning is hindered or its appearance suffers. Such damaging effects can occur, for example, as a result of time-dependent deformations of unforeseen severity, as in the case of a slender beam of large span supporting sliding doors, which became wedged and could not be moved owing to excessive, permanent deformation of the beam under loading.

Some structural components are particularly sensitive to deformation limit states since exceeding these can lead to increases in loading. In the case of roof slabs, for example, excessive deflections can lead to ponding and could lead to collapse. Lateral deformation of slender members can in turn lead to large increases in internal forces, leading to the collapse of members not normally regarded as slender.

Local damage limit states. These can be reached by damage to specific parts of a structure leading to excessive maintenance works or corrosion, thereby affecting the appearance or the efficient functioning of the whole structure. Such damage can occur as a result of cracking, spalling, local buckling of compression bars, splitting near anchorages, etc.

Local damage can lead to an ultimate limit state if neglected or if the local damage spreads over a substantial and structurally significant part of the structure, particularly where it cannot be subjected to adequate inspection or where repairs are frustrated because the damaged parts cannot be reached.

Vibration limit state. This is rarely found to affect the efficient functioning of the structure itself, but it can impair the enjoyment of the building by a user owing to discomfort or alarm caused by wind forces, impact, machinery or the movement of vehicles, as in the case of concert halls placed adjacent to railway lines. It can lead to structural problems in buildings used for certain industrial processes, e.g. in the press-shops of motor car body building plants.

Other limit states can become of decisive importance and may have to be avoided where a structure is designed to fulfil specific purposes. Such cases occur in industry, e.g. radiation hazards in nuclear installations, escape of dangerous substances in chemical plants and many others.

Safety standards

Having defined the ultimate serviceability and intermediate special limit states most frequently encountered it is necessary to determine the safety coefficients which determine the margin of safety against reaching a particular limit state. Since reaching particular limit states may result in widely differing degrees of damage it would seem logical to impose different margins of safety against their being attained. The determination of the degree of safety to be attained is a matter partly for the government which represents the community and its individual citizens and partly for the engineering profession in whom is vested the duty to exercise their knowledge for the benefit of the community it serves. Different degrees of safety will apply to different types of building as well as to different limit states.

The actions or loads upon a structure are defined in terms of their characteristic values.[20] Ideally, these values should be based on a statistical analysis of evidence obtained from observation for given return periods. However, such evidence is often not available and then characteristic values are determined from an appraisal of experience or from informed forecasts of the consequences of future developments. Many actions, moreover, are random occurrences (e.g. accidental loadings) and not capable of statistical treatment.

The strengths and other properties of the materials used are defined in terms of their characteristic values determined by statistical methods from comparable tests using standard test specimens and procedures.

It follows from the definition of characteristic values for strengths and actions that two main types of partial safety coefficient are needed to derive design values for strengths and actions respectively. Thus, a design value for the action or action effect is derived from $\gamma_f F_k$ where F_k is the characteristic action and γ_f is a partial safety coefficient. A design value for the strength of the section is obtained by dividing characteristic strengths by a materials safety coefficient. γ_m. The partial safety factor for actions might be assumed to be a function of three factors, γ_{f1}, γ_{f2} and γ_{f3}, each of which takes account of given risks:

γ_{f1} takes account of possible inaccuracies in the assessment of the characteristic values.

γ_{f2} (or ψ_0) takes account of the reduced probability of the combination of actions, all at their characteristic value. γ_{f2} is therefore not a safety coefficient but a combination factor for actions.

γ_{f3} takes account of possible inaccuracies in the assessment of action effects and variations in the dimensional accuracy of the cross sections in construction, as they affect the action effects.

It should be noted, however, that for most practical cases a global γ_f value will suffice for each type of load.

Similarly, the partial safety coefficient γ_m for stresses takes account of a number of specific uncertainties and might be considered to be a function of γ_{m1}, γ_{m2} and γ_{m3}, where

γ_{m1} takes account of the possibility of unfavourable inaccuracies in the assessment of the characteristic strengths of the materials used in the structure as a whole.

γ_{m2} takes account of possible local variations between the strength or other properties of the actual structure or component and that of the control test specimens and of possible weakness in the material or component arising from the construction process itself.

γ_{m3} takes account of possible inaccurate assessment of the resistance of the elements, derived from test results, including the effect of dimensional inaccuracies.

In addition to the γ_m and γ_f values an additional special factor γ_n may be needed to modify the γ_m and γ_f values in the light of the inherent structural behaviour of a member or structure. Thus it can be assumed that:

γ_{n1} takes account of the type of fracture, i.e. whether the structure is brittle or ductile.

γ_{n2} takes account of the consequences of failure in loss of life and in terms of economic consequences, viz. loss of use of the structure and need for replacement and repair.

γ_{n3} takes account of the degree of control exercised in construction.

In practice for most structures it will suffice to take account of the two global safety coefficients γ_m and γ_f, as in CP 110. The use of the modifying factor γ_n has not been formally established. It serves as a rational way of modifying γ_m and γ_f appropriately.

Levels of safety approach

The Draft International Safety Code (Volume 1) identifies three levels at which structural safety problems can be treated.[18]

Level 1. This is a semi-probabilistic design process using design loadings and strengths derived from characteristic values obtained by statistical treatment, increased or reduced with the aid of practical safety coefficients, modifying factors and combination factors respectively, as required. Level 1 is identical with the limit state processes described above. For Level 1 processes the complexities of lifelike consideration of local service conditions are attained through a series of partial factors which are deemed to constitute the two main practical safety coefficients γ_f and γ_m. For the *simplified Level* 1 *process* these complexities are reduced by adopting global γ_m and γ_f values from the start, relating to a single limit state which is taken as the critical one. The design is then carried through by adjusting the safety factors relating to that single limit state and by adopting practical design rules to cover all the other limit states.

Level 2. This is an advanced fully probabilistic design approach. The Draft International Code for Safety (Volume 1)[18] defines Level 2 as 'a design process in which the loads or actions and the strengths of materials and sections are represented by their own or postulated distributions (defined in terms of relevant parameters such as type, mean or standard deviation) and some formal probability of failure is accepted'. The fully probabilistic Level 2 approach can be further refined by treating economic optimisation as well as distribution of loads and stresses on a statistical basis (Level 3).

For practical purposes, the Level 2 processes are unlikely to be of use in design except for some specialised structural problems where it could be appropriate. Thus it could be so used for the design of pylons for electric overhead cables and it has been successfully used for the design of a large, prestressed lightweight concrete floating dock constructed in Genoa, Italy. Level 2 processes might be useful however in checking the appropriate γ_f and γ_m values for Level 1. If it can be so used it could ensure that for different methods of construction those values are mutually compatible. For example, after agreeing the selection of practical safety coefficients for loading, these being applicable for all types of construction, in the absence

TABLE 14.4
DESIGN LOADS (CP 110)

Characteristic load combinations	*Design loads = $f \times$ Characteristic load*	
	Ultimate limit state	*Serviceability limit state*
1. Dead load Q_k	$1 \cdot 4 Q_k$	$1 \cdot 0 Q_k$
Imposed load Q_k	$1 \cdot 6 Q_k$	$1 \cdot 0 Q_k$
2. Dead load Q_k	$0 \cdot 9 Q_k$	$1 \cdot 0 Q_k$
Wind load W_k	$1 \cdot 4 W_k$	$1 \cdot 0 W_k$
3. Dead load Q_k	$1 \cdot 2 Q_k$	$1 \cdot 0 Q_k$
Imposed load Q_k	$1 \cdot 2 Q_k$	$0 \cdot 8 Q_k$
Wind load W_k	$1 \cdot 2 W_k$	$0 \cdot 8 W_k$

of a check on the overall safety achieved, different code committees could validly adopt γ_m values which in cost competition would unduly favour the particular material or method of construction for which they are responsible. Level 2 is thus at present to be regarded as—at best—a checking procedure for code drafting bodies.[21]

As stated earlier, for design Level 2 can at present only be used in

TABLE 14.5
DESIGN STRENGTHS (CP 110)

Type of limit state	*Design strength = $\dfrac{Characteristic\ strength}{m}$*	
	Concrete	*Steel*
Ultimate limit state for: the strength of structure	$\dfrac{f_{cu}}{1 \cdot 5}$	$\dfrac{f_y}{1 \cdot 15}$
the effects of excessive loads or local damage	$\dfrac{f_{cu}}{1 \cdot 3}$	$\dfrac{f_y}{1 \cdot 0}$
Serviceability limit state for: deflections	$\dfrac{f'_{cu}}{1 \cdot 0}$	$\dfrac{f_y}{1 \cdot 0}$
cracking or stresses	$\dfrac{f_{cu}}{1 \cdot 3}$	$\dfrac{f_y}{1 \cdot 0}$

conjunction with very approximate and rough calibration processes as a result of which the complex sophistication inherent in fully probabilistic methods becomes unnecessary and ineffectual.

Values of partial safety coefficients

Following the CEB–FIP International Recommendations[2] the British code has established values for the partial coefficients of safety for concrete construction. (Tables 14.4 and 14.5).

SHEAR

Where the unit shear stress derived from the conventional method of design

$$q = \frac{Q}{bl_a}$$

does not exceed the permissible shear stress for the concrete, according to the British codes of practice CP 114 and CP 116 reinforced concrete beams may be designed without shear reinforcement. Here q denotes the unit shear stress, Q the shear force at the section, b the breadth of the section, and l_a the lever arm of the internal forces in the cross-section.

For slabs, this conventional design method is generally safe. Indeed, in most cases, the safety of slabs against failure in shear is so little in question that design calculations to check shear stresses may seem superfluous. For beams, however, the actual load factor obtained with the conventional method of design without shear reinforcement may not always be adequate. Hanson's tests[22] on a large number of gravel concrete and lightweight concrete beams showed that in some cases the load factor against shear failure barely rises above 1·2 and is rarely greater than 1·7 (Fig. 13.3). Similarly disquieting results were obtained by Taylor[23] for beams without shear reinforcement.

To obtain a more realistic basis for the shear design of beams that do not contain shear reinforcement, empirical rules have been drawn up by various research workers. Taylor's ultimate strength formula for example

$$Q = q_{cr}db$$

gives the diagonal cracking load in relation to a unit nominal shear stress which is assumed to be dependent on the cube strength and on the longitudinal reinforcement. Assuming a load factor 3·0 against failure in shear, the permissible shear stress for gravel aggregate concrete for different tensile stresses in the longitudinal reinforcement is given in Ref. 34. These data apply to cross-sections where the bending moment is not less than one-half the resistance moment corresponding to working loads;

where this rate is less than half, the nominal shear stresses given in Ref. 34 may be increased by 10 per cent.

The nominal shear stresses given in Ref. 34 apply to gravel aggregate concrete of a given cube strength. Lightweight concrete beams without shear reinforcement fail in shear at a load that may be 10–20 per cent lower than those calculated for beams made with gravel concrete.

Whether the design method based on the elastic theory or that based on the ultimate strength is used, however, it is clearly desirable that the permissible stresses or loads should be such that the performance of gravel concrete and lightweight concrete beams is comparable. It is therefore necessary to reduce the permissible stress or permissible load in shear for lightweight concrete members by 20–25 per cent compared with gravel concrete ones.

It is axiomatic in modern reinforced concrete design that, owing to the suddenness and unpredictability of shear failures, structures should not be liable to fail in shear under an overload but that failure should occur as a result of yielding of the reinforcement in bending. We cannot be certain of this unless the shear forces are resisted by properly designed shear reinforcement, since in beams without shear reinforcement diagonal cracking, leading to shear failure, can occur at relatively low loads as a result of unforeseen weakness in the concrete. With the exception of slabs, where shear stresses are generally low, and of subsidiary members, such as lintels, reinforced lightweight concrete flexural members of major importance should, therefore, always contain shear reinforcement. The permissible shear stresses laid down for lightweight concrete flexural members therefore only apply to slabs or subsidiary members. Where the shear stress in these exceeds the maximum permissible shear stress, then either the cross-section must be increased sufficiently to resist the shear forces or, alternatively, shear reinforcement must be introduced. Whether a load-bearing flexural member should be regarded as one of major importance is in practice largely a matter for the engineer to decide. For general guidance, those members might be reasonably regarded as structural components of major importance which, through their collapse, could vitiate the continued functioning of the entire structure for a prolonged period or would cause injury to occupants. Where such consequences would be remote even in case of sudden shear failure, then the member might be regarded as a subsidiary component.

Where shear reinforcement is provided and is designed to resist the whole of the shear in a cross-section, in accordance with CP 114 and CP 116, the shear stress in the concrete should still not exceed four times the permissible stress in the concrete, i.e. the shear resisted by the shear reinforcement must not be greater than four times that which could be resisted by the concrete without any shear reinforcement.

Where shear reinforcement is provided in accordance with the earlier

British code, i.e. disregarding the shear resistance of the concrete, the spacing between stirrups should not exceed a distance equal to the moment arm l_a. The actual spacing may be calculated from the following equation:

$$s = \frac{p_{st} A_w l_a}{Q}$$

where s is the maximum spacing between stirrups; p_{st} is the permissible tensile stress in the reinforcement; A_w is the cross-sectional area of the stirrup and Q is the total shear in the section.

The design of the stirrups, and indeed of all other reinforcement in lightweight concrete, must comply with the standards recommended for dense gravel concrete members in the code.

The ACI Building Code Requirements only require a proportion of the shear force to be resisted by shear reinforcement, the rest being resisted by the concrete. In this way some account is taken of the resistance to shear forces which is exerted by the longitudinal reinforcement as well as by the concrete section.

Sir Owen William's work on the shear stress in reinforced lightweight concrete ships' hulls[24] indicates that the diagonal strain in lightweight concrete members is considerably higher than in similar dense gravel concrete ones. He suggested therefore that the permissible stress in the shear reinforcement should be reduced for reinforced lightweight concrete. On the face of it, the differences between gravel and lightweight aggregate concretes do not appear to support the introduction of considerable restrictions, but the problem deserves further and more detailed experimental examination.

For gravel concrete beams the web reinforcement arrived at by the conventional theory recommended by CP 114 is usually much more than is required to prevent shear failure. Particularly with heavily reinforced beams, therefore, a considerable reserve of strength is present which is in fact being taken into account by the Russian and American codes of practice for reinforced concrete, as well as in CP 110.

The calculation of the shear resistance provided by inclined tension bars generally proceeds from the assumption that these bars form the tension members of a system of lattice girders in which the concrete forms the compression members. The shear resistance may then be taken as the sum of the vertical components of the internal tension and compression forces in the cross-section, but stresses in the horizontal reinforcement must not exceed the permissible steel stresses.[13] In continuous beams it is usual to continue the bent-up bars over the supports so thay they may act as top tensile reinforcement. Tests show that in the case of simply supported beams, also, the continuation of the bent-up bars will lead to enhanced shear resistance, because they inhibit the start of shear cracks and also due to the contribution to the shear resistance made by the longitudinal bars.

Other methods than the lattice girder analogy are also used and may be considered admissible for lightweight concrete as well as for gravel concrete members but all these methods suffer from the defect of attempting to simulate in theory the behaviour of some type of structure that is different from the one considered, i.e. a reinforced concrete beam. Such analogies are necessarily incomplete and may be misleading.

The shear provisions of CP 110:1972[1,25] are simpler. Design of lightweight concrete beams is governed by data provided in two tables.

TABLE 14.6

ULTIMATE SHEAR STRESS v_c IN LIGHTWEIGHT CONCRETE BEAMS[1]

$\dfrac{100A_s}{bd}$	v_c for concrete grade (28-day cube strength)									
	15 (2 200 psi)		20 (2 900 psi)		25 (3 600 psi)		30 (4 350 psi)		40 (4 800 psi) or more	
	(MPa)	(psi)	(MPa)	(psi)	(MPa)	(psi)	(MPa)	(psi)	(MPa)	(psi)
0·25	0·15	22	0·28	41	0·28	41	0·28	41	0·28	41
0·50	0·20	29	0·36	52	0·40	58	0·44	64	0·44	64
1·00	0·20	29	0·48	70	0·52	75	0·56	81	0·60	87
2·00	0·25	36	0·64	93	0·68	99	0·72	105	0·76	110
3·00	0·30	44	0·68	99	0·72	105	0·76	110	0·80	115

Where the shear stress v calculated from the equation $v = V/bd$ exceeds v_c given in Table 14.6, then special shear reinforcement must be provided. In this equation V is the shear force due to ultimate loads; b is the breadth of the section or—for a flanged beam—the rib width; and d is the effective depth of the section.

In any case, however, the shear stress must not exceed that given in Table 14.7, even with special shear reinforcement.

The spacing of links used as shear reinforcement should not exceed $0·75d$ and the following requirement should be satisfied:

$$\frac{A_{sv}}{S_v} \geq \frac{b(v - v_c)}{0·87fyv},$$

where fyv is the characteristic strength of the link steel, but not more than 425 MPa (about 62 000 psi); A_{sv} is the cross-sectional area of two legs of one link in mm^2; and S_v is the spacing of the links in mm.

The special shear reinforcement should thus be capable of resisting safely that part of the shear force only which is in excess of that resisted by the concrete section, subject to some additional safeguards. The shear stress which is assumed to be resisted by the concrete alone in lightweight concrete

TABLE 14.7

MAXIMUM ALLOWABLE SHEAR STRESS v_{max} FOR LIGHTWEIGHT CONCRETE BEAMS[1]

v_{max} *for concrete grade (or 28-day cube strength)*									
15 (2 200 *psi*)		20 (2 900 *psi*)		25 (3 600 *psi*)		30 (4 350 *psi*)		40 (5 800 *psi*) or more	
(MPa)	*(psi)*	*(MPa)*	*(psi)*	*(MPa)*	*(psi)*	*(MPa)*	*(psi)*	*(MPa)*	*(psi)*
2·30	335	2·68	390	3·00	435	3·28	475	3·80	530

beams (Table 14.7) is 20 per cent lower than that for gravel concrete and the maximum shear stress allowed to occur in the concrete, in lightweight concrete beams with shear reinforcement is also 20 per cent lower than for dense concrete beams. The shear stress in solid slabs is calculated as for beams and no special shear reinforcement is required where $v < \xi_s v_c$, where v_c is given in Table 14.6 and ξ_s in Table 14.8.

TABLE 14.8

VALUES OF ξ_s

Overall depth of slab		ξ_s
(mm)	*(in.)*	
250 or more	10 or more	1·00
225	9	1·05
200	8	1·10
175	7	1·15
150 or less	6	1·20

For slabs at least 200 mm (8 in.) thick, where $v > \xi_s v_c$, shear reinforcement must be provided as for beams but the spacing between links may be increased to d instead of $0.75d$ as for beams. The maximum shear stress given in Table 14.7 should be halved for slabs. The shear stress in slabs less than 200 mm (8 in.) thick should not exceed $\xi_s v_c$ and shear reinforcement is not normally provided.

Bond

The development of adequate anchorage bond along a sufficient bar length or at the ends of bars is essential for both reinforced and prestressed concrete to ensure effective composite action between concrete and reinforcing bars or tendons. This is clearly a fundamental technical feature of these methods of construction.

Many tests on the bond properties of different types of concrete and of reinforcing bars indicate some factors on which the anchorage bond and local bond depend (Chapter 12). Various national and international codes differ somewhat in their assessment of the relative importance of these factors. The US codes, as well as the CEB–FIP International Recommendations[21] and the Draft International Code, Volume 2,[16] regard the position of the bars in the cross-section in respect of the top edge of importance, in addition to the type of bar surface (plain or deformed), the strength of the concrete and the type of aggregate used. Some codes single out the bar diameter as having an important effect. The British Code CP 110:1972[1,23] establishes allowable stresses for local bond and for anchorage bond, depending on the concrete strength and the type of steel, the allowable bond stresses for deformed bars being 25–30 per cent higher than for plain bars for local bond, about 40 per cent higher for anchorage bond.

For lightweight concretes, design stresses for local and anchorage bond are reduced by 50 per cent for plain bars and by 20 per cent for deformed bars compared with the values given for concretes made with normal dense aggregates. There is, however, little or no justification for reducing bond stresses in lightweight concrete for bars held vertically during casting.

The Draft International Code[16] distinguishes between 'good bond conditions' and 'bad bond conditions', the former being related to reinforcement which is inclined at 45° to 90° to the horizontal during casting, to any reinforcement placed at any angle in the lower half of the section or not less than 300 mm (12 in.) from the upper face or from a construction joint [(450 mm, 18 in.) for lightweight concrete]. All other reinforcement is deemed to be in bad bonding conditions and the allowable bond is reduced by 50 per cent for lightweight concretes.

Columns

Short columns of lightweight concrete are designed in the same manner as those of gravel aggregate but for lightweight concrete the slenderness ratio which defines the boundary between short columns and long columns is usually fixed at a somewhat lower value than for gravel concretes. For long columns, lightweight concrete is at a disadvantage. Lateral deformations are larger and the resulting secondary stresses due to lateral deformation tend to become higher, thereby reducing the ultimate loadbearing capacity of a lightweight concrete column. There is also the tendency of lightweight concrete to fail in compression at a lesser ultimate strain and to display a quasi-brittle rupture pattern due to the more rapid decline of the descending branch of the load-deflection diagram (Fig. 14.1). Particularly with single, relatively isolated columns where redistribution of load affects is less likely to take place effectively, this—in theory—could lead to sudden collapse.[14,15]

In the case of the British Code[1] a slender column is designed for its ultimate axial load N together with a moment M_t which consists of two components; an initial moment M_i due to ultimate loads and an additional moment depending on the axial load and the dimensions of the column. This additional moment is increased by a factor of about 1·5 for lightweight concrete. The design of slender columns can be based, however, on a variety of theoretical limit state approaches since it is clearly not merely a problem of elastic instability. These are set out in the CEB Design Manual for Buckling[6] by a group of collaborators led by Professor Franco Levi and Dr Aas-Jakobsen. All these methods take account of the effect of secondary deformations at varying levels of accuracy and expand the methods given in the International Recommendations.[2] The additional moment method used in CP 110 is one of these.

For lightweight concrete, the effect of secondary deformations due to larger compressibility and in some cases to larger creep must be taken into account by a suitable increase of the design load, varying from 1·1–1·3.

PERMISSIBLE STRESSES IN THE CONCRETE

Compression

Normally, as mentioned before, the earlier British Codes of Practice [3–5] require that for concrete in compression a safety factor 3·0 be applied to the cube strength for flexural members, when using the elastic method of design. For the design calculations based on ultimate strength an overall load factor of about 2·0 is generally required. It is assumed, however, that at failure the actual strength of the concrete in flexural members is only two-thirds of the cube strength, thus increasing the load factor against failure, where failure is likely to be due to crushing of the concrete. It follows then that the same permissible stress, i.e. one-third of the cube strength, may be used for the ultimate strength method of design with a load factor of about 2·0 as is used with the elastic method with a safety factor 3·0 in compression.[13]

The factor 3·0 is applicable to nominal mixes in CP 114 where the aggregate used complies with BS 882 and also to lightweight aggregate concretes. For designed mixes a somewhat lower factor is applied (Table 14.9).

Few reinforced concrete members are so over-reinforced that in case of overloading they would fail as a result of compression of the concrete. A higher safety factor or load factor in compression will not therefore greatly affect the ultimate loadbearing capacity of a structure, although it will affect some other properties and, of course, its cost.

Better concrete having a higher compressive strength will also possess a higher initial modulus of deformation, thus reducing somewhat the deflections of flexural members made with such concrete; it will also lead to less creep. There are more efficacious and less expensive methods of increasing the stiffness of structural members than reducing the permissible stresses in compression, and on balance this discrimination did not seem to be justified. A safety factor 4·0 against crushing of the concrete appeared to be excessive for concrete made to consistent standards of quality, and gave way for lightweight concrete to the more usual safety factor of about 3·0 on cube strength and a load factor that is somewhat higher than 2·0 on flexural strength where failure is caused by crushing of the concrete (Table 14.9).

TABLE 14.9
PERMISSIBLE COMPRESSIVE STRESSES FOR DESIGNED CONCRETE MIXES

Specified works cube strength at 28 days	Permissible compressive stresses	
	Direct	*Bending*
u_w	$u_w/3·65$	$u_w/2·73$

The ACI Code of Building Requirements which incorporates the recommendations of the ACI–ASCE Joint Committee on ultimate strength design, provides for a minimum load factor 1·8 for beams, while assuming that the maximum fibre stress in compression does not exceed 85 per cent of the 28-day cylinder strength (approximately equivalent to 60–70 per cent of the cube strength). Using the elastic method of design, the permissible stress in compression for flexural members is limited to 45 per cent of the cylinder strength (approximately 30–35 per cent of the cube strength).

With regard to compression members, for short columns with a slenderness ratio of less than 10, the permissible stresses in direct compression given in the codes of practice for gravel concrete are also applicable to lightweight aggregate concrete. Tests indicate that under the same load, axially applied, lightweight concrete columns are shortened more than comparable dense concrete ones, leading to higher stresses in the steel reinforcement. The difference will depend on the moduli of deformation of the two types of concrete and on the reinforcement percentage. It has been found, however, that the ultimate strength of short columns does not differ greatly, whatever the type of aggregate used, if the compressive strength is the same.[27]

Long columns made of lightweight concrete have a lower failing load than comparable gravel concrete columns, owing to the effect of the lower modulus of deformation, and other factors.

In design, the reduction coefficients applicable to the permissible loads on slender columns must be lower. For reinforced lightweight concrete

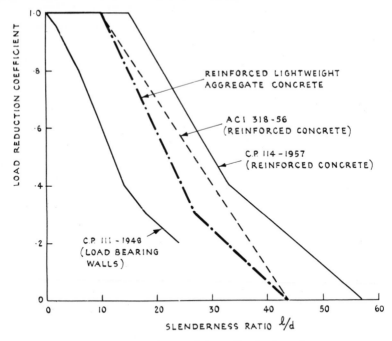

FIG. 14.2   Reduction coefficients for slender columns.

columns and walls, therefore, the reduction coefficients given in Fig. 14.2 have been adopted in the British Codes CP 114 and 116.

Shear

In the British Codes CP 114 and 116 the permissible stress in shear for gravel concrete in flexural members must be not more than one-eleventh of the permissible stress in compression for designed mixes having a specified works cube strength of 21 MPa (3000 psi) or less. For higher strengths the proportion of permissible shear and compressive stresses is somewhat less, reaching, for example, one-seventeenth for a cube strength of 42 MPa (6000 psi). For lightweight concrete members the permissible shear stress is reduced by 25 per cent.

The ACI Code 318–71 as amended in 1975[6] presents a number of variants for the approach to the assessment of shear and for the provision of shear reinforcement.[27] It includes provisions for shear in both ordinary reinforced and prestressed concrete members and for torsion in non-prestressed members only; it gives detailed rules for the design of brackets and corbels, deep beams, slabs, footings and shear walls, and a special section is included for lightweight concrete.

For reinforced concrete beams without special shear reinforcement, shear is assumed to be carried by the concrete web and the stresses are calculated with the basic equation first given in the 1963 edition of the ACI Code:

$$v_c = 1 \cdot 9(f_c')^{1/2} + 2500 \rho_w \frac{V_u d}{M_u}$$

where f_c' is the compressive strength; ρ_w is the steel proportion in the section; V_u is the shear force; M_u is the moment at the section, and d is the effective depth of the section.

It has been recognised that in some ways this equation does not accurately represent shear flow in a beam. For example,[27] it is known that it overestimates the effect of the compressive strength f_c' compared with other factors in the equation and does not take into account recent research which seems to indicate that shear strength decreases with the depth of the beam. The shear strain must not exceed $3 \cdot 5(f_c')^{1/2}$, but for most practical design cases it will suffice to assume by simplification that

$$v_c = 2 \cdot 0(f_c')^{1/2}$$

even where the calculated shear strain in the concrete is low—except where it is less than one-half of the nominal permissible shear strain, or in slabs and footings—when a minimum shear reinforcement should be provided. Such reinforcement restrains the spread of diagonal cracking and is a safeguard against sudden failure due to an unexpected tensile force or accidental loading.

For lightweight concrete members the expressions for the shear strain v_c apply with two alternative modifications: (1) $(f_c')^{1/2}$ (the square root of the specified compressive strength) shall be replaced by $f_{ct}/6 \cdot 7$ (where f_{ct} denotes the average tensile strength of the lightweight aggregate concrete) but $f_{ct}/6 \cdot 7$ must not then exceed $(f_c')^{1/2}$; or alternatively, where f_{ct} is not specified: (2) $(f_c')^{1/2}$ for lightweight concrete shall be substituted by $0 \cdot 75(f_c')^{1/2}$ for 'all-lightweight' concrete and $0 \cdot 85$ for 'sand-lightweight' concrete, respectively. Where the lightweight fines are partially replaced by sand a linear interpolation is permissible. These ratios imply some movement from the previous assessment of the splitting tensile strength in relation to $(f_c')^{1/2}$. In the 1963 Code the assumed value of $f_{ct}/(f_c')^{1/2}$ was $4 \cdot 0$. Using the factors given in the 1971 Code that ratio now assumes values of $5 \cdot 0$ and $5 \cdot 7$, respectively, based on many tests.

Bond

The permissible bond stresses are defined in codes of practice in relation to the compressive strength. The British codes relate them to the cube strength, the American to the cylinder strength, as in the case of the permissible shear stresses. A reliable direct experimental determination of the bond strength is not possible at present. Even as a comparative index of the bond strength for different types of concrete or steel bar, the results obtained from bond tests are not always dependable, particularly with pull-out specimens.

The results of comparative bond tests made with beams indicate that the bond strength of lightweight concrete with plain round reinforcing bars is usually lower than that obtained with gravel concrete of equal compressive strength. In the case of deformed bars the ultimate bond-anchorage strength is of the same order for all types of concrete having the same compressive strength, whatever the aggregate used. On the other hand, the force required to produce a given critical slip, say 0·025 mm (0·001 in.), between concrete and an embedded deformed bar is less for lightweight concrete than for gravel aggregate concrete.

For gravel concrete, the permissible average bond stress laid down in the CP 114:1957 for plain round bars ranges from about one-ninth to about one-fifteenth [for 42 MPa (6000 psi) concrete] of the permissible compressive stress in flexure. The corresponding ratio in American practice appears to be about one-tenth for normal use but somewhat lower for top bars and for bars in footings. In view of the results obtained from tests on bond beams, it is necessary in lightweight concrete flexural members to allow for a permissible bond stress that is about one-half of that permitted for plain round bars embedded in gravel aggregate concrete having the same compressive strength.

For deformed bars, the British code permits an increase of 25 per cent over and above the bond stress permitted for round bars, provided that the bond strength of the deformed bars used can be shown by pull-out tests to be actually at least 25 per cent higher than that of plain round bars. American usage allows a much greater increase, i.e. about 100 per cent. In view of the behaviour of the bars at a slip of 0·025 mm (see Chapter 12), the permissible bond stresses for deformed bars are also reduced by one-half, in British practice, when using lightweight concrete.

In fact, however, the ultimate bond strength of deformed bars with lightweight concrete is usually 3 to 4 times as high as that obtained with plain round bars, while the bond stress obtained for a slip of 0·025 mm is normally about twice as high as with plain bars. Similar relationships can be observed with gravel aggregate concrete beams. On the face of it, therefore, the permissible bond stresses in CP 114 are perhaps too cautious for all types of concrete with regard to deformed bars. On the other hand, it has been shown that permissible stresses for plain round bars embedded in gravel concrete are such as to result in a load factor against bond failure which may be too low in those cases where bond is the governing factor for strength. A reduction of the normal permissible stresses for plain bars and a slight upward adjustment of those relating to deformed bars in the British code of practice would appear to be justifiable.

For the ACI Code 318–71 the concept of bond strength is replaced by the concept development length and the emphasis on the calculation of nominal peak bond stresses has been replaced by the use of average bond resistance over the full development length. The method used and the minimum development lengths adopted are intended to safeguard against the danger of highly strained bars being placed in thin cross-sections, leading to splitting of the concrete section.

For lightweight concrete two alternative methods can be used. With one method the basic development length determined for gravel aggregate concrete shall be multiplied by a factor 1·33 for 'all-lightweight' concrete and by 1·18 for 'sand-lightweight' concrete, linearly interpolated intermediate values being used where the fines are only partially replaced by sand. Alternatively, where the splitting strength f_{ct} is specified, the development length can be obtained for lightweight concrete by multiplying the basic development length by a factor

$$\frac{6·7(f_c')^{1/2}}{f_{ct}} > 1·0$$

where f_c' is the specified compressive strength.

The British Code CP 110:1972 introduces the concept of anchorage bond. For lightweight concrete the bond stresses for mild steel plain bars are required not to be in access of 50 per cent of those allowed for ordinary gravel concrete, to take account of lower bond strengths. For deformed bars the corresponding proportion is 80 per cent, to take account of the possibility of slip. In the main these recommendations follow those in the previous Code, CP 114.

For the Draft International Code the zone when bad load conditions are assumed to prevail is increased somewhat, but otherwise lightweight concrete is treated in the same way as ordinary gravel aggregate concrete.

For deformed bars used in lightweight concrete it would seem sufficient if the permissible bond stresses for normal concrete were reduced somewhat less than for plain round bars. A reduction of 25–30 per cent would seem appropriate, similar to that adopted in the CEB Recommendations.

PERMISSIBLE STEEL STRESSES

The criteria which appear to govern the permissible stresses in the reinforcement of flexural members are:

(1) The yield point stress or—where no distinct yield point is present—the proof stress of the steel.
(2) The deflections of the flexural member.
(3) The distribution and width of the cracks under working loads.

Due to the lower modulus of deformation of lightweight concrete the deflections of lightweight concrete flexural members are likely to be somewhat higher than those of similar beams made of dense concrete. Moreover, due to the lower bond strength of lightweight concrete, the crack distribution is such that the crack widths become greater for the same steel stress. Nevertheless, for ordinary round mild steel bars, the maximum crack widths are not of such a magnitude as to require a reduction of the permissible steel stress. The maximum deflection, on the other hand, can be controlled by means other than a reduction of the steel stresses.

TABLE 14.10

PERMISSIBLE STEEL STRESSES WITH REINFORCED LIGHTWEIGHT CONCRETE[3] IN
CP 114

Designation of stress	Permissible stress			
	Mild steel to BS 785		*Deformed bars with a guaranteed yield stress*	
	Up to and including $1\frac{1}{2}$ in. dia. (37 mm)	*Over $1\frac{1}{2}$ in. (37 mm) dia.*	*Shear reinforcement*	*All other reinforcement*
Tension	140 MPa (20 000 psi)	124 MPa (18 000 psi)	55 % the guaranteed yield stress,[1] but not more than 170 MPa (25 000 psi)	208 MPa (30 000 psi)
Compression	124 MPa (18 000 psi)	110 MPa (16 000 psi)	55 % the guaranteed yield stress, but not more than 170 MPa (25 000 psi)	

Experiments have shown that the maximum crack width in lightweight concrete beams reinforced with plain round mild steel bars was of the order of 0·125 mm (0·005 in.) or less, at a steel stress of about 138 MPa (20 000 psi) i.e. at about half the yield stress of mild steel. The position of the neutral axis tends to be lower for lightweight concrete beams for working loads, due to the lower E-value; this leads to somewhat higher steel stresses than in equivalent gravel concrete beams for the same load. Nevertheless, there appears to be no justification for a reduction in the permissible steel stress in lightweight concrete flexural members compared with gravel concrete ones on account of increased crack widths. The same permissible steel stress may therefore be used for any type of aggregate (Table 14.10) for plain round mild steel reinforcement.

For deformed high tensile bars having a guaranteed yield stress or 0·25 per cent proof stress, CP 114 allows a permissible stress equal to 55 per cent of that stress but not more than 228 MPa (33 000 psi) (207 MPa (30 000 psi) for lightweight concrete) in tension and 173 MPa (25 000 psi) in compression or 173 MPa (25 000 psi) for the shear reinforcement.

For lightweight concrete *slabs*, the use of deformed bars should be allowed on the same basis as for ordinary gravel concrete slabs. Some restrictions should apply to *beams*, however. When deformed bars are used in beams, the crack widths are somewhat greater than with gravel concrete beams. Because of the lower position of the neutral axis in lightweight concrete flexural members a larger proportion of the compressive zone is used effectively in compression after cracking. These somewhat smaller concrete stresses and reduced moment arm are balanced however by higher steel stresses. For equal loads the steel stress might be about 10 per cent higher in lightweight concrete than in similar gravel concrete members.

To take account of higher actual stresses and crack widths, the permissible stresses for deformed high-tensile steel bars in lightweight concrete might be reduced to approximately nine-tenths of those allowed for gravel concrete beams. Nevertheless, even at the maximum permissible tensile stress allowed by the code, crack widths are likely to remain smaller than those which in normal conditions could encourage dangerous corrosion of the reinforcement. It would appear reasonable, therefore, to allow the use of the full permissible stresses laid down in the code for members used internally, in cases where the surroundings are not corrosive.

In American practice the same steel stresses may normally be used for all types of concrete.

For CP 110:1972[1] the characteristic strength of reinforcing steel is assumed to be its yield or proof stress or—in the case of prestressing

TABLE 14.11
STRENGTH OF REINFORCEMENT[1]

Designation	Nominal sizes		Specified characteristic strength, fy	
	(mm)	*(in.)*	*(MPa)*	*(psi)*
Hot rolled mild steel	All sizes		250	36 500
Hot rolled high yield	All sizes		410	60 000
Cold-worked high yield	Up to and including			
	16	0·63	460	67 000
	over 16	over 0·63	425	62 000
Hard drawn steel wire	Up to and including			
	12	0·48	485	71 000

tendons—the ultimate load; not more than 50 per cent of the test results are permitted to fall below the characteristic strength, in accordance with the statistical basis of the design calculations. The actual values of the characteristic steel strengths are those given in the appropriate British Standards (Table 14.11).

STIFFNESS AND CRACKING

International agreement on what are acceptable maximum deflections which must not be exceeded in various types of structure has yet to be obtained. They vary from 1/180th of the span as a limiting deflection laid down for some cases in the American Codes to 1/300th in usual British Practice. CP 110:1972 requires that the final deflection (including the effects of temperature creep and shrinkage) should not exceed 1/250th of the span.

The stiffness of reinforced concrete members must be such that excessive deflections do not impair their performance, e.g. will not produce cracks in the finishes or partitions. For all normal cases this condition can be taken to be satisfied for lightweight concrete beams and slabs where the ratio of the span to the overall depth does not exceed the values given in Table 14.12.[3,5] These span–depth ratios are somewhat lower than those allowed in the code

TABLE 14.12

MAXIMUM VALUES OF THE PERMISSIBLE SPAN–DEPTH RATIO OF REINFORCED LIGHTWEIGHT AGGREGATE CONCRETE FLEXURAL MEMBERS[3,5]

	Support conditions	*Ratio of span to overall depth*	
		CP 114	*CP* 110
Rectangular	Simply supported	17	17
Beams	Continuous	21	22
	Cantilever	8	6
Slabs	Spanning in one direction:		
	Simply supported	26	
	Continuous	30	
	Spanning in two directions:		
	Simply supported	30	
	Continuous	34	
	Cantilever	10	

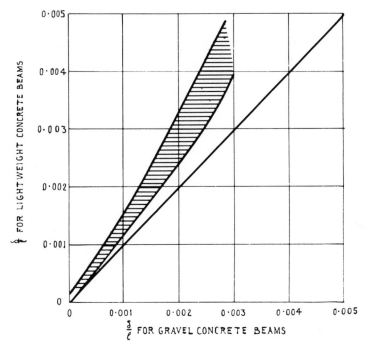

FIG. 14.3 Comparison of deflection/span ratios for gravel concrete and lightweight concrete beams.

for dense concrete, so as to take account of the propensity of lightweight aggregate concrete members to deflect somewhat more than dense concrete ones, on account of their lower modulus of deformation.

Tests indicate that the differences in deflection may vary between 10 and 50 per cent (Fig. 14.3), depending on the reinforcement percentage and cracking behaviour as well as on E-value.

The simplicity of this method of ensuring adequate stiffness for reinforced concrete flexural members is often outweighed, however, by its uncertainty. Experience has shown that the deflections obtained with members designed with the span–depth ratios laid down in the codes for gravel concrete are not excessive if the steel stress in the tensile reinforcement does not exceed 140 MPa (20 000 psi) for beams and 200 MPa (30 000 psi) for slabs. There is less information on the behaviour of lightweight concrete members, particularly for higher stresses. Moreover, where beams are made with higher steel stresses using deformed high-tensile steel bars, the deflections at such stresses are bound to be higher, although no special provision is made for reducing the span–depth ratios. In fact, therefore, with this method, different standards of stiffness are used for different types of reinforcing bar.

In view of the larger initial elastic deflections and because of the somewhat larger creep of most lightweight aggregate concretes, it seems advisable to check the deflections by calculations, particularly for high-tensile steel reinforcement and not to rely entirely on the permissible span–depth ratios to ensure adequate stiffness. Provision is made for this in CP 110:1972.

In the case of precast members where a large number of identical units are made to the same design, it is preferable to use loading tests to check the stiffness of the members concerned. An imposed load equal to one-and-a-quarter times the specified imposed load should be maintained for a period of at least 24 h and the deflection measured should not exceed 1/250th of the span. On removal of the load the member should recover at least 75 per cent of the maximum deflection measured during the test.

Slender beams of large span exposed to the weather tend to develop excessive deflections after a time due to the creep of the concrete. These deflections may hinder the performance of the functions for which the structure was designed. Where there is a greater propensity to creep, lightweight concrete beams can be more likely to develop excessive permanent deformations and this should be taken into account in design.

Where the laterally unsupported length of a slender beam is large in relation to the width of its cross-section, for example where this ratio is greater than 30, the danger of failure due to torsional instability cannot be disregarded. CP 114:1957[3] therefore provided for a progressive reduction of the permissible stresses in the concrete for such slender beams (Table 14.13). In any case, however, the height of the cross-section of such beams should not exceed eight times the width.

Evidence obtained from tests made at the Building Research Station on slender gravel concrete beams on which these provisions are based showed that where lateral movement was prevented at the ends, failure was more likely to occur as a result of lateral bending and particularly shear, than

TABLE 14.13
STRESS REDUCTION COEFFICIENTS FOR SLENDER
BEAMS IN CP 114

Slenderness ratio $= \dfrac{L}{b}$	30	40	50	60
Coefficient	1·00	0·75	0·50	0·25

L is the length of the beam between lateral restraints.
b is the breadth of the beam.

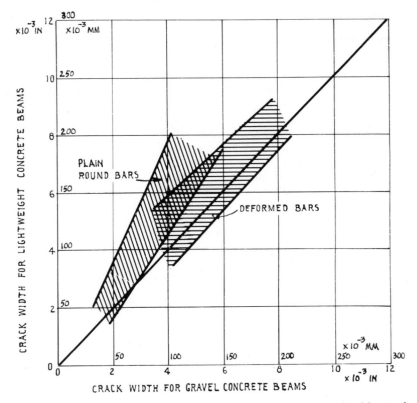

FIG. 14.4 Crack widths for equal steel stress obtained in beams made with gravel concrete and lightweight concrete.

elastic torsional instability. Propensity to such failure is further increased by initial inaccuracies in the alignment of the beam.

The stress reduction coefficients adopted in the code of practice allow for a high factor of safety against failure by lateral instability before full flexural strength has been attained. Although special measures other than those laid down for ordinary gravel or crushed rock concrete[13] are not normally required for lightweight concrete, in the case of abnormally slender lightweight concrete beams the stress reduction factors given in the code may have to be further reduced in view of the lower modulus of deformation of lightweight concretes.

Cracking is usually more severe in lightweight concrete beams than in similar gravel concrete members whatever type of lightweight aggregate used; this is independent of the reinforcement percentage. For plain round mild steel reinforcing bars the difference between gravel concrete and lightweight concretes increases with increasing load (Fig. 14.4). With deformed bars the difference tends to remain constant. The crack spacing diminishes slightly with increasing load, but is almost always greater for lightweight concrete than for gravel concrete beams.

The greater crack widths and crack spacing would be explained by the lower bond strength and anchorage strength of lightweight concrete by greater deflections and by its lower tensile strength.

For normal conditions the safety and durability of lightweight concrete members is not greatly affected by this tendency to develop greater crack widths. Where corrosive conditions are likely to occur, however, special measures of protection may be necessary and the permissible steel stresses may have to be reduced. The use of a cement slurry poured over the bars before casting the concrete increases their resistance to corrosion. For adequate corrosion resistance the cover over steel bars in lightweight concrete members should be slightly greater in exposed positions; in severe exposure, the increase might reach 10 mm (0·4 in.).

TRANSVERSE REINFORCEMENT

Whatever aggregate is used, solid reinforced concrete slabs must have reinforcement in at least two directions, whether supported on two, three or four sides. In either direction the reinforcement of normal gravel concrete slabs must be at least 0·15 per cent of the gross cross-sectional area of the concrete.[3] In the case of slabs supported along two opposite edges only, the transverse reinforcement should be not less than 10 per cent of the longitudinal reinforcement. The pitch of the bars must not exceed five times the effective depth but this minimum pitch only applies to thin slabs. The spacing of distribution bars should nowhere exceed 0·46 m (18 in.).

According to the ACI 1963 Code the transverse reinforcement is determined according to the type of steel used, being not less than 0·18 and 0·25 per cent of the gross cross-sectional area of concrete.

The main purpose of the transverse reinforcement is to ensure the distribution of the bending moments caused by concentrated loads or strip loads, so as to increase the effective width over which the load can be distributed. Solid slabs are frequently calculated on the assumption that their behaviour under loading is akin to that of the isotropic plate. The inclusion of transverse reinforcement ensures that the bending moment and shear force distribution across the slab is similar under loading to. that which is expected to occur in the plate.

In addition, transverse reinforcement enhances the resistance of the slabs to the incidence of shock effect and the punching shear due to concentrated loads. It also helps to resist thermal and shrinkage stresses.

Transverse reinforcement cannot prevent cracking due either to shrinkage or temperature stresses, but it can prevent the formation of very wide cracks, it can ensure that the number of cracks is larger, that cracking is evenly distributed, and that the crack width is small enough not to be conducive to the development of corrosion.

In some cases, transverse reinforcement is also a useful aid in erection, since, when assembled with the main longitudinal reinforcement, it forms mats which are easier to handle, place and transport than single bars.

The presence of adequate transverse reinforcement is an important feature of any type of reinforced concrete construction but is especially important for lightweight concrete, in view of the tendency of lightweight concrete to develop wider cracks under load than dense concrete. Tests have shown that under concentrated loads lightweight concrete slabs tend to fail earlier than dense concrete slabs in the absence of adequate transverse reinforcement.

Temperature effects in lightweight aggregate concrete may take longer to become effective, due to better insulation properties, than with gravel concrete. The coefficient of expansion of lightweight concrete is also generally lower and due to its lower modulus of elasticity the stresses associated with these thermal changes are therefore much smaller. On the other hand, the temperature gradient across a lightweight concrete cross-section is likely to be steeper than in dense concrete, due to its better insulation properties and in severe cases this may be conducive to higher shear stresses. On balance, the resistance of lightweight concrete to stresses due to thermal changes is likely to be greater in most cases than that of gravel concrete.

The deformation of most lightweight concretes due to shrinkage and moisture movement tends to be greater than that of gravel concrete of equal strength; this is due to their greater initial water requirement and generally to the increased cement content for the same strength. For some types of lightweight concrete greater shrinkage is counteracted to some degree by greater creep under stress.

For unreinforced concrete the greater shrinkage of lightweight concrete is broadly balanced by its lower modulus of elasticity, so that where the concrete is restrained by the adjacent members, for example, in unreinforced walls, the shrinkage stresses are of the same order as they would be for gravel concrete or even lower. Where reinforcement is present, however, it can be easily shown that the shrinkage stresses in lightweight concrete, particularly for lightly reinforced members, may well be much higher than for gravel concrete.[24]

PRESTRESSED CONCRETE

The advantages of prestressed concrete construction are not perhaps as great for lightweight as for gravel aggregate concrete. Because of the softness of lightweight aggregates, compared with gravel or most crushed rock aggregates, the required compressive strength can only be attained by using a large proportion of cement in the mix, so that the matrix may well be more than a mere binder providing for the adhesion of the aggregate grains. Nor, on the face of it, is the reduction in weight compared with gravel concrete as great as for reinforced concrete. Concrete made with lightweight aggregate such as sintered pulverised-fuel ash or expanded clay, and having a strength of 41·5 M Pa (6000 psi) at 28 days, may vary in density from about 1680–2000 kg/m^3 (105–125 pcf). The weight of gravel concrete of such strength is about 2300–2400 kg/m^3 (145–150 pcf).

Owing to the elimination of cracking, prestressed concrete cross-sections can be fully utilised throughout their depth. The economic advantage of utilising the whole construction depth of lightweight concrete flexural members is not, however, as great as with dense concrete, since the position of the neutral axis in ordinary reinforced lightweight concrete is lower than in dense concrete members and thus the concrete is already more fully utilised.

Nevertheless, for bridge girders of large span, for example, the dead weight of a member can be of decisive importance. In the USA, the use of prestressed lightweight concrete girders with post-tensioned steel enables the designer to use this cheaper method of construction instead of steel girders, where the use of gravel concrete girders would not be economic, e.g. for haulage distances greater than 100 miles or where the allowable weight is limited because of restrictions imposed on the load capacity of overland transport facilities or of the cranes used for handling and erection. Precast roof-slabs with pre-tensioned reinforcement have also been used with advantage.

CP 115:1959[4] and CP 110:1972 are relevant to the design of both dense and lightweight prestressed concrete structures. The design of prestressed concrete is simply and fully explained in the *Guide to the BS Code of Practice*[30] and in other text books[25,31,32] and these are applicable to prestressed lightweight concrete in most respects. Some brief comments are necessary, however, at least on bond strength and on losses due to the elastic deformation, the creep and shrinkage of lightweight concrete, and relaxation of the steel.

Most of the information on bond strength relates to lightweight concrete having a compressive strength of less than 31 M Pa (4500 psi). Little information is at present available on the bond strength of lightweight concrete of high compressive strength.

Bate's tests at the Building Research Station on gravel concrete and lightweight concrete containing foamed slag, sintered pulverised-fuel ash, and expanded clay aggregates respectively,[31] with a cube strength of 35–40 M Pa (5000–6000 psi) at transfer, with 13 mm ($\frac{1}{2}$ in.) dia. strand, indicate that the transmission lengths in concrete made with lightweight aggregates may not be substantially different from those of gravel aggregates of similar strength. A transmission length of about 640 mm (25 in.) might be assumed in design, for a cube strength of 35 MPa (5000 psi) at transfer.

The loss of prestress due to the elastic deformation of gravel concrete can be calculated with the E-values of the concrete. For lightweight concrete the values for this loss should be doubled in the calculations since, for the same compressive strength, the modulus of deformation of lightweight concrete

TABLE 14.14

MODULAR RATIO FOR THE CALCULATION OF LOSSES
OF PRESTRESS IN LIGHTWEIGHT CONCRETE

Cube strength of lightweight concrete at transfer		Modular ratio to be used for the calculations
(MPa)	*(psi)*	
20	3 000	18·5
27·5	4 000	14
35	5 000	12·5
42	6 000	11
55	8 000	9·5
70	10 000	8·5

is about half that of gravel aggregate concrete. For pre-tensioning, the loss of stress in the tendons at transfer in lightweight concrete should be taken as the product of the modular ratio in Table 14.14 and the stress in the adjacent concrete. The cube strength of the concrete should preferably not be less than 35 MPa (5000 psi) at transfer.

For post-tensioned wires, bars or strand that are stressed successively, the resulting loss of stress in the tendons should be taken as half the product of the modular ratio given in Table 14.14 and the stress in the adjacent concrete. The modular ratio corresponding to a cube strength of 20 MPa (3000 psi) is included in Table 14.14 for the purposes of interpolation, for post-tensioning only.

The loss of stress which takes place in the prestressing tendons owing to shrinkage of the concrete is greater where lightweight concrete is used than with gravel concrete because the shrinkage is generally much higher. For average conditions of exposure, the contraction of lightweight concrete owing to shrinkage, for a cube strength of not less than 42 MPa (6000 psi) at 28 days, may be assumed at about 600×10^{-6} for pre-tensioning and at about 400×10^{-6} for post-tensioned tendons. Higher contraction should be assumed to take place where post-tensioning of the tendons is carried out less than two to three weeks after concreting.

The loss of stress in the prestressing steel due to creep of the concrete should be calculated on the assumption, as for gravel concrete, that creep is proportional to the initial compressive stress in the concrete. The loss of stress in the tendons due to contraction caused by creep of the concrete is obtained by multiplying the modulus of deformation of the steel (taken as 19×10^4 MPa (28×10^6 psi), by the creep of the concrete adjacent to the prestressing tendon. The loss of stress in the prestressing tendons due to creep to be assumed for the calculations is given in Table 14.15 for the most unfavourable creep development. Normally the loss due to creep is closer to that for gravel concrete.

TABLE 14.15

LOSS OF STRESS IN THE STEEL DUE TO CREEP OF LIGHTWEIGHT CONCRETE

Cube strength of the concrete at transfer		Loss of stress in the prestressing steel (psi) per unit compressive stress in the concrete			
(MPa)	(psi)	For pre-tensioning		For post-tensioning[a]	
		(MPa)	(psi)	(MPa)	(psi)
35	5 000	0·13	19	0·10	14·5
42	6 000 and more	0·11	16	0·08	12

[a] Where stressing takes place about 14 days after concreting.

The total eventual loss of stress in the prestressing steel used with lightweight concrete can be about 25–35 per cent of the initial stress; for gravel concrete the corresponding loss is normally about 20–25 per cent.

Dimensionally the high-tensile steel wires and strands used for prestressed concrete are not entirely stable under high stress, particularly in high ambient temperature. Under a constant tensile stress they tend to lengthen permanently; if a sensibly constant length is maintained, under the conditions that occur in prestressed concrete members, there is a noticeable relaxation of stress, even in normal room temperature.

According to CP 115:1959, the initial tensile stress immediately after anchorage in the prestressing steel should not exceed 70 per cent of the ultimate strength of the steel. To counteract the greater loss of stress caused by shrinkage and possibly by creep of the concrete, it has been proposed in some countries in Europe to use higher initial steel stresses with prestressed lightweight concrete. With increasing initial prestress, however, the loss of stress by relaxation will increase at a much higher rate[30] and this loss of stress must be taken into account in design.

Prestressed concrete members are normally so designed that they do not crack under working load. In addition, the concrete has a higher compressive strength and its quality is therefore higher than in normal reinforced concrete. In general, therefore, the stiffness of prestressed concrete flexural members is greater than that of reinforced concrete members of the same depth.[24] This applies to both gravel and lightweight concrete members.

With lightweight concrete, the effect of the lower modulus of deformation and greater creep of the concrete on the deflections is more marked in prestressed concrete than in reinforced concrete flexural members. The stiffness of a prestressed concrete member is dependent almost entirely on the properties of the concrete used, whereas in reinforced concrete members of the same depth, part of the concrete is cracked and the reinforcement contributes considerably, particularly in lightweight concrete, to the stiffness of the structure.

In design, the recommendations for prestressed gravel concrete in respect of limitations on permissible stresses and depth of members are normally also applicable to lightweight concrete, but the lower *E*-value and greater creep and shrinkage must be taken into account.

Where finishes are applied, the total camber of prestressed concrete beams due to prestressing should not in general exceed 1/300th of the span.[1,3]

REFERENCES

1. British Standard Code of Practice CP 110:1972. 'The Structural use of Concrete', British Standards Institution.
2. CEB–FIP International Recommendations for Concrete Construction (1970), CEB, Paris.
3. British Standard Code of Practice CP 114:1969, Pt 2, (metric units 1965, 1967 and 1969). 'The Structural use of Reinforced Concrete in Buildings', British Standards Institution.
4. British Standard Code of Practice CP 115:1969. 'The Structural use of Prestressed Concrete in Buildings', British Standards Institution.
5. British Standard Code of Practice CP 116:1969. 'The Structural use of Precast Concrete', British Standards Institution.
6. American Concrete Institute Standard ACI 318 71 (1971–1975). 'Building Code Requirements for Reinforced Concrete', ACI, Detroit.
7. British Standard 882:1965. 'Coarse and Fine Aggregates from Natural Sources for Concrete', British Standards Institution.
8. Edwards, A. G. 'Scottish Aggregates: Their Suitability for Concrete with Regard to Rock Constituents', Current Paper, 28/70, Building Research Station, Garston, Watford.
9. 'Shrinkage of Natural Aggregates in Concrete', BRS Digest No. 35, 1963, revised 1968, Building Research Station, Garston, Watford.
10. British Standard 877:1967. 'Foamed or Expanded Blast-furnace Slag Lightweight Aggregate for Concrete', British Standards Institution.
11. British Standard 3797:1964. 'Lightweight Aggregate for Concrete', British Standards Institution.

12. Thomas, F. G. (1955). 'Load Factor Methods of Designing Reinforced Concrete', *Reinforced Concrete Review*, **3**(8).
13. Scott, W. L., Glanville, W. H. and Thomas, F. G. (1965). *Explanatory Handbook on the British Standard Code of Practice for Reinforced Concrete CP 114:1957 (Amended 1965)*, Concrete Publications, London.
14. Short, A. (1973). 'Lightweight Concrete', CEB Course for Limit State Design. National Laboratory for Civil Engineering, Lisbon.
15. Grimer, F. J. and Hewitt, R. E. (1969). 'The Form of the Stress–Strain Curve of Concrete Interpreted with a Diphase Concept of Material Behaviour'. Proc. International Conference on Structure, Solid Mechanics and Engineering Design, Southampton University, April 1969.
16. 'International System of Standard Codes for Civil Engineering', Draft (1977), Vol. 2, 'Model Code for Concrete', CEB, Paris.
17. Soviet Standard Code GOST 11051–70. 'Lightweight Aggregate from Porous Aggregates: Concrete Mix Test Methods', Moscow.
18. 'International System of Standard Codes for Civil Engineering' Draft (1977), Vol. 1, 'Unified Common Rules', CEB, Paris.
19. Ministry of Housing and Local Government (1968). Report of the Inquiry into the Collapse of Flats at Ronan Point', HMSO.
20. Mathieu, H. (1974). 'Manual on Structural Safety', Bulletin No. 102, CEB, Paris.
21. CIRIA (1976). 'Rationalisation of Safety and Serviceability Factors in Structural Codes', London.
22. Hanson, J. B. (1961). 'Tensile Strength and Diagonal Tension Resistance of Structural Lightweight Concrete', *Amer. Const. Inst. J.*, **34**(1).
23. Taylor, R. (1960). 'Some Shear Tests on Reinforced Concrete Beams without Shear Reinforcement', *Mag. Concr. Res.*, **12**(36).
24. Williams, Sir E. Owen. (1945). 'Shear Stresses in Reinforced Concrete with Particular Reference to Concrete Ships', *J. Inst. Civ. Eng.*, **26**(7).
25. Bate, S. C. C., Cranston, W. B., Rowe, E. R. *et al.* (1972). *Handbook on the Unified Code for Structural Concrete (CP 110:1972)*, Cement and Concrete Association, London.
26. CEB Manual for Buckling (1975). Bulletin No. 103, CEB, Paris.
27. Commentary on Building Code Requirements for Reinforced Concrete (ACI 318-71). American Concrete Institute, Detroit.
28. Grimer, F. J. (1965). 'Tests on Lightweight Concrete Columns', *Struct. Concrete*, **2**(6).
29. Marshall, W. T. (1961). 'Shrinkage and Temperature Stresses in Reinforced Concrete Section', *Civil Engineering and Public Works Review*, **56**(665).
30. Walley, F. and Bate, S. C. C. (1959). *A Guide to the British Standard Code of Practice for Prestressed Concrete 115:1959*, Concrete Publications, London.
31. Bate, S. C. C. (1961). 'Prestressed concrete', *Civil Engineering Reference Book*, Vol. 3, Second Edition, Butterworths, London.
32. Gerwick, Ben C. Jr. (1971). *Construction of Prestressed Concrete Structures*, Wiley, New York.
33. Bate, S. C. C., Building Research Station, Private Communication.
34. Short, A. and Kinniburgh, W. (1968). *Lightweight Concrete*, Second Edition, CR Books, London, p. 180 (Table 14.3).

CHAPTER FIFTEEN

Insulation-Grade Aggregate Concretes

SUMMARY

Certain aggregates are eminently suitable for making concretes of very low density and low thermal conductivity. These aggregates are exfoliated vermiculite and expanded perlite. In general, concretes made from such aggregates have insufficient strength for load-bearing purposes but are particularly suitable as thermal insulating materials.

The concretes considered in the earlier chapters have been those particularly suitable as loadbearing materials, but at the same time having moderate thermal insulation value. This chapter deals with the very light concretes with high thermal insulation but generally with quite low strength. It is true that with the aggregates considered here, very rich mixes can in some cases produce strength sufficient for loadbearing purposes, but such have inferior insulation value and are generally uneconomical, since concrete of comparable properties can be produced with less expensive aggregate using leaner mixes.

EXFOLIATED VERMICULITE

Raw vermiculite is a micaceous mineral and, as such, has a laminar structure. When heated, it expands by delamination in much the same way as slate expands, a process which was described in an earlier chapter. It does not, however, show any noticeable fusion, as does slate. This type of expansion is termed 'exfoliation' and during this process the vermiculite may expand to many times its original volume. The product thus formed has a golden lustre and has a density of only a few pounds per cubic foot. Exfoliated vermiculite is illustrated in Fig. 15.1.

To obtain the exfoliated product, the raw ore is dried to about 3 per cent moisture at a temperature of 100–120 °C, and is then crushed and screened. The crushed material is dropped into a horizontal stream of air where the particles are transported varying distances according to their particle size, a process termed 'winnowing'. In this way it is separated into three or four size grades which are exfoliated separately by dropping the material through an intense flame, thus subjecting it for a few seconds to flash-roasting at a temperature approaching 2000 °C.

FIG. 15.1   Exfoliated vermiculite aggregate.

Vermiculite was first exfoliated during the First World War, using material mined in Colorado, but it is now obtained from other parts of the USA, notably Montana, North and South Carolina, as well as from South Africa. It is said to be available also in the USSR (Urals) and in Australia.

Until 1940, exfoliated vermiculite was used principally as a loose-fill insulation for roofs of houses, a purpose for which it is still used, but it has now become of some importance as an aggregate for wall-plaster and, to a lesser extent, as an aggregate for concrete.

Exfoliated vermiculite concrete may be used for blocks and panels, as screeds for flat roofs, for shell type roofs, thermal protection for steel structures, and for furnace fire bricks.

TABLE 15.1

PROPERTIES OF VERMICULITE CONCRETE

Dry density of concrete		Compressive strength at 28 days		Drying shrinkage (per cent)	Thermal conductivity, k-value	
(kg/m^3)	(pcf)	(MPa)	(psi)		(W/m °C)	(Btu in/ft² h °F)
368	23	0·86	125		0·10	0·7
464	29	2·00	290	0·35–0·47	0·12	0·8
576	36	3·24	470		0·14	1·0
672	42	4·03	585		0·17	1·2

The density of the aggregate depends on the conditions of heating as well as on the grading, while the properties of the concrete reflect not only the density of the aggregate and the mix proportions, but also the methods of mixing. In this connection it is claimed that an air-entraining agent can be used with advantage. The properties of vermiculite concrete are shown in Table 15.1.

EXPANDED PERLITE

Perlite is one of the natural volcanic glasses and is thus related to pumice. It has not, however, a physical structure like pumice, but is a dense glassy rock and, as its name implies, has an onion-like concentric form. When the crushed rock is flash-heated to the point of fusion, about 1800 °C, it expands, often with decrepitation, to form a light cellular material with a density of 4–15 pcf, which has been found useful as an aggregate. In practice the rock is crushed to carefully graded size and then subjected to rapid heating in a specially designed furnace which permits of close control of temperature and retention time. This heating produces physical and chemical changes which lead to the formation of minute voids which, in turn, create the expansion and the cellular form, thus giving the lightness and the insulation value of this aggregate.

FIG. 15.2   Expanded perlite aggregate.

Although it was known as early as 1836 that perlite would expand when heated under certain conditions, it was not until 1946 that expanded perlite was first used as an aggregate. The raw material was obtained originally from Arizona, USA, but Sardinia in the Mediterranean is also an important source. More recently, deposits in Antrim, Northern Ireland, have been processed and the Irish product was for some years available on the British market. In England it is not much used yet as a concrete aggregate, but is finding favour as an aggregate for wall-plaster. In the USA, however, it has been used as a concrete aggregate for blocks, wall-panels and for the fire protection of steel.

Figure 15.2 shows a sample of expanded perlite. Table 15.2 gives the results which can be expected from perlite concrete. Shrinkage figures have been derived from various sources.

TABLE 15.2
PROPERTIES OF EXPANDED PERLITE CONCRETE

Dry density of concrete		Compressive strength at 28 days		Drying shrinkage (per cent)	Thermal conductivity, k-values	
(kg/m^3)	(pcf)	(MPa)	(psi)		$(W/m\ °C)$	$(Btu\ in/ft^2\ h\ °F)$
320	20	0·55	80		0·09	0·6
400	25	0·96	140		0·10	0·7
480	30	1·65	240	0·1–0·3	0·12	0·8
560	35	2·75	400		0·13	0·9
640	40	3·44	500		0·16	1·1

It will be observed that the density, strength and thermal conductivity of these very lightweight aggregate concretes are close to those of autoclaved aerated concrete which is considered in a later chapter. Aerated concrete, however, was not being made in the USA at the time when the perlite and vermiculite concretes were first established there and it may be that these aggregate concretes would not have been so readily accepted for their purpose, had aerated concrete been available at the time. In many countries in Europe and elsewhere, on the other hand, aerated concrete has been used successfully for many years, and it does not seem likely that in these countries perlite and vermiculite could have the popularity they enjoy in the USA.

CHAPTER SIXTEEN

Lightweight Aggregate Concrete in Practice

SUMMARY

The application of lightweight aggregate concrete in practice is illustrated by examples.

Lightweight aggregate concrete may be used with advantage simply to replace gravel concrete, e.g. for precast or cast-*in-situ* loadbearing members. It is, however, a material specifically suited in its own right for particular purposes, e.g. where thermal insulation is an important consideration or where selfweight must be reduced, as for bridge beams of large span. With very few exceptions, any one of the several available types of lightweight aggregate may be used for any of the purposes for which lightweight concrete is needed, but some aggregates are less suitable, others are more suitable for particular applications. Pumice aggregate, for example, is not generally used for cast-*in-situ* construction, because of its tendency to float to the surface and cause segregation of the mix. Nevertheless, this difficulty has been successfully overcome in some instances; for example, large numbers of houses have been constructed with cast-*in-situ* floor and roof slabs of pumice concrete in Nairobi, Kenya. The very light aggregates are another example. In general these materials, such as vermiculite and perlite, are only used for insulation, e.g. in roof screeds. They have also been used, however, for the construction of reinforced concrete shells; cube strengths of 7 MPa (1000 psi), and even more, have been obtained with them. At the other end of the scale, foamed slag concrete, when fully compacted for reinforced concrete construction, was found to have considerably higher density/strength ratios than lightweight concrete made, for example, with sintered clay, shale, or pulverised-fuel ash aggregate. By using suitable mixes, foamed slag concrete can reach very high strengths and can be used economically for structural purposes, depending on the cost of material and transport in particular cases but the weight of the resulting structure will tend to be higher with foamed slag concrete than with some other aggregates. When used with a porous no-fines mix, most lightweight aggregates at present in production in the UK are equally suited for loadbearing as well as for non-loadbearing types of plain concrete construction. Where reinforcement is used it must be protected against corrosion in exposed conditions. Although rapidly diminishing in supply, clinker will still be available in some areas. Provided it fulfils the necessary requirements (BS 1165), clinker is suitable for making precast blocks but should not be used for reinforced concrete work.

WALLS

When using lightweight aggregate concrete, designers expect two main advantages, namely, reduced weight and high thermal insulation; these

Fig. 16.1   Unrendered external foamed slag block walls.

may be combined with high strength where the concrete is used for structural purposes. In many cases lightweight concrete is preferred, although on the face of it the initial price of the material may appear higher than that of dense gravel aggregate concrete; in the USA, lightweight aggregates have found an increasing market in spite of their higher price.

Masonry block walls were the first type of lightweight concrete loadbearing element used on a large scale. While in the rest of Europe and in the USA solid single-leaf walls were required, in Britain, cavity walls with a loadbearing inner leaf and a non-loadbearing or partly loadbearing outer leaf are more usual. The inner loadbearing leaf is frequently made of lightweight concrete blocks or cast-*in-situ* lightweight concrete, the outer leaf being unrendered facing bricks or rendered masonry, or even unrendered masonry blocks (Fig. 16.1). Until recently, most masonry blocks in the UK were made with clinker aggregate; in Western Europe pumice or foamed slag were mainly used. In the US, unrendered block walls are commonly used.

PRECAST PANELS

The size of masonry blocks is usually such that they can be lifted by one man, their chief advantage being that, owing to their lower density and the cored cavities they often contain, the rate of building can be greatly speeded up and transport costs can be reduced. A further step towards site mechanisation was the introduction in East Germany of large blocks 1 m (3′ 3″) square 300 mm (1 ft) thick, placed by light cranes. The buildings made with such blocks are somewhat difficult to make architecturally pleasing and tend to be monotonous. The blocks were made of porous, non-compacted foamed slag or expanded slate concrete at or near the sites.

As the lifting capacity of tower cranes increased, experience with precast work led to the development of storey-high panels made of lightweight concrete, with embedded reinforcement. These methods of construction were originally pioneered in the UK, mainly in Glasgow, where large municipal blocks of flats were constructed with precast foamed-slag panels. Development took place independently in Eastern European countries where considerable progress was made with automatic precasting methods in large factories and the introduction of mobile precasting works erected in the centre of neighbourhood units and then moved to the next site when its work in one place was completed. In East Germany three types of large panel were standardised, having maximum weights of 0·75, 2 and 5 tons, respectively, depending on the size of the unit and the material used (Fig. 16.2) Cranes with appropriate lifting capacity were designed for each type of panel.

Loadbearing crosswall construction is usually employed, the outer walls serving for insulation only. Window and door frames are included in the moulds during casting and the units are ready to be decorated after erection. The panels are held together by welding the protruding reinforcing bars at ceiling and floor level; additional bars are placed at the external walls. The panels are made of foamed slag or expanded slate concrete, using non-compacted porous mixes. Six men, including the crane driver, can assemble the structure of a block of 40 dwellings units in about 5 weeks.

Many different types of large-panel structure similar to that described above have been developed in different countries. In the USSR, expanded clay (Keramzite) was mainly used. In general, both the wall and floor slabs are precast, but while the wall units are made with porous, non-compacted lightweight concrete mixes, the floor and roof units are made with compacted concrete. Recent practice has been to steam-cure the units.

FIG. 16.2   Precast concrete wall panels made with expanded slate aggregate, stored at a site at Leipzig, GDR, awaiting erection.

FIG. 16.3   Multi-storey block of apartments constructed with precast foamed slag and gravel concrete sandwich panel with cast-*in-situ* joints at Metz, France, using a light prefabricated steel frame for erection.

Precasting has considerable advantages in that some of the building operations usually carried out on the open site, exposed to the weather, are converted into manufacturing operations capable of being closely controlled in a factory. The large investment required for such a production line is only worthwhile, however, if the number of units needed of any one type is very large. In many cases, however, the cost of transporting the materials from their source to the factory added to the cost of moving the finished products to the building site exceeds the savings gained from factory production. Mobile precasting factories can provide a solution, not perhaps as efficient as the large enclosed works, but avoiding some of the handling operations which are necessary with the latter. In recent years large-panel, high-rise buildings have become less popular, partly because of the widespread social rejection of tall buildings, particularly for dwelling accommodation and partly as a reaction to the Ronan Point failure, which was due to an accidental gas explosion. For a large block of flats near Metz, France, loadbearing sandwich units were produced on the site, consisting of a foamed slag concrete core and dense concrete outer and inner layers. The storey-high units were attached to a light steel frame erected progressively storey by storey together with the panels, the joints being cast *in situ* (Fig. 16.3).

Smaller precast units spanning up to 3 m (10 ft) have long been made in Germany as standard building components with pumice or foamed slag concrete. Owing to their light weight and high thermal insulation, these units are particularly suitable for industrial roofing (Fig. 16.4); to reduce deflections, tension reinforcement is placed *in situ* over the supports, in

FIG. 16.4   Industrial building in Germany constructed with precast reinforced pumice concrete slabs covering the north-light roof.

grooves left in the top of the slabs. Narrow, storey-high precast foamed slag concrete slabs are used widely in Czechoslovakia for the construction of multi-storey buildings.

For such generally applicable standard units, precasting in large works has often proved to be both technically and economically advantageous. Where very large numbers of units are required, units of storey height and comprising an entire room could be made economically in such large precasting works with semi-automatic systems of production.

Precast prestressed floor and roof slabs made of expanded clay aggregate concrete are being made in the UK. The cross-section of these slabs is cored; their maximum span is 6 m (about 20 ft). Some are manufactured in a similar manner to the Schäfer slabs; these are sandwich units, the top and bottom layers of which consist of ordinary dense gravel concrete of high strength in which the prestressing wires and other reinforcement are embedded, while the middle layer is made of non-compacted foamed slag concrete. The slabs are made in continuous strips several hundred feet long, the material being prepared in a mobile tower and cast. The metal cores are withdrawn automatically as the tower passes along the slabs. The slabs are then cut, the maximum length of Schäfer slabs normally being 4 m (approximately 12 ft).

Precast box units of room size are being made mainly in the USSR. In other countries the difficulties of transporting such large, bulky elements

FIG. 16.5 Footbridge at Wiesbaden-Schierstein, West Germany, during construction (Werk foto Dyckerhoff and Widmann).

across country were found to inhibit the adoption of this type of component on a large scale.

BRIDGES

Precast prestressed beams with post-tensioned reinforcement have found increasing use in the USA for bridge deck systems. The use of prestressed

FIG. 16.6 Footbridge at Wiesbaden-Schierstein, West Germany (werk foto Dyckerhoff and Widman).

concrete beams above certain spans is limited not merely by the increasing dead weight which absorbs a large proportion of the loadbearing capacity of the beams but also by the facilities which are required for transporting such beams to the sites where they are to be erected. The use of prestressed lightweight concrete with high-tensile steel strand reinforcement stressed at 80 per cent or even more of the ultimate strength of the steel, to allow for the larger losses due to creep and shrinkage of the concrete, led to a considerable reduction in the selfweight of the beams. Available lifting and transport facilities could thus be used for large spans. The advantage of lower weight for transport and erection is also apparent in the case of precast pier sections. These can be transported to the site in ordinary rail or road vehicles in much larger single units than would be possible with dense gravel concrete. Similarly, the weight of plate girders with encased bottom flanges where these are used as shoulders to support cast-*in-situ* jack-arches can be reduced substantially by using lightweight concrete.

FIG. 16.7   Footbridge at Kenilworth, England made with Lytag (sintered fly-ash) aggregate.

FIG. 16.8   Road bridge at Fuehlingen/Cologne, West Germany of continuous prestressed girders made with expanded clay aggregate concrete (Werk foto Dyckerhoff and Widmann).

Some of the most imaginative recent applications of high-grade, lightweight aggregate concretes in Europe are the series of medium-span bridges built in West Germany and The Netherlands. Figures 16.5 and 16.6 show a footbridge near Wiesbaden (Dickerhoff and Widmann) where the central prestressed lightweight concrete arch is supported on short fixed end sections made of ordinary gravel concrete. Expanded clay aggregate was used here. An elegant bridge construction made with Lytag aggregate concrete is shown in Fig. 16.7. Figure 16.8 shows a roadbridge in West Germany, consisting of continuous girders and deck, made with expanded clay aggregate concrete.

COMPOSITE MEMBERS

Composite methods of construction have been used extensively both for bridge deck and floor systems, combining steel girders and reinforced concrete slabs or prestressed precast girders and cast-*in-situ* slabs. Prestressed gravel concrete girders have been used in Great Britain, together with a lightweight concrete filling (Fig. 16.9), thus greatly reducing weight and also improving the impact characteristics of the system owing to

FIG. 16.9 Composite bridge deck system for the Staffordshire Motorway in England; prestressed concrete beams 11 m (36 ft) span with Lytag concrete deck.

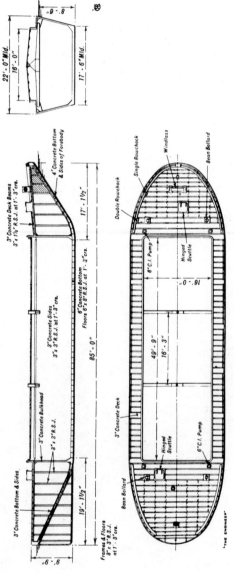

FIG. 16.10 Details of lightweight concrete barge.

the lower *E*-value of the lightweight aggregate concrete. The use of compacted lightweight concrete with composite steel-concrete slab-and-girder systems can increase the useful loadbearing capacity of the structure. Here the steel girders and the reinforced concrete top slab are combined through shear connectors. These can be rigid steel sections or flexible bars and are usually welded to the top flange of the girders. In this way the stiffness and ultimate loadbearing capacity of the composite system are greatly increased over those of the separate girder and slab, since the deflections are small. In any case the use of lightweight concrete has little untoward effect on stiffness. The neutral axis of a composite slab-and-girder system is usually close to the top flange of the steel girders, thus leading to inadequate use of the steel section, particularly at working loads. Owing to the lower modulus of elasticity of lightweight concrete than of dense gravel concrete, the neutral axis of lightweight concrete flexural members tends to be lower and thus allows slightly higher stresses to be reached in the top flange of the steel girder. By the more efficient use of the compressive flange some economies may be achieved.

The design of composite lightweight concrete members can be carried out in accordance with the rules laid down in the Code of Practice of the American Concrete Institute.

SHIPS

Perhaps the earliest experimental application of reinforced concrete was in boat-building. Later, during the Second World War, lightweight concrete was used both in Great Britain and in the USA for the construction of sea-going ships (Fig. 1.4) and barges (Fig. 16.10) to save steel and other scarce materials. The aggregate used for the ships' hulls was mainly expanded clay and the hull was usually protected by a bituminous outer layer. Foamed slag aggregate was used for parts of the mobile harbour installations known as Mulberry Harbour (Fig. 11.5).

MULTI-STOREY BUILDINGS

The development of high-grade, lightweight aggregates made it possible to use lightweight concrete for the construction of large framed cast-*in-situ* loadbearing structures. The consequent saving in weight permitted the use of larger spans in design; it also led to less easily quantifiable but no less real savings on site work by reducing the cost of transportation and erection on the site. In the USA, expanded clay aggregates were used for most lightweight concrete work but other types of lightweight aggregate—such as expanded slate and sintered pulverised-fuel ash—are becoming more widespread.

Aglite concrete was used for the construction of the loadbearing structure of the framed building shown in Fig. 16.11, the first of its kind in the UK. The precast exposed mullions, cast-*in-situ* internal columns as well as the floor and roof slabs were made with the same material. In the course of the service life of the completed building the mullions did not exhibit excessive crazing due to exposure.

FIG. 16.11   Framed multi-storey office building during construction in London using expanded clay (Aglite) aggregate concrete.

Reinforced concrete floor and roof slabs form part of a number of large multi-storey buildings in London (Fig. 16.12) and elsewhere. These were made with Aglite and with other types of lightweight aggregate concrete. The Central Administration building of BMW in München (Fig. 16.13) was designed by Bomhard for Dyckerhoff and Widmann. It is an ingenious application of lightweight concrete for which successive floors, 17 in all, were constructed at ground level and lifted as construction progressed (Fig. 16.14). The concrete was made with Liapor expanded clay aggregate having a density of $1660 \, \text{kg/m}^3$ (105 pcf).

Lytag sintered pulverised-fuel ash aggregate concrete was used for the new Guy's Hospital (Fig. 16.15), one of the great London teaching hospitals, and also for the new construction at Carlton House Terrace in

FIG. 16.12   Multi-storey office building in London constructed with expanded clay aggregate (Aglite) concrete cast-*in-situ* floors and roof.

London (Fig. 16.16). The 60-storey Marina City Towers, Chicago, nearly 180 m (588 ft) high, was built at the astonishingly fast rate of one storey per day, the entire floor structure, including the radial beams being made of lightweight concrete (Fig. 16.17). Lightweight concrete floors and columns were also used in One Shell Plaza, Houston, Texas, a building of 52 storeys, 215 m (705 ft) high (Fig. 16.18). The Water Tower Plaza, Chicago, completed in 1976 is the largest lightweight concrete building in the world (Fig. 16.19). It contains both offices and apartments.

The spread of tall buildings in the great conurbations of industrialised countries has not been without social consequences, which led to an aversion towards such buildings in the USA and elsewhere, particularly against the use of tall buildings for housing. Increasingly it is being accepted that if tall buildings of any kind are to continue to form a sizeable sector of building activities in the cities of the future it will be necessary to re-assess the way in which they function in practice. Even at increased cost their

FIG. 16.13   The BMW administration building in Münich, West Germany, in the course of construction (Werk foto Dyckerhoff and Widmann).

FIG. 16.14 The completed BMW administration building in München, West Germany (Werk foto Dyckerhoff and Widmann).

FIG. 16.15   Guy's Hospital in London, England, built with sintered fly-ash (Lytag) concrete.

populations will need to be split into distinct, smaller communities, thus reducing their immense physical size to the level of human dimensions.

OTHER BUILDINGS

Lytag sintered pulverised-fuel aggregate concrete formed the loadbearing wall and overhanging balcony slab in a church at Orpington (Fig. 16.20),

FIG. 16.16   New buildings at Carlton House Terrace, London, England.

where the reduced selfweight of the structure permitted a more daring and more slender design than would have been possible with gravel concrete.

Prestressed concrete roofs have been built for industrial and other buildings with lightweight concrete, saving material costs and reaching greater spans.

One of the most notable lightweight concrete buildings erected in recent years has been the grandstand at Doncaster. Designed by Bobrowski, its overhanging roof consists of Lytag concrete precast prestressed shell units (Fig. 16.21) 110 m (360 ft) long. For economy, speed of construction and originality of conception it has not been surpassed for this type of structure and forms a prototype for several similar lightweight concrete roofs in the UK and Canada.

Figure 16.22 shows the ski-jump platform at Oberstdorf in West Germany. By using Liapor expanded clay aggregate concrete, savings were obtained on rock anchors and prestressing of the huge cantilever beam supporting a platform at the free end of the beam.

FIG. 16.17   Marina City Towers, Chicago, USA.

FIG. 16.18   One Shell Plaza, Houston, USA.

The nuclear research laboratory at Oxford is an outstanding industrial building, designed by Arup Associates and constructed of Lytag concrete (Fig. 16.23).

Some of the component units of the wartime Mulberry floating harbour structure which enabled the Allied Armies to land in Normandy were constructed of foamed slag concrete. They performed satisfactorily and survived extremely severe conditions in the Channel.

More recently, in Genoa harbour in Italy construction has been proceeding on a floating dock consisting of eight separate prestressed lightweight concrete units made with expanded clay aggregate. When completed, the eight units will be assembled by prestressing with post-tensioned cables, and will be capable of containing the largest ships afloat (Figs. 16.24–16.26).

Figure 16.27 shows Kensington Maintenance Depot in London. The roof consists of radial lightweight concrete beams supported on a central concrete column at one end and on a loadbearing circular wall at the other.

CAST-*IN-SITU* WALL CONSTRUCTION

With some structural lightweight concrete (e.g. Lytag) it has been found that, owing to lower moisture absorption, internal renderings such as plaster, occasionally tend to peel off cast-*in-situ* or precast walls unless the wall surface is treated before the rendering is applied by roughening or

FIG. 16.19   Water Tower Plaza, Chicago, USA.

FIG. 16.20   Cantilevered gallery made of sintered fly-ash (Lytag) concrete, in a
church at Orpington, England.

FIG. 16.21   Grandstand at Doncaster Racecourse, England.

FIG. 16.22   Ski jump at Oberstdorf, West Germany (Werk foto Dyckerhoff and Widmann).

using a bonding agent. With masonry block walls or cast-*in-situ*, loadbearing walls of non-compacted lightweight concrete this difficulty does not arise. Buildings up to 21 storeys high have been erected with cast-*in-situ* loadbearing walls using different types of proprietary shuttering system (Fig. 16.28). It is usual to cast the first few storeys with compacted gravel concrete or with Thermocrete (lightweight concrete containing crushed slag fines) to provide an adequately rigid base on which the upper storeys can be built with non-compacted porous lightweight concrete.

Loadbearing crosswall construction is frequently used with rectangular slab-shaped or tower types of multi-storey building with various plan patterns. In general the latter is more economical.

FIG. 16.23   Nuclear physics research laboratory, Oxford, England.

The outer face of cast-*in-situ* walls is usually rendered but more recently various types of ceramic cladding have also been used (Fig. 16.29). In the UK, expanded clay (Fig. 16.30), foamed slag and sintered pulverised-fuel ash as well as gravel aggregates, have been used for two-storey as well as for multi-storey no-fines concrete buildings of this type (Chapter 7).

OTHER USES

Owing to its low modulus of deformation (E-value), the resistance of lightweight concrete to impact forces and vibration is greater than that of dense gravel concrete. It can be used with advantage for machine foundations. When used for road surfaces it has also been found to be less likely to become smooth and slippery.

FIG. 16.24 Floating dock in Genoa, Italy; section being constructed in dry dock.

FIG. 16.25 Floating dock in Genoa, Italy; tendons and reinforcement being placed in the dry dock during construction. Completed units floating in the harbour beyond.

FIG. 16.26   Floating dock section in Genoa, Italy being towed into the harbour from dry dock.

FIG. 16.27   Kensington Maintenance Depot, London, England.

FIG. 16.28 Shuttering system for cast-*in-situ* walls made with Leca aggregate concrete in London, England.

FIG. 16.29 Ceramics—faced cladding panels for no-fines, foamed-slag concrete external walls of multi-storey building in Düsseldorf, West Germany.

FIG. 16.30 Multi-storey building in London constructed with expanded clay (Leca) aggregate concrete cast-*in-situ* walls.

FIG. 16.31   Screen wall made with precast interlocking units of Lytag concrete.

A special use has been found for precast lightweight concrete hollow blocks as filler elements in some types of lightweight floor construction. With the well-known Stahlton floors, for example, hollow foamed-slag concrete blocks are used. They span between adjacent prestressed Stahlton members to form a base on which cast-*in-situ* concrete is poured, forming the compression zone of the cross-section. A pleasing decorative feature of interlocking precast elements for a screen wall 24 m (80 ft) high and 90 m (300 ft) long has been made of lightweight concrete using suitably pigmented cement (Fig. 16.31). By using lightweight concrete larger individual units can be made.

SCREEDS

Lightweight aggregate concrete is frequently used as a screed on flat roofs and floors, since it can easily be laid in thicknesses which will provide falls for drainage or carry services without increasing the weight unduly. Advantage can also be taken of its thermal insulation. The screed is often

FIG. 16.32   Roof screed made with Leca aggregate laid loose for solar insulation in 75 mm (3 in.) thickness for hospital at Bishop's Stortford, England.

given a topping of 1:4 cement and washed sand or other fine aggregates on which to lay the roof covering or floor finish (Fig. 16.32).

The screed should never be less than 40 mm ($1\frac{1}{2}$ in. thick), but on roofs where it is intended to provide thermal insulation, (thus minimising thermal movements in and heat loss from the structural roof), greater thicknesses will usually be required. To demonstrate this point, Table 16.1 compares three types of lightweight concrete used at specified densities and shows the thickness of screed required in each case, to produce a U-value of $1\cdot25$ W/m^2 °C ($0\cdot22$ Btu in/ft^2 h °F) in a roof of specified construction. The thickness needed for other materials, densities, or U-values may be calculated from published data on thermal conductivity.

High strength is not usually required in a roof screed; probably the roughest treatment which it will receive is from workmen carrying out the next operation on the roof. Foamed slag, sintered pulverised-fuel ash and expanded clay, are suitable aggregates. For producing screeds of about 1100 kg/m^3 (70 pcf) density, mixes of 1:8–1:10 are recommended. For

TABLE 16.1
THERMAL INSULATION OF LIGHTWEIGHT CONCRETE SCREEDS

Insulation material	Approximate density		Thermal resistivity $(1/k)$		Average thickness	
	(kg/m^3)	(pcf)	$(W/m^2\ °C)$	$(Btu\ in/ft^2\ h\ °F)$	(mm)	$(in.)$
Foamed slag concrete	1 120	70	4·3	0·6	150 falling to 100	6 falling to 4
Aerated concrete	640	40	6·9	1·0	100 falling to 50	4 falling to 2
Vermiculite concrete	640	40	6·9	1·0	100 falling to 50	4 falling to 2

screeds of density lower than 650 kg/m³ (40 pcf), exfoliated vermiculite or expanded perlite can be employed, in which case the mix proportions should be about 1:5. Aerated concrete in this density range can also be used.

Porous aggregate absorbs water in the mixing process and high water contents are required to obtain workable mixes. A lightweight concrete screed usually contains a large amount of water when first laid and such screeds take a long time to dry out. On roofs, the screed is usually given two or more weeks to dry out, but if it is not protected from rain it may gain rather than lose moisture. If the roof covering when laid contains substantial amounts of water, serious troubles may ensue. This difficulty, and some ways of dealing with it are discussed in *Building Research Digest No. 8* (Second Series).

In a recent proprietary development, relating particularly to asphalt coverings, bitumen is used in place of cement as the binder for the lightweight aggregate, and the asphalt is bonded directly to the screed, thus avoiding the use of water.

Since floors are subject to much heavier traffic and greater loads than roofs, the design of a lightweight floor screed must take into account the characteristics of the floor finish to be applied. Flexible floor finishes that are incapable of spreading point loading—e.g. linoleum, rubber, sheet vinyl—require a topping of at least 12 mm ($\frac{1}{2}$ in.) of 1:4 cement and sand. Topping requirements are not so stringent where rigid finishes such as wood blocks are used.

Many finishes (or adhesives used to fix them), are susceptible to moisture so that it is important to allow the screed to dry out before the finish is applied, and to take the usual precautions against rising ground moisture.

CHAPTER SEVENTEEN

Aerated Concrete—Manufacture and Properties

SUMMARY

Aerated concrete is a lightweight material. It is unlike other concretes inasmuch as it does not normally contain aggregate, and can be regarded as an aerated mortar.

Typically, aerated concrete is made by introducing air or other gas into a slurry of cement and fine sand and allowing this to set, but in commercial practice the sand is often replaced by pulverised-fuel ash or other siliceous material, and lime may be used instead of cement.

There are two forms of aerated concrete, the in situ *type and the precast products. The latter are usually cured in high-pressure steam.*

Precast aerated concrete is made in the form of loadbearing blocks and reinforced wall, roof and floor units in densities of 500–1000 kg/m³ (31–62 pcf). It has been used for 45 years or more and is manufactured in many countries.

GENERAL

What is termed 'aerated concrete' in the UK and the USA may be defined as a more or less homogeneous, fine-grained siliceous structure enclosing largely non-communicating air-cells. In continental Europe, the terms 'gas concrete' and 'foam concrete' distinguish the mode of manufacture. Figure 17.1 shows a section through aerated concrete and illustrates well its cellular structure.

Although in the Chapter 1 aerated concrete was described, for the sake of simplicity, as a cement paste into which gas bubbles had been introduced, in commercial manufacture aerated concrete almost always contains a considerable proportion of siliceous material in the form of silica flour, pulverised-fuel ash, ground burnt shale or ground burnt blast-furnace slag. Such a siliceous ingredient functions partly as a filler and partly as a chemical reactant with the binder, which may be Portland cement or lime or a mixture of these. This will be dealt with more fully below.

By suitable adjustment of its composition and its method of manufacture, aerated concrete can be produced in a range of densities from 500–1000 kg/m³ (31–62 pcf). Clearly, a product made in so wide a range of density has necessarily a correspondingly wide range in other properties, as will be demonstrated later.

Although aerated concrete is functionally a concrete, its composition is very dissimilar to that of concrete as it is generally understood, and the material could be described more aptly as an aerated mortar or aerated sand–lime block. Indeed, the term 'concrete' is misleading, and it has been suggested that 'aerated silicate' or 'cellular silicate' would be more descriptive. However, the terms aerated concrete and gas concrete are very well established and likely to remain in common use. It is this fundamental

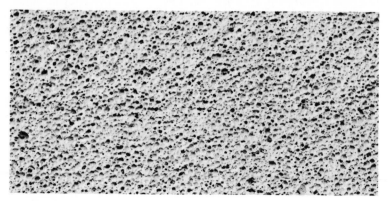

FIG. 17.1   Cut face of aerated concrete, showing cellular structure.

difference from conventional concrete, in composition and structure, which leads to the combination of properties which is characteristic of aerated concrete. In contrast, lightweight aggregate concrete is but a modification of conventional concrete, the difference in this case being one of degree rather than of kind.

Aerated concrete is used in two forms, precast units and *in situ* concrete. Precast units, which include building blocks, are usually steam-cured at high pressure; *in situ* material is necessarily air-cured. This is an important distinction as only by this high-pressure steam-curing (usually termed 'autoclaving') is it possible to obtain a really light material at acceptable levels of strength and drying shrinkage. Air-cured aerated concrete has often less than half the strength of autoclaved material of the same density and it may have four or five times as much drying shrinkage. Moreover, air-cured aerated concrete cannot be made with lime as the cementing agent.

Precast units are produced as plain blocks and as reinforced units such as wall, roof and floor slabs and lintels. *In situ* aerated concrete is used for insulation roof screeds, pipe-lagging and other such purposes for which low thermal conductivity is the principal object and for which high strength and low drying shrinkage are not required. Precast aerated concrete was originally produced only as building blocks and although some producers have for many years made reinforced structural units, the production of blocks still represents the major proportion of the output of this material and may continue to do so for some years. Whilst such blocks are a great asset to the building industry inasmuch as they greatly reduce the dead-weight of structures and make corresponding savings in handling loads, it is in the form of large reinforced units that aerated concrete may yet make its greatest contribution to the building industry. From many points of view the prefabrication of large sections of buildings is a rational approach to building construction and the introduction of reinforced units at densities from 500–750 kg/m³ (31–47 pcf) for loadbearing purposes has given encouragement to this mode of construction in countries where increasing labour cost is seriously affecting building costs.

To the advantages of reduction in weight must be added that of low thermal conductivity. Doubtless on account of an abundance of cheap coal, there was in Britain, until the last war, a great indifference to fuel efficiency but, because the present-day demand for a higher level of comfort, particularly in terms of warmth, both in dwellings and in industrial buildings, coincides with a rapidly advancing cost of fuel, there is now a growing awareness of the need for the more efficient utilisation of fuel. This can be achieved in two ways, by improved heating appliances and by improved insulation. Lightweight concrete in general and aerated concrete in particular provide this improved insulation. No other structural material other than timber provides such a high degree of thermal insulation.

The basic principles of aerated concrete manufacture have been known and understood since the beginning of the century, but significant commercial production did not begin until 1929, when a factory was erected in Sweden to produce this material using a process based on the work of Axel Eriksson. From that date there has been great progress in the development of aerated concrete and in Sweden it is a major material for buildings of all kinds. Nor is it in Sweden alone that the development has taken place. The world-wide use of aerated concrete in climates ranging from the Arctic to the Equator indicates its adaptability to a wide range of weather conditions. Aerated concrete is now being made in the 'developing' countries as well as in countries with a high level of building and civil engineering technology, where it is often in competition with long-established materials of high technical merit. It is clear therefore that economic as well as technical advantages are obtained from the use of aerated concrete. It should be pointed out, however, that in Sweden, the country of its origin, certain conditions exist which were particularly favourable to its development. First, in Sweden there is no brick production comparable with that of the English Fletton brick industry which produces very cheap bricks in vast quantities. Secondly, the climate in much of Sweden is sufficiently severe for good thermal insulation to rank high among the functional requirements for a building material, and aerated concrete goes a long way to meeting U-value requirements. Thirdly, timber, the Swedish traditional building material, has become too valuable as an export to be used extensively in building work, and this has favoured the application of aerated concrete, which has many of the characteristics of timber. It is as light as wood, and can be sawn, chiselled, planed, screwed and nailed; units which have been planed can be glued together. Although it lacks the tensile strength of timber, it has one overwhelming advantage—it is non-combustible.

Licensees of the Swedish companies operate in nearly 30 countries and, in addition, a few countries operate independently. In Britain, 13 factories produce about 2 million m³ autoclaved aerated concrete annually while the USSR makes about 5 million m³ per annum. Factories in several countries produce air-cured units and a number of contractors produce *in situ* aerated concrete for roof screeds and for pipe insulation.

MANUFACTURE

Aerated concrete, as we have already seen, is made by introducing air or other gas into a slurry composed of Portland cement or lime and a siliceous filler, so that when the mixture sets hard, a uniformly cellular structure is formed. (In Chapter 2 an outline was given of the chemical reactions involved in the setting of cement and the combination of lime and silica. Reference to this should assist the understanding of what follows.) There are several ways in which air-cells or other voids may be formed in the slurry, the principal of which may be described thus:

(1) The formation of gas by chemical reaction within the mass during the liquid or plastic stage, in much the way that carbon dioxide is formed and used in aerating bread and other baked products.

(2) Introduction from outside, either by adding to the slurry in the mixer a preformed stable foam such as is used in fire-fighting, or by incorporating air by whipping (with the aid of an air-entraining agent), in the manner in which egg-white may be whipped to a light cream or foam.

In the gasification method, a finely powdered metal (usually aluminium) is added to the slurry and this reacts with the lime which has been used as the cementing agent or which has been formed in the matrix by the setting of the cement.

The gas formation may be illustrated in the following equation which has been simplified for clarity. Other aluminates may also be formed.

$$2\,Al + 3\,Ca(OH)_2 + 6\,H_2O \rightarrow 3\,CaO \cdot Al_2O_3 \cdot 6\,H_2O + 3\,H_2$$

Aluminium powder   Hydrated lime   Tricalcium aluminate hydrate   Hydrogen

Powdered zinc may be used instead of aluminium, in which case calcium zincate and hydrogen are formed. In either case the hydrogen produced in the cells is quickly replaced by air, so that no fire hazard whatever exists when these blocks are used in building.

Alternatively, if hydrogen peroxide and bleaching powder are used instead of metal powder, the following reaction takes place, in which oxygen is evolved instead of hydrogen.

$$\underset{\substack{\text{Bleaching}\\\text{powder}}}{CaCl(OCl)} + \underset{\substack{\text{Hydrogen}\\\text{peroxide}}}{H_2O_2} \rightarrow \underset{\substack{\text{Calcium}\\\text{chloride}}}{CaCl_2} + \underset{\text{Oxygen}}{O_2} + \underset{\text{Water}}{H_2O}$$

This process was formerly used commercially but is believed to be no longer in use.

Of the various methods of generating gas, the one of chief practical importance today in the manufacture of precast units and blocks is the aluminium powder process. The foam methods of aeration are used only to a limited extent in the making of autoclaved precast products but they are eminently suitable for making *in situ* aerated concrete, and are much used for this purpose.

High-pressure steam-curing is practically unavoidable in making aerated concrete of first quality when cement is used as the binder, and absolutely essential when lime is used. With Portland cement, the initial development of strength in the product depends primarily on the normal setting of the cement, and autoclaving is used to improve the characteristics of the aerated concrete. With lime as the binder, the development of useful strength depends entirely upon reaction between the lime and the siliceous component, and such reaction takes place only under autoclaving conditions, as in the manufacture of sand–lime bricks. In other words, autoclaving is necessary to make a product at all. After autoclaving, the aerated sand–lime product is essentially similar to that in which cement was used; the bonding matrix in both cases is substantially mono-calcium silicate hydrate. That this must be so will be clear by reference to the explanation on mono-calcium silicate formation in Chapter 2. (Although it has been stated or implied repeatedly that cement *or* lime may be used, some manufacturers do, in fact, use a mixture of both.)

In addition to the cement (or lime), siliceous material and aluminium powder, other ingredients may be added for a variety of reasons. For example, a wetting agent is used to assist the wetting of the powdered ingredients, sugar in one form or another is sometimes added to induce solubility of the lime, saponin or other like material to stabilise the cells, and soluble alkali, such as caustic soda, to initiate the reaction between the metal powder and the lime liberated from the cement.

Although simple in principle, the commercial production of autoclaved precast units is quite elaborate in practice. The sand or other siliceous

FIG. 17.2   Casting hall of aerated concrete factory.

material is ground in ball-mills to the required degree of fineness which is, as a rule, comparable with the fineness of ordinary Portland cement. (In the UK many of the aerated concrete factories use pulverised-fuel ash, which requires no grinding.) Where grinding is necessary, it may be by dry mill, but wet-grinding is more often used. When the latter mode of comminution is adopted, the fine sand produced is held as a slurry or suspension and adjusted with water to a predetermined density, and maintained thus by agitation. If dry-grinding is employed, the fine siliceous material is held as a dry powder in silos, usually by this stage having been blended with the cement or lime.

In the wet process, the measured quantity of slurry representing a known quantity of sand or other siliceous material is transferred to the mixer, the cement added by weigh-batching, and the other chemicals added at this stage. The mixing is batchwise, normally one batch to each mould. The mix is transported by an agitated rail tank to the particular mould to be charged, although in some cases the mould may be brought to the mixer.

In the dry process, the procedure is similar, except that a dry-blended mixture of sand and lime (or cement) is added to the mixer together with the water and other ingredients.

The same moulds can be used whether the product is to be in the form of building blocks or reinforced units. Indeed, the reinforced slabs and the blocks are frequently made together in the same mould, the blocks occupying the part of the mould beyond that required for the reinforced units. When reinforced units are to be made, the prefabricated reinforcement mats are placed in the mould, prior to casting, and are located very accurately, so that when the original casting is subsequently cut into slabs, the reinforcement will be exactly where it is required in each individual slab. The batch of slurry is then run into the mould, which is only partly filled, but after about 5–20 min the mixture becomes sufficiently aerated (by virtue of gas formation) to fill the mould. The rate of rise depends on the composition; the extent to which the moulds are filled with the slurry depends on the density of product which is to be made, and so on the amount of expansion which is expected. Figure 17.2 shows the casting hall of an aerated concrete factory.

After a period of about 5–6 hrs the casting will have set sufficiently to withstand cutting. At this point the mould is transferred to the cutting machine and after trimming off the material standing proud of the mould edges (which is recovered as rework,) the mould sides are removed to expose the casting for cutting. Figure 17.3 shows blocks being formed in the vertical cutting machine.

When the parallel cuts have been made, usually in two directions at right angles, by tensioned wires, so as to produce the required blocks or slabs, the mould sides are replaced, and the whole transported to the autoclaves. The retention of the product within the moulds enables the material to be stacked in layers for steam-curing. In some processes, however, the 'green' units are removed from the moulds and placed in frames which are stacked prior to autoclaving, thereby relieving the moulds for further casting.

The autoclaves are frequently about 2·4 m (8 ft) in diameter and more than 24 m (80 ft) in length, and hold 12 moulds in four bogie-loads. A battery of autoclaves is shown in Fig. 4.6.

The aerated concrete within the moulds remains in the autoclaves for 10–18 hrs at 11–15 atmospheres pressure, corresponding to a temperature of 180–210 °C. At the end of the cycle period the moulds are withdrawn, the sides removed, and the product, after being checked for quality, packed for transport to the site or transferred to the stock-pile.

Outside the main stream of the process, a number of essential operations

Fig. 17.3   Blocks being cut on the vertical cutting machine.

take place; for example, reinforcement rods have to be cut, welded into suitable mats, and dipped into the coating mixture which will subsequently protect them from corrosion (Fig. 17.4). Moulds have to be cleaned, re-oiled, and returned to the casting-hall for refilling. An outline of the process is shown diagrammatically in Fig. 17.5.

Reinforced roof, floor and wall slabs have edge grooves for jointing. In some factories such grooves are formed by a travelling depression-tool or else by edge-milling at the wirecutting stage when the material is still somewhat plastic; in other factories the grooves are cut in the hardened slabs after curing, by passing them through high-speed milling machines.

In the modern aerated concrete factory all the handling is done by electric overhead cranes, the hinged mould sides are dropped by electric relay switches, cutting is done by self-locating fully-automatic machinery. Only a few men are required to operate a large factory.

The description given is a composite one inasmuch as it does not describe any particular factory or proprietary product. It does, however, give the broad pattern of procedure within which the various brands of autoclaved aerated concrete are produced. Manufacturers of such products differ in the relative importance which they attach to particular details of manufacture, such as the optimum times, temperatures, pressures, etc. But on one thing they do not differ, that is the rigid control which they exercise over whatever

FIG. 17.4

routine they have adopted. This is reflected in the remarkable consistency of the product compared with conventional concrete.

Factories to produce autoclaved precast products in aerated concrete on an economic scale of output are costly to lay down, the capital investment being of the order of 2–3 million pounds, according to size and location. On the other hand, they produce material of consistently high quality and their efficiency is high, particularly with respect to manpower. In contrast, *in situ* aerated concrete, in which such properties as strength and drying shrinkage are of secondary importance because of the purposes for which it is used, can very conveniently be made by one of the foaming methods for which relatively inexpensive, portable equipment is sufficient. Such a method is the preformed foam process. In this, cement and sand are made into a slurry in a standard concrete mixer and into this is introduced a stable foam produced in a special foam-generator by means of a proprietary foaming

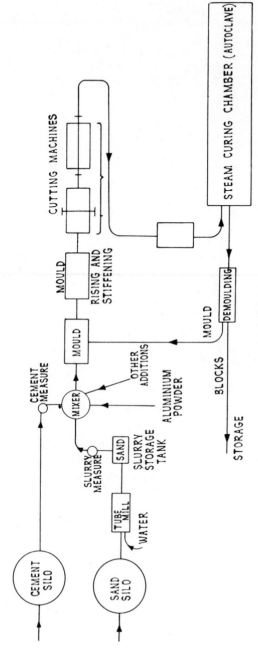

Fig. 17.5   Flow sheet of the manufacture of aerated concrete.

FIG. 17.6 Generator for *in situ* aerated concrete.

agent. Mixing is continued after the introduction of the foam in order to ensure good distribution of the air-cells throughout the mixture. The equipment for making foamed concrete by this method is shown in Fig. 17.6.

A variation of this process is one in which an air-entraining emulsion is added to the mortar in the mixer and air is enveloped during the mixing, thus producing an aerated mortar which sets as aerated concrete. By the preformed foam method aerated concrete of a wide range of densities can be produced, and with the air-entrained method products can be made with dry density as low as $300 \, \text{kg/m}^3$ (19 pcf). At such low density the aerated concrete is strictly an insulating material.

PROPERTIES

Density

Low density is probably the most characteristic feature of aerated concrete, although it has other properties which are possibly of even greater interest to engineers and builders.

The figures quoted for density in the commercial literature usually refer to oven-dry specimens or in some cases to material which has reached equilibrium with normal air conditions, a difference which for most purposes is not very important. Figures seldom refer to the material as delivered to the site, which because of its moisture content may be 15–25 per cent heavier than the oven-dry material.

The density of steam-cured aerated concrete is within the range 400–1000 kg/m^3 (25–62 pcf). Although the lowest density is approved for loadbearing purposes in some countries, the most common density for loadbearing products and reinforced flexural members is 500 kg/m^3 (31 pcf), or more. The moisture content of the concrete when removed from the autoclaves may be 20–35 per cent by weight of the dry density. This moisture dries out gradually and an equilibrium in buildings is reached at 3–5 per cent.

The specific gravity of the solid mineral material is about 2·5.

The low density of aerated concrete leads not only to a substantial reduction in the dead weight of the buildings in which it is used, but also in the loads which have to be transported and handled. That the weight reduction is indeed very substantial may be appreciated when it is recalled that in Sweden for many years, and more recently in Britain and elsewhere, autoclaved structural reinforced aerated concrete has been used at densities of 480–800 kg/m^3 (30–50 pcf), that is one-fifth to one-third of that of conventional concrete (see Fig. 1.1), and although greater sections may sometimes be necessary with aerated concrete in order to obtain the required rigidity or other structural characteristics, the saving in weight is always very considerable.

Compressive strength

The compressive strength which can be expected from aerated concrete having a dry density within the range 500–880 kg/m^3 (31–55 pcf) is shown in

TABLE 17.1
DRY DENSITY AND COMPRESSIVE STRENGTH

Dry density		Approximate compressive strength (tested dry)	
(kg/m^3)	(pcf)	(MPa)	(psi)
500	31·25	2·8	405
600	37·50	3·2	465
750	46·75	3·9	565
800	50·00	4·2	610
830	51·75	4·5	650
880	55·00	6·0	870

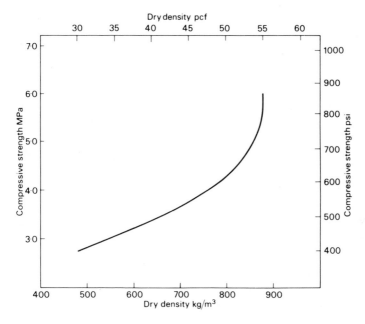

FIG. 17.7   Relationship between density and compressive strength.

Fig. 17.7 and Table 17.1. It can be seen from this relationship that aerated concrete of 500 kg/m³ (31 pcf) can be expected to show a compressive strength of 2·8 MPa (400 psi), which is accepted for lightweight building blocks in British Standard BS 2028. There may, however, be considerable departure from the values shown in this figure in cases where the composition is substantially different from that implied in the description of manufacture given above.

In reference to Fig. 17.7 it should be noted that the compressive strength depends on the conditions at which the tests are made, e.g. the size of the test specimens, their moisture content, their planeness or capping material. It is therefore important that test methods are standardised in order to obtain comparable results.

Modulus of elasticity

The modulus of elasticity or E-value of concrete is a measure of the deformation which the material will suffer under short-term loading, and is thus a significant factor in design. A low E-value means a relatively large deformation for a given stress. The modulus of elasticity of aerated concrete is low when compared with conventional concrete.

The E-value of aerated concrete can be compared with that of lightweight aggregate and dense concrete by employing the following formula given by Schäffler:[1]

$$E = 6000(\gamma_t^3 W)^{1/2}$$

where E is the modulus of elasticity; γ_t is the density in the dry condition, and W is the compressive strength.

Although values obtained with this formula may differ somewhat from test results for certain makes of aerated concrete, it can be used by the designer to estimate elastic deformation of unreinforced material. The E-value is slightly influenced by the moisture content in that a higher moisture content will give a lower E-value. The formula above assumes air-dry material at 3–5 per cent moisture by volume.

Creep

In addition to the elastic deformation thus described above, aerated concrete like other cement products, undergoes plastic deformation or 'creep' under sustained loads. As a general rule it can be assumed that the plastic deformation of a flexural unit containing both top and bottom reinforcement will amount to the same value as the elastic deformation.

Drying shrinkage

All cement products are subject to small changes in volume, accompanying changes in moisture conditions. Though small in actual dimensions, such changes are of great importance to the functional behaviour of the concrete or mortar. The tensile strength of concrete is relatively low and the tensile stress which is set up in restrained units can cause shrinkage cracking.

Lightweight aerated concrete produced by ordinary air-curing has very high drying shrinkage. However, when the same product is cured in high-pressure steam, fundamental changes take place in the mineral constitution which reduce the shrinkage to one-quarter or even one-fifth of what it would have been with air-curing. Midgley[2] has shown that in autoclaved aerated concrete, the main cementing agent is well-crystallised tobermorite, a mono-calcium silicate hydrate, giving in an X-ray diffraction pattern a well-defined reflection at about 11·4 Å. On the other hand, air-cured aerated concrete even from the same manufacturing batches indicate poorly crystallised tobermorite or tobermorite-gel, the X-ray diffraction showing it to be in a highly disorganised state. This work demonstrates for aerated concrete a belief which has been held for many years in respect to other concretes, that a gel-form of set cement is associated with high shrinkage and that this gel-form is changed to a micro-crystalline form by the conditions of high-pressure steam-curing. It might therefore be considered that an effectively autoclaved aerated concrete is a basically different material from the corresponding air-cured product even when made at the same time from the same ingredients. Figure 5.1 shows the drying shrinkage of both air-cured and autoclaved aerated concrete measured as a function of relative humidity.[3] The drying shrinkage is usually determined from the water-saturated condition to equilibrium at some nationally accepted level, e.g. 43 per cent r.h. and 20 °C or 17 per cent r.h. and 50 °C. Attempts are being made to have a standard level of relative humidity accepted internationally.

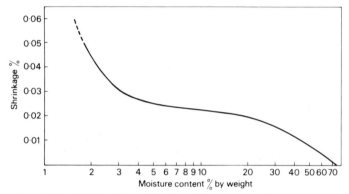

FIG. 17.8   Relationship of drying shrinkage to moisture content.

All cement products are subject to attack by the carbon dioxide of the atmosphere, but this is of small importance in heavy, well-consolidated concrete, which is practically impervious. In aerated concrete, however, there is a ready access for gas diffusion and in such products the silicate can become partially carbonated with the liberation of silica-gel. It has been found that under certain conditions of moisture content the effect of carbonation is to double the amount of shrinkage.[3,4] In other words, a large irreversible shrinkage is due not to moisture changes but to atmospheric carbonation. It seems, however, that the aerated concrete will usually have gained a large measure of stability in this respect before being delivered to the user.

The relationship between drying shrinkage and moisture content is shown in Fig 17.8.

Thermal conductivity

One of the principal features of aerated concrete is its relatively very low thermal conductivity, this being roughly proportional to the density of the material, as shown in Fig. 17.9. The insulating character of building materials is expressed either as k-value, or U-value, as defined in Chapter 6. Table 17.2 shows the typical k-values for four densities of aerated concrete, compared with that for heavy concrete.

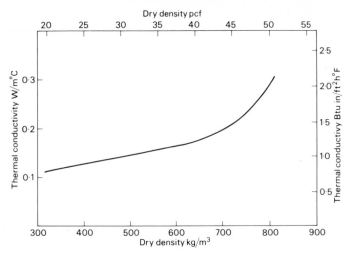

FIG. 17.9 Relationship between density and thermal conductivity.

Moisture substantially increases the thermal conductivity of materials. The interpretation of conductivity values with regard to moisture content is discussed in Chapter 6. Many workers have reported on the moisture content of aerated concrete in equilibrium with normal air humidity and the mean value of these reports is about 5 per cent by weight for external walls and 3 per cent for protected walls.

Conductivity values quoted for aerated concrete have often been derived from oven-dried specimens so that it is important when assessing the k-values of materials to know the moisture content at which the tests were made. Ideally, the tests should be done at the moisture content which is likely to prevail in the situations in which the material will be used. Failing this, a procedure in which the test specimens are brought to equilibrium

TABLE 17.2
THERMAL CONDUCTIVITY OF AERATED CONCRETE

Material	Dry density		Thermal conductivity, k-value	
	(kg/m^3)	(pcf)	$(W/m\ °C)$	$(Btu\ in/ft^2\ h\ °F)$
Aerated concrete	320	20	0·11	0·78
Aerated concrete	480	30	0·14	0·95
Aerated concrete	640	40	0·17	1·20
Aerated concrete	800	50	0·23	1·60
Dense concrete (1:2:4)			1·30–1·73	9–12

with the air at some standard condition of humidity such as 40 per cent or 65 per cent r.h. is the one giving the most realistic results. This is discussed at length in Chapter 6.

Fire resistance

Because of its particularly low thermal conductivity, aerated concrete is well suited for the protection of steel structures from exposure from fire. Apart from this use in fire protection, structural aerated concretes themselves behave well in fire. Official fire resistance tests made in accordance with British Standard BS 476 on British brands of aerated concrete are given in Chapter 6. Results of fire tests on walls, roofs, and floors, carried out in Sweden, Germany, Denmark, and America, have been published by Engwall.[5]

Other properties

Coefficient of linear expansion. 8×10^{-6}–10×10^{-6} per °C
Specific heat capacity (dry material). $1 \cdot 0$–$1 \cdot 1$ kJ/kg °C
Vapour resistivity. 40–55 MN s/gm
Sound absorption characteristics. Table 17.3 shows values of the sound absorption coefficient of unplastered aerated concrete at various frequencies.

TABLE 17.3

SOUND ABSORPTION BY UNPLASTERED, AERATED CONCRETE

Mean frequency (Hz)	Sound absorption coefficient
125	0·00–0·15
250	0·10–0·15
500	0·15–0·25
1 000	0·15–0·20
2 000	0·15–0·20
4 000	0·20–0·25

GASCON

As mentioned briefly in Chapter 1, a form of aerated concrete can be made incorporating lightweight aggregate. Such a product was developed in the UK under the name Gascon.[6] The process broadly follows that employed for conventional aerated concrete but necessarily differs in a number of respects. For example, because of the presence of coarse aggregate, certain measures are necessary to prevent segregation and irregular distribution of

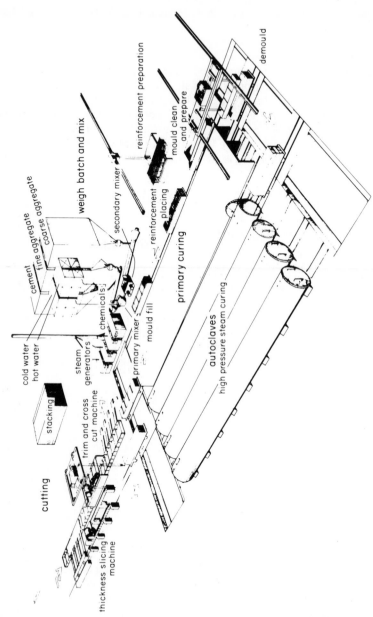

FIG. 17.10 The Gascon production plant layout.

gas bubbles. Moreover, it is not practicable to cut up the cast cake in the green state as is done with aerated concrete, since the aggregate would drag through the soft matrix by the action of the cutting wires: cutting is done after autoclaving, by means of multiple diamond saws.

Gaston contains the same raw materials as aerated concrete but has in addition a proportion of coarse aggregate, which can be any of those normally used for lightweight concrete, for example, expanded clay or pumice, this having a maximum size of 20 mm. Gascon has a high strength-to-density ratio, and is used for large structural units. Fig. 17.10 shows the plant layout for the production of Gascon.

REFERENCES

1. Shäffler, H. (1960). RILEM Symposium on Steam-Cured Lightweight Concrete, Gothenburg.
2. Midgley, H. G. Building Research Establishment, Private Communication.
3. Kinniburgh, W. (1960). 'Comparison of Drying Shrinkage of Autoclaved and Air-Cured Concrete at Different Humidities', RILEM Symposium on Steam-Cured Lightweight Concrete, Gothenburg.
4. Verbeck, G. V. (1958). 'Carbonation of Hydrated Portland Cement', ASTM Special Technical Publication No. 205, ASTM, Chicago.
5. Engwall, A. (1960). 'Fire Resistance of Siporex Products', RILEM Symposium on Steam-Cured Lightweight Concrete, Gothenburg.
6. Urmston, C. W. B. and Bessey, G. E. (1973). 'Structural Lightweight Concrete using Lightweight Aggregate with Aeration', *Chemistry and Industry*, **1973,** 7 April.

CHAPTER EIGHTEEN

Protection of Aerated Concrete against Deterioration

SUMMARY

The risk of corrosion of the embedded reinforcement in aerated concrete members is mainly governed by the climatic conditions to which they are exposed. The embedded reinforcement must be protected by coating the bars with a protective layer or by some other suitable and effective method. Where aerated concrete units are exposed to specially injurious, sulphur-laden and humid atmospheric conditions, the concrete itself must also be protected.

When used internally under cover or externally with proper protection, the durability of reinforced aerated concrete elements is not in doubt.

CORROSION OF STEEL EMBEDDED IN AERATED CONCRETE

Consider first the possible corrosion of steel in ordinary, dense concrete. Bare steel bars embedded in well-compacted gravel concrete or lightweight aggregate concrete are given a measure of effective protection against corrosion by being surrounded by a dense, alkaline mass of concrete. Moreover, the presence of moisture and oxygen, essential for the formation of rust, is also inhibited by the resistance of the concrete cover against penetration of liquids and gases. Where the concrete surrounding the embedded bars loses its alkaline character, perhaps as a result of carbonation or through leaching-out of the free lime, corrosion of the embedded bars is likely to follow. The severity of the ensuing corrosion will depend on the type of concrete used and the conditions to which it is exposed.

Turning to aerated concrete, it is obvious that because of its overall macro-porosity and cell-like structure and also because of the possible porosity of the cell walls the cellular material is inherently less resistant to the penetration of moisture and vapour than dense, compacted concrete. Aerated concrete is also capable of taking up carbon dioxide from the air much more readily than dense concrete, thus accelerating the process of carbonation in the concrete although this is not perhaps critical, since carbonation of the free lime in the outside layers is likely to have been very nearly complete by the time the units are taken out of the autoclave. Moreover, the autoclave treatment itself may have some effect on the durability of aerated concrete, for example through rusting of the bars embedded in it,[1] if they have not been given some form of protection beforehand.

It has been shown in practical conditions as well as *a priori* that unprotected steel embedded in aerated concrete is exceptionally vulnerable. The durability of aerated concrete components containing bare steel reinforcement may thus suffer as a result of corrosion of the steel if exposed to the weather or to humid, polluted ambient conditions. Such conditions can occur not only in the open but also inside buildings for example with certain industrial processes such as in steelworks or cotton mills or in unventilated roof-spaces subject to condensation. In the absence of adequate protective measures which can be taken, such exposure is likely to lead to corrosion of the embedded reinforcement and to some deterioration of the concrete itself if sulphur is present in the atmosphere.

Nevertheless, for some 20 years floor and roof members and reinforced wall slabs were made and used in Sweden on a considerable scale, with bare mild steel reinforcement without any special protection against corrosion.[2] It appears that at least in the case of domestic buildings, serious damage due to rusting of the reinforcement has not been reported to the manufacturers. Since, however, unprotected bare bars are no longer used as reinforcement in structural aerated concrete members, it seems reasonable to infer that the incidence or risk of failures due to corrosion in aerated concrete units reinforced with bare steel bars and exposed to severe conditions was in fact greater than was considered to be tolerable in the industry.

In many parts of the UK, of the USA and Western Europe, acid atmospheric conditions aggravated by sulphurous pollution in the neighbourhood of centres of industry, have been generally present since the industrial revolution. Precautions which appeared to be reasonable in Sweden, with its generally unpolluted alkaline atmosphere, are therefore even more necessary in countries with an acid atmosphere.

This is confirmed by tests made by the Building Research Station with specimens made of aerated concrete having a dry density of about $800 \, \text{kg/m}^3$ (50 pcf) in a severely polluted industrial atmosphere, without any external covering to protect them. The bare mild steel bars embedded in these specimens have sufficiently corroded after two to three months' exposure to cause cracking of the concrete (Fig. 18.1). In fact, the bars appear to have corroded more rapidly when encased in aerated concrete than when they were exposed to the air on open racks. This may have been caused by the relative ease with which electrochemical processes can start with embedded steel bars by the longer time needed for the evaporation of moisture inside the concrete than in the open, and also by the penetration and accumulation of sulphurous substances.

No damage has occurred, however, where the bars embedded in aerated concrete were coated with a suitable protective material.

FIG. 18.1   Aerated concrete specimens.

METHODS OF PREVENTING CORROSION

In the case of well-compacted dense concrete the thickness of the concrete cover is of great importance in preventing or retarding the corrosion of the embedded steel reinforcement. In the case of aerated concrete, however, it seems that the thickness of the cover is only of subordinate importance for the protection of the embedded steel. The resistance of aerated concrete against moisture penetration is less than that of dense concrete, so that however thick the surrounding layer of aerated concrete may be, eventually moisture will penetrate to the reinforcement through the pore structure of the material, if the circumstances are favourable to such penetration, e.g. where the surface of the concrete is exposed to the weather without being protected by a suitable rendering. As shown by tests made by the Building Research Station however, in exposed aerated concrete specimens an adequate cover tends to delay corrosion somewhat (Fig. 18.2). The main purpose of providing a substantial cover in aerated concrete members, however, is not the protection of the reinforcement against corrosion, but rather to ensure safety against fire and the safe transmission of the internal forces without dangerous and unsightly cracking or spalling along the embedded reinforcement.[3]

In general, aerated concrete structures are protected against the danger of corrosion of embedded bars by providing an impermeable coating on the surface of the reinforcement. In the factories the reinforcing bars or welded mats are dipped—usually twice—in a bath of protective liquid and the adhering material is allowed to dry on the steel before the reinforcement is placed in the mould, preparatory to the commencement of casting (Fig. 17.4). The material used for this impermeable coating must be capable of fulfilling stringent requirements so that it may resist successfully the severe conditions to which it has to be exposed during casting and in the

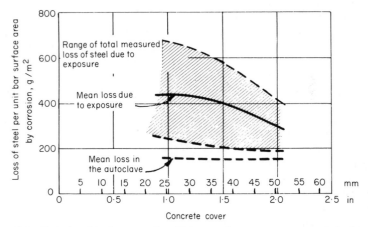

FIG. 18.2 Relationship between the thickness of concrete cover and the loss of steel by corrosion for bare bars embedded in aerated concrete, after three months' exposure to the weather.

autoclave. After drying, therefore, the newly formed protective coating must be resistant to moist heat, it must be chemically inert towards the steel and adhere to it, and must have sufficient mechanical strength to resist impact and abrasion in handling; it must not be brittle or deteriorate with age.

Standard tests for the assessment of different types of anti-corrosive surface treatment for the reinforcement are laid down in some detail by the German code of practice for reinforced aerated concrete,[4] which establishes both sustained and short duration corrosion tests.

The sustained tests are carried out on three or more slabs, each slab being 400 mm (16 in.) square in plan and not less than 100 mm (4 in.) thick, with a 10 mm (0·4 in.) cover for the embedded steel bars. Following the autoclaving process, the specimens are subjected to a loading test and after being relieved of the load, each specimen is kept under constant atmospheric conditions at 20 °C and 95 per cent r.h. for not less than one year. The method of treatment is deemed to have passed the test if, at the end of this period, pitting or scaling of the surface has not taken place, and only slight rust can be observed on not more than one-twentieth of the surface area of the bars tested.

The short duration corrosion tests are made on nine specimens taken from current production units. Six of these specimens, which must be 400 mm (16 in.) square in plan, are stored under constant atmospheric conditions, at a temperature of 10–20 °C and at 40–70 per cent r.h. The remaining three specimens are first subjected to a loading test and are then alternately immersed in brine and dried in the air. This process is repeated 10 times in the course of 30 days, and the specimens are then broken up. Three of the six specimens stored under constant conditions are also broken up at the same time. To pass this short duration test, the condition of the bars that were immersed in brine must not be worse than the condition of those stored under constant conditions and not more than one-twentieth of the total surface area of the bars may be affected by rusting; heavy flaking or pitting must not occur.

An alternative short duration test is carried out on the remaining three specimens previously kept under constant conditions; these are placed in an insulated curing chamber under conditions of alternating temperature and humidity. To pass this test, the specimen bars must fulfil the same conditions as those laid down for the previous test.

These standard tests are based on Schäffler's work,[5] which indicates that a protective covering that is capable of satisfying the requirements laid down in the German code can provide adequate long-term protection to embedded bars in practice.

Research on the suitability of different materials[6] for use as a protective coating indicates that most paints, ordinary bitumen emulsions, and mineral oil are not suitable for this purpose because these materials are not capable of resisting the conditions present in an autoclave.

Galvanising is expensive and is also subject to deterioration in the autoclave because zinc combines chemically with the alkaline substances present in the cement. The resulting oxidation products may not be effective as protection against corrosion of the steel underneath the zinc coating. Other types of metallic coating are either similarly vulnerable or too expensive to be used in this way.[2]

Phosphate treatments create a surface layer which may give temporary protection to the steel but some types of phosphate coating may be removed by the alkaline substances present. Although they form a hard-wearing surface, phosphate films tend to have low resistance against damage through impact and this must cause difficulties in transportation and handling. Tests made by the Building Research Station indicate that paint and phosphate coatings are damaged by autoclave treatment. Rusting becomes more severe during subsequent exposure but is generally much less severe than for bare bars (Fig. 18.3), and does not cause spalling of the concrete.

Natural rubber is capable of resisting steam-curing, in the autoclave but by itself it is not suitable as a bar coating because of its elastic properties and it deteriorates in a marine environment. Chlorinated rubber paint is also unsuitable because it tends to attack the concrete. Among artificial materials, *epoxy resins* can provide a satisfactory and corrosion-proof

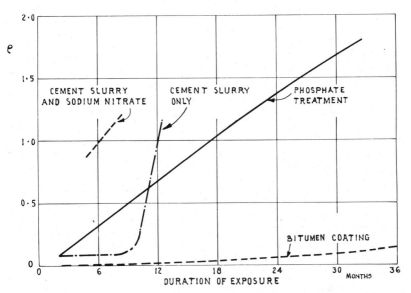

FIG. 18.3 Relationship between the duration of exposure and the corrosion of steel embedded in aerated concrete for different surface treatments of the bars ($\rho = S/S_c$, where S denotes the weight of steel per unit bar surface area lost by a treated bar through corrosion and S_c the weight of steel per unit bar surface area lost by a bare bar to cause cracking of the surrounding concrete).

surface cover, especially if sprayed with sand, to improve their adherence to the surrounding aerated concrete. Epoxy resins and the methods used to apply these materials to the surface of steel bars are still rather too expensive, however, and are outside the economic range for use as a surface coating in aerated concrete. *Ceramic surface treatments*, on the other hand, are both expensive and inadequate.

Special bituminous layers have been widely used as a protective coating by various manufacturers. They provide adequate protection over a long period if the coating remains continuous over the whole bar surface after removal from the liquid. The bitumen used should have a relatively high softening temperature and is generally used with a solvent. It is usually desirable to include a mineral filler as well, so that a fairly thick surface layer is formed; the mineral filler also tends to prevent the porous concrete from absorbing the bitumen during steam-curing in the autoclave. The resulting surface layer is hard and may have a rough texture, but it must be carefully handled for it can be easily damaged. The use of some bituminous coatings can lead to almost complete loss of bond strength, but some types of oxidised bitumen harden in the air; droplets are formed along the bars and create corrugations which may considerably improve the anchorage strength between steel and concrete. This may help with the bond strength but is not desirable for protection against corrosion because the uneven coating may be more susceptible to damage than a smooth one. Tests made by the Building Research Station indicate that after several years' exposure in severe conditions of industrial pollution, the corrosion of bitumen-coated bars embedded in aerated concrete is negligible (Fig. 18.3), but still later results show that substantial corrosion can occur with bitumen-coated bars.

For improved performance at least one manufacturer of reinforced concrete units uses bars covered by one coat of a rubber latex mix followed by a second coat of bitumen on top.

For sustained protection, a simple cement slurry coating seems to be of little value by itself. Tests by the Building Research Station showed that corrosion is delayed but not prevented by such a coating (Fig. 18.3). Adequate protection against corrosion was achieved, however, if the slurry contained some *rubber latex* and a colloidal material such as casein, in addition. Not only is this type of proprietary material not damaged by autoclaving, but in fact it needs steam-curing in the autoclave in order to attain its full hardness and compressive strength, which is said to be very high, about 100 MPa (14 000 psi).[2] It is also highly resistant to mechanical damage and moisture penetration, and adheres well to the steel. The effective bond strength developed by bars coated with it, tends to be higher than with any other type of coating,[3] although in design this is relied on.

Certain types of material, such as burnt shale, are inherently corrosive when in contact with steel; in some countries such materials are widely used for the manufacture of aerated concrete units. Where such a material is used, an oil wash is sometimes added to the usual cement–rubber–casein or bitumen coating, to protect the steel. Fortunately, none of the materials at present used, or likely to be used, in the UK or in the USA, is inherently corrosive, all these materials being in fact chemically inert.

Coating of the reinforcement with an impermeable protective stratum has been discussed in some detail because this method has been generally adopted in current manufacturing practice. It would be wrong, however, to assume that this was the only method that can be used for this purpose. Some manufacturers, for example, have adopted *composite methods of construction* for flexural members with the reinforcing steel embedded in ordinary dense concrete which is combined with aerated concrete placed in the compression zone. Thus the steel reinforcement is rendered immune against corrosion without any special treatment other than the effect of the surrounding relatively impermeable dense precast concrete, which may be prestressed. Such beams are being made by the Ytong Company in Sweden and also by factories in the USSR[7] using a corrugated type of cross-section. Owing to the complex manufacturing techniques used for aerated concrete flexural members, large-scale production tends to become difficult, however, where precast dense concrete is used in conjunction with aerated concrete in this way.

In place of steel bars or welded mats, the use of *prestressed 'pencils'* has also been proposed. These are pre-tensioned, high-tensile wires or strand, encased in concrete of high strength and density, resistant to moisture penetration, and capable of combining readily with the aerated concrete through surface bond or anchorage, to transmit the forces developed under loading. This is an expensive method of construction and would be, moreover, somewhat difficult to apply for reinforcing the compression zone—an important feature of reinforced aerated concrete in view of its low *E*-value—or as transport reinforcement.

Some experiments have been carried out by the Building Research Station and by other research establishments to change the *environmental conditions* in the concrete by adding chemicals, such as sodium nitrite or potassium nitrite[8] to the mix. These tests do not, however, appear to have led to more than partial success.

An altogether different approach would be to replace ferrous reinforcement with glass fibre. The use of glass fibres of very small diameter and combined into a rod by bedding in a plastic protective material has been tried with both reinforced and prestressed concrete.[9] It appears, however, that the great strength of the material cannot as yet be adequately utilised, nor is it certain that the glass fibres can be reliably protected against the alkaline substances present in the concrete. For these reasons, as well as because of its costliness, this method of construction, which raises as many difficult problems as it appears to solve, is not likely to be of any great practical importance in the immediate future for any kind of concrete construction.

Total immersion of completed aerated concrete units in a protective sealing substance has been proposed, following experience with some types of precast prestressed construction. Such a method of protection, however, can only be successful if complete continuity of the cover can be permanently ensured, without serious risk of a breakdown due to mechanical damage during transport or erection or due to cracking. It also uses a large quantity of coating material and is likely to be expensive for this reason as well as because of the large capital installation required.

PREVENTION OF THE DETERIORATION OF AERATED CONCRETE

It can be shown that the protection afforded to embedded steel against corrosion is as important a criterion for the durability of aerated concrete as for any other reinforced construction, but the protection of the aerated concrete itself against deterioration is obviously of equal importance. Aerated concrete is generally accepted as being adequately durable when used under cover, in normal atmospheric conditions, but unless special precautions are taken, its durability becomes doubtful if exposed to a very humid sulphur-laden atmosphere. Such conditions are not uncommon in industrial areas and with certain industries they may prevail even indoors but such special precautions are not difficult to introduce.

Exposure to humid, sulphurous conditions may result in leaching-out of residual free lime and soluble salts which are sometimes present, the presence of soluble salts being dependent on the materials used. Moreover, the material tends to expand, differential expansion being followed by excessive deformations in bending by cracking, and weakness in shear. Evidence for this was obtained from a study made by the Building Research Station on some reinforced aerated concrete slabs exposed to the weather under load or without imposed loading, without any cover, in a highly contaminated industrial atmosphere in East London (Fig. 18.4). Efflorescence and the growth of algae on the surface was followed by cracking along the longitudinal reinforcement, probably as a result of inadequate cover. The observations made here refer to unusually severe conditions of exposure: not only was the atmosphere very heavily polluted, but the slabs had none of the normal protection they would have had in an actual building, such as an external rendering.

During the time that the slabs were exposed on this site, their deflections increased considerably under load. Although these permanent deflections were much greater than those observed in the laboratory under controlled conditions of temperature and atmospheric humidity, they did not appear to be greater than those of some dense concrete members tested by other research workers under similar conditions.[10] Sustained loading by itself appears to have little influence on the ultimate loadbearing capacity of aerated concrete slabs, but exposure to the weather in a polluted atmosphere may lead to a loss of about 40 per cent in loadbearing capacity, compared with that of slabs under cover. Moreover, the manner in which failure occurred also changed. Whereas in the case of new slabs tested in the laboratory, primary failure was due to yielding of the steel in tension or to crushing of the concrete in compression, those units which had been exposed to the weather tended to fail in shear. Thus it appears that the tensile strength and crack resistance of aerated concrete is affected to a greater extent than its compressive strength. The lower ultimate

Fig. 18.4   Aerated concrete slabs exposed to the weather at Beckton, London.

loadbearing capacity of flexural members after exposure was probably caused in part by the development of surface cracks along the reinforcing bars.

It is of interest to compare the effects of severe exposure of slabs without cover in a polluted atmosphere with the results obtained from a field survey made in Sweden[11] of the moisture content and structural performance of a large number of aerated concrete structural roofs in practice. These results showed that the great majority of the roofs examined behaved satisfactorily and that the mean moisture content of all but three was less than 3 per cent by weight.

Nevertheless, severe exposure can and has been found to occur. The effect of exposure of a roof structure to the polluted atmosphere in an iron and steel works over the cupola was studied with exemplary care by Bergström.[12] Owing to the air pollution and elevated temperature reaching 200 °C at the underside of the roof slabs, increased deformations and loss of strength were observed in some slabs after three years of service. The slabs so affected were replaced and various protective treatments were applied to the soffit, with satisfactory results. On the other hand, experience in a steel works at Sheffield in England showed that after 10 years' service, an aerated concrete roof was still in excellent condition, although no special treatment had been applied to the underside of the roof system. The top surface was covered with felt.

Bergström suggested that better resistance to sulphurous fumes and elevated temperature can be obtained by using aerated concrete having a density of about 700 kg/m³ (45 pcf) or more. As with many other building materials, experience both in the laboratory and in practice indicates that it is desirable for building components made of aerated concrete to be protected against the weather both before and during erection. If used in a very moist atmosphere, at least one surface of all roof members should be ventilated to prevent the accumulation of moisture in the material. For use in a polluted internal atmosphere it is recommended nowadays that the soffit of roofs should be sealed by a protective coat, usually of bituminous paint, which may be subsequently covered by aluminium paint, as a decorative finish. Before sealing the top surface with a waterproof membrane, and the soffit with paint that is resistant to vapour penetration, the roof slabs should be dried out. It is also desirable that the outside surface of external walls should be given a suitable rendering, to maintain the thermal insulating properties of the material. The rendering should be both resistant to moisture and vapour penetration from the outside, and should allow water trapped in the wall to evaporate to the outside through the rendering.

In summary, if used in a dry, covered position, the durability of aerated concrete is clearly satisfactory, and it can be used without any special protective measures. Where the units are exposed to the weather or used in a polluted, very moist atmosphere, then they must be suitably protected.

REFERENCES

1. Short, A. (1960). 'Tests on the Bond Strength and Durability of Reinforced Aerated Concrete'. RILEM Symposium on Steam-Cured Lightweight Concrete, Gothenburg.
2. Ulfstedt, L. T. (1960). 'Korrosion und Korrosionsschutz der Bewehrung in Siporex Platten' ('Corrosion of the Reinforcement and its Prevention in Siporex Slabs'), RILEM Symposium on Steam-Cured Lightweight Concrete, Gothenburg.
3. Schäffler, H. (1960). 'Gas und Schaumbeton; Verankerung der Bewehrung' ('Aerated Concrete; Bond Strength'), Bull. No. 136, Deutscher Ausschuss für Stahlbeton.
4. German Standard DIN 4223, 'Bewehrte Dach- und Deckenplatten aus dampfgehärtetem Gas- und Schaumbeton' ('Reinforced Roof and Floor Slabs of Steam-Cured Aerated Concrete'), Deutscher Ausschuss für Stahlbeton.
5. Schäffler, H. (1960). 'Rostschutz der Bewehrung' ('Protection of the

Reinforcement against Corrosion'), RILEM Symposium on Steam-Cured Lightweight Concrete, Gothenburg.

6. Short, A. and Kinniburgh, W. (1961). 'The Structural Use of Aerated Concrete', *The Struct. Engineer*, **39**(1).
7. Makarichev, V. (1960). 'The Cellular Concrete Structure and Methods of its Designing in the USSR', RILEM Symposium on Steam-Cured Lightweight Concrete, Gothenburg.
8. Alexeev, S. M. and Rozenfeld (1958). 'On the Corrosion of the Reinforcement in Autoclaved Aerated Concrete Containing Ash', *Beton i Zhelezobeton* (10).
9. Biryukovich, K. K. and Biryukovich, Yu. L. (1957). 'Concrete Reinforced with Glass Fibres', *Stroitel. Prom.*, **35**(6).
10. Båve, G. (1960). 'Plastic Flow of Reinforced Siporex Slabs', RILEM Symposium on Steam-Cured Lightweight Concrete, Gothenburg.
11. Hallgren, A. (1952). 'Roofs of Reinforced Siporex Slabs for Industrial Buildings', *Cement och Betong*, **26**(1).
12. Bergström, S. G. (1957). 'Skador på Siporextak över järnverk' ('Damage in a Siporex Roof in an Ironworks'), Svenska Forskningsinstitutet för Cement och Betong, Utredningar No. 2., Stockholm.

CHAPTER NINETEEN

Bond Strength in Reinforced Aerated Concrete

SUMMARY

The bond strength of aerated concrete is affected by a number of factors, viz. the bar diameter and position, the embedment length, autoclaving, the compressive strength of the concrete, and its saturation, the effect of different types of coating on the steel bars and of different types of anchorage arrangement.

GENERAL

Effective composite action between the concrete and the embedded steel reinforcement is the essential basis on which the stiffness and strength of any type of reinforced concrete structure primarily depends and the degree of composite action also affects the cracking characteristics of flexural members. For the examination of the bond strength of aerated concrete and of the effect of various factors on this, research workers are mainly dependent on the results of pull-out tests. It is known, that such tests do not provide accurate quantitative evidence on the bond strength of different types of concrete and steel reinforcement, because the stress conditions in pull-out specimens differ so much from the stress conditions in actual flexural members. The methods used for making these specimens are also different from the methods usually employed for producing reinforced aerated concrete members in practice. Pull-out specimens, however, are undoubtedly much cheaper and easier to make than beams and they do provide a basis for a qualitative and comparative assessment of the effect of different factors on bond strength. Tests on flexural members have also been made, however, to provide information on loadbearing capacity, deflections, and cracking, as well as on bond properties; these were compared with the results obtained from pull-out tests.

It is now generally accepted that the use of bare bars—i.e. bars not covered with any protective coating against corrosion—is not usually desirable with aerated concrete members. Moreover, for the design of mass-produced reinforced concrete members, sole reliance is not placed on the inherent bond resistance of individual bars; normally the transmission of internal forces is provided for by anchorage bar. On the face of it, therefore, the performance in bond of bare, round reinforcing bars would not seem to be relevant to reinforced aerated concrete. It is, nevertheless, an important structural property of the material, and much of the evidence on the bond strength of aerated concrete has been obtained with pull-out specimens containing bare bars. In any case, it has been found that the effects of some important factors, such as those of the diameter of the embedded bar or of its embedment length, do not appear to differ greatly in character for bars having different surface characteristics and can be assessed with reasonable precision from the behaviour of bare reinforcing bars.

The following factors appear to have an influence on the bond strength and slip of bare bars embedded in aerated concrete:

the diameter and position of the embedded bars;
the position of the bars during casting;
the length of embedment of the bars;
the effect of autoclaving or other method of curing on the surface texture
    of the embedded bars;
the moisture content and
the crushing strength of the concrete;
the surface characteristics of the bars and
the type of anchorage arrangement used.

The effect of these factors and of others related to them will be discussed here.

EFFECT OF THE DIAMETER AND POSITION OF THE EMBEDDED BARS AND THEIR EMBEDMENT LENGTH

For bar diameters of 6–25 mm (0·25–1 in.) the pull-out strength of aerated concrete generally tends to decrease somewhat with increasing bar diameter (Fig. 19.1),[1] as it does, indeed, for ordinary dense aggregate concrete, but the effect of the bar diameter is not very great.[2] This holds independently of the nature of the bar surface—i.e. whether the bars are coated or bare—and also of the position of the bars during casting, although the variation with bar diameter seems more pronounced for bars held in a vertical position during casting than for horizontal bars. For horizontal bars taken from the upper part of the 'cakes' there is, on the contrary, a tendency for a decrease in bond strength for bar diameters diminishing below 12 mm ($\frac{1}{2}$ in.) compared with thicker bars. This is probably caused by the higher steel stresses in thinner bars, aggravated by indifferent bond formation near cavitations formed particularly in the upper part of the moulds, mentioned below. It does not generally occur with specimens taken from the lower parts of the mould. The test results show considerable scatter, but for bars held horizontally in the upper part of the moulds they indicate that there is

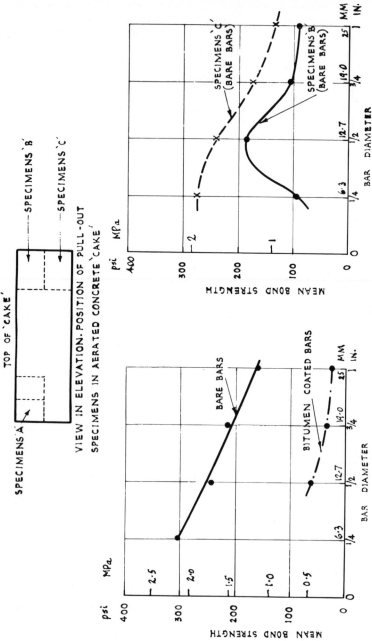

FIG. 19.1   Mean bond strength of bright mild steel bars embedded in autoclaved aerated concrete pull-out specimens. (*Left*) bar held vertically during casting (specimens 'A'); (*right*) bar held horizontally during casting (specimens 'B' and 'C').

an optimum bar diameter for maximum bond strength for a particular material and conditions.

Pull-out tests with embedment lengths of 200–400 mm (8–16 in.) indicate that as with ordinary concrete, the bond strength is not likely to vary greatly with the embedment length.[2]

The bond strength appears to be greatly affected by the position of the pull-out specimens in the cake during casting. The average bond strength of specimens taken from the lower part of the cake was generally higher than that of specimens taken from the upper part of the same cake. The difference is nowhere less than about 25 per cent of the bond strength taken from the bottom; it becomes greater for thinner bars.

FIG. 19.2   Cavity formed above a horizontal reinforcing bar embedded in aerated concrete ('shadow effect').

It is probable that a reduction in strength in the upper part of the mould—including the reduction in bond strength—is caused by a feature of the method of manufacture which is common to most types of autoclaved aerated concrete. During manufacture the reinforcing bars placed in the lower part of the mould are initially covered with the liquid mix when casting begins. These bars remain enveloped in the concrete mix throughout the successive stages of manufacture while the bars placed above are gradually covered by the rising material. These bars tend to hinder the expansion of the 'dough' which, therefore, leaves cavities of varying shape and size immediately above the bars. This is often referred to as the 'shadow effect' (Fig. 19.2). Although manufacturers have not found it possible to eliminate the shadow effect entirely, they have succeeded in reducing it by controlling the rate at which the dough is made to rise and by other proprietary means.

Owing to the shadow effect, a substantial part of the surface area of the embedded bars is not in contact with the surrounding concrete, particularly in the case of bars placed in the upper part of the mould. The bond strength of these bars is therefore reduced. It seems also that for thinner bars the proportion of the circumferential area of the bars affected by the shadow effect is greater than with thicker ones; the corresponding reduction in bond strength is therefore also greater. Manufacturers of aerated concrete slabs using cement–rubber–casein coated reinforcement claim, however, on the basis of tests, that the bond strength of the top bars is as great, or greater, than that of the others, owing to the mechanical bond effected by the coating.

Because of its very nature, the shadow effect is much more pronounced for horizontal bars than for vertical ones. In the upper parts of the cakes the difference between the bond strength of vertical and horizontal bars is about 25 per cent of the mean bond strength.

EFFECTS OF AUTOCLAVING, OF THE COMPRESSIVE STRENGTH AND OF THE SATURATION OF THE CONCRETE WITH WATER

Reinforced aerated concrete members are usually cured by subjecting them for about 16 hours to a steam pressure of about 1 MPa (150 psi) gauge in an autoclave, corresponding to a temperature of about 185 °C. Under this pressure and temperature, moisture penetrates through the material and embedded bare steel bars are invariably covered throughout their surface

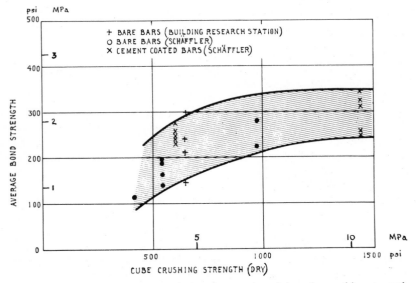

FIG. 19.3   Relationship between the bond strength and the cube crushing strength of autoclaved aerated concrete.

area with a layer of rust.[3] Owing to this rust, the surface of the bars becomes somewhat rougher and the bond is improved.

In the case of bars treated with an anti-corrosive surface coating, autoclaving rarely leads to extensive rusting of the embedded steel. Some types of coating, such as paint, and phosphate-treated or galvanised surfaces, tend to deteriorate, however, in the autoclave and as a result their bond properties also become worse. Bars coated with a plain cement slurry usually develop slight rusting during steam curing, but this tends to improve its bond, as in the case of bare bars.[2]

With increasing crushing strength, the bond strength also increases (Fig. 19.3), but the relationship is not linear in character. Variations in surface characteristics have a greater effect on bond strength than changes in the crushing strength.[4]

Saturation of aerated concrete with moisture reduces its average oven-dry compressive strength by as much as 25 per cent. The reduction of the bond strength due to saturation is of the same order.

EFFECT OF BITUMINOUS COATING

None of the impervious coatings used for the protection of the reinforcement against corrosion is without some influence on the bond strength of the embedded bars. For bituminous coating materials the bond strength of the embedded bars depends largely on the initial surface characteristics of the bars, on the thickness of the coating and on the properties of the bituminous material used for the coating. For crushing strengths of about 3·5–5·5 MPa (500–750 psi) the bond strength varies from nil to about 1·1 MPa (150 psi) but the scatter of the bond strength for any one type of bituminous coating is generally considerable. For design, the bond strength of bitumen-coated bars is not taken into account.

When dipping slightly rusted ordinary round bars in some viscous types of bituminous solution, droplets tend to form along the bars, thus creating a corrugated surface when dry. After hardening, such a surface has considerable resistance against slip under short duration loading. In general, however, the slip of bars coated with bitumen is greater than that of bare bars under the same load.

For aerated concrete having a compression strength of about 2·8 MPa (400 psi) the bond strength of bitumen-coated bars subjected to sustained loading is about 20 per cent lower than the bond strength of identical bars under short duration loading.[2] The slip of bitumen-coated bars under sustained loading is also about 25 per cent greater than under short duration loading, for the same load.

For smooth bars covered with bitumen, the average bond strength is low and tends to diminish with increasing bar diameter (Fig. 19.1).

EFFECT OF CEMENT–CASEIN–RUBBER COATING

The bond resistance of bars embedded in autoclaved aerated concrete after coating with a propietary material consisting mainly of cement casein, and rubber, has been found to be satisfactory, mainly as a result of anchorage forces developed along the length of the coated bars, aided by corrugations on the bar surface formed by hardened droplets of cement slurry. Even without this additional anchorage effect, however, the bond of cement-slurry-coated bars is normally greater than that of bitumen-coated bars.

The pull-out strength of cement–casein–rubber-coated bars embedded in aerated concrete having a crushing strength of about 2·8 MPa (400 psi) ranges from about 1·1–1·6 MPa (150–220 psi).[3] Failure occurs generally as a result of a breakdown of the concrete along the length of the bar in shear, on a circumference which is about the same as the maximum diameter of the corrugated bar surface. Adhesion between the steel bars and the coating, and also between the coating and the aerated concrete adjacent to it, is not affected. With smaller diameter bars the failing stress is somewhat lower, but the position of the bars in the mould has little effect on the bond strength of bars coated with cement–casein–rubber slurry. The influence of the 'shadow effect' on the pull-out strength of such bars is not appreciable because, compared with the anchorage forces acting through the hard material of the coating, bond adherence becomes of subordinate importance. In addition, later the cementitious coating material enters into chemical combination with the surrounding concrete.

EFFECT OF USING DEFORMED BARS

In flexural members made with aerated concrete, adhesion and friction between steel and concrete surfaces usually cannot be relied on to balance the external forces and bending moments. After slip has taken place, these forces are resisted by mechanical anchorage due to the corrugated surface texture formed by some types of anti-corrosive coating, by welded crossbars or by other types of anchorage element. Where ribbed deformed bars[5] are used covered with a cement coating, the space between the ribs is filled with the protective material. Failure then takes place due to shear in the concrete along the bar, as in the case of ordinary round bars, around a circumference determined by the size of the ribs on the bar and by the hardened droplets of cement slurry. With cement-coated bars, therefore, there is little advantage in using deformed bars.

For deformed bars coated with a thin bituminous coating, on the other hand, the bond adherence is low and crushing of the concrete can occur at the interfaces between the steel ribs and the aerated concrete at relatively low loads, owing to excessive bearing stresses. Again, the use of deformed bars is of doubtful benefit.

EFFECT OF END ANCHORAGES

Bond and continuous anchorage along the length of the embedded bars can be effectively assisted by anchorage elements placed at the ends of bars or intermediately at intervals along them. By providing end hooks, the pull-out strength can be increased by as much as 30 per cent compared with straight bars. Failure usually occurs through splitting of the concrete.[2,4] Anchorage plates or angle-section shear connectors welded to the ends of embedded bars are effective in concentrating anchorage forces near the supports of beams and slabs and in preventing anchorage failure. The failing load is generally increased considerably;[4] at failure the bearing stress on the compressed surface of the anchorage plates in pull-out specimens is usually about double the normal crushing strength of the concrete. In beams and slabs, intermediate and end anchorages perform a similar function to shear connectors in composite construction and, again, bearing stresses at failure are usually considerably in excess of the crushing strength of the concrete, mainly due to triaxial stress conditions at the interfaces.

Compared with welded crossbars, the pull-out strength obtained with end anchorage plates is about 20–40 per cent greater[2] and the slip of the bars for the same load is also reduced appreciably.

EFFECT OF WELDED CROSSBARS

In floor and roof slabs, the reinforcement is usually in the form of welded mats containing transverse bars at the ends and intermediately along the length of the longitudinal bars; the crossbars thus provide mechanical anchorage. With greater bond strength, the effect of such anchorage elements generally becomes smaller. This is not unexpected since, for increasing bond strength transmission of the internal forces becomes less dependent on the anchorage elements welded to the main bars. Thus it is found that in general transverse bars are more effective in the case of reinforcement coated with bitumen than with cement–casein–rubber-coated bars, because of the better bond properties of the latter.

The anchorage strength generally increases with the length and diameter of the crossbars, and is reduced somewhat if the spacing between adjacent crossbars is increased.[2] The anchorage force can be enhanced by increasing the number of crossbars; the increase in strength is not proportional to the number of crossbars but somewhat less. Slip is also reduced with an increasing number of crossbars, although for flexural members this seems to have little effect on the deflections and on crack formation. With not less than three crossbars, even the type of anti-corrosive surface treatment used has little effect on slip, but with fewer than three bars at each end, this effect can be considerable.

Inclined and vertical stirrups are more effective in resisting anchorage forces, as well as shear, than plain transverse bars.[5] Vertical stirrups can withstand a pressure that is 50 per cent higher than the pressure resisted by simple transverse bars; stirrups inclined at about 45 degrees, however, can resist bearing pressures about three times as high as transverse bars. Some types of reinforced member contain a few vertical bars welded to the mats at the corners near the supports, but because of production difficulties vertical or inclined stirrups are not at present used, except in the case of lintels.

To evaluate the effect of crossbars on the loadbearing capacity and on the resistance to bond or anchorage failure in flexural members, the concept of a 'specific transverse bar area' has been introduced by Granholm.[6] This concept is similar to that of the 'specific area' adopted for the definition of the anchorage properties of deformed bars.[7] The specific transverse bar area has been expressed as a proportion of the net diameter of the bar and is defined as the total frontal bearing area of the transverse bars, divided by their spacing and equally distributed between the longitudinal bars. With anchorage systems having a large specific transverse bar area, resistance against slip and against failure at the anchorages is greater.

Transverse anchorage bars are most effective if they are placed in positions where the bond stresses are highest. For simply supported members, therefore, they should be placed near the supports. However, their equally important function is to locate the main bars of the reinforcing mat securely during casting and some bars must therefore be placed in the mats along the span.

To ensure that the internal forces are securely transmitted between the steel reinforcement and the concrete, it is essential that the concrete cover should be adequate, not only over the main bars but also over the transverse bars. Where the concrete cover is too thin, cracks tend to occur either immediately after manufacture or later during the life of the unit, leading to failure in severe cases of loading or of exposure to the weather, as in the case of ordinary reinforced concrete. Where the concrete cover is less than 12 mm ($\frac{1}{2}$ in.), bond and anchorage strengths are reduced considerably.

REFERENCES

1. Short, A. (1960). 'Tests on the Bond Strength and Durability of Reinforced Aerated Concrete', RILEM Symposium on Steam-Cured Lightweight Concrete, Gothenburg.
2. Schäffler, H. (1960). 'Gas- und Schaumbeton; Verankerung der Bewehrung'

('Aerated Concrete; Bond Strength'), Bull. No. 136, Deutscher Ausschuss für Stahlbeton.
3. Short, A. and Kinniburgh, W. (1961). 'The Structural Use of Aerated Concrete', *The Struct. Engineer*, **39**(1).
4. Schäffler, H. (1960). 'Versuche über die Verankerung der Bewehrung in Gasbeton' ('Tests on the Bond Resistance of the Reinforcement in Aerated Concrete'), RILEM Symposium on Steam-Cured Lightweight Concrete, Gothenburg.
5. Cederwall, K. (1960). 'Tests on Reinforced Lightweight Concrete Beams', RILEM Symposium on Steam-Cured Lightweight Concrete, Gothenburg.
6. Granholm, H. (1960). 'Reinforced Lightweight Concrete', RILEM Symposium on Steam-Cured Lightweight Concrete, Gothenburg.
7. Granholm, H. (1959). 'Kam 40, Kam 60 and Kam 90', Publ. No. 213, Gothenburg, Chalmers Technical University.

CHAPTER TWENTY

Design Considerations for Reinforced Aerated Concrete

SUMMARY

General information on aerated concrete methods of construction developed in different countries is followed by a consideration of the flexural rigidity and the actual load factor against failure, obtained with flexural members. Relatively high resistance against cracking is obtained with some types of aerated concrete. Codes of Practice and design practice in different countries are discussed. Design methods are given for bond and anchorage, shear strength and stiffness in aerated concrete flexural members.

METHODS OF CONSTRUCTION

It has been shown previously that autoclaved aerated concrete, although adequately strong for its purpose is a relatively friable, weak material compared with gravel or lightweight aggregate concrete and its deformations are greater under load. When using it for reinforced units these characteristics must be taken into account in design. It might be difficult to ensure, for example, that bending moments are fully transmitted at the corners or joints of building frames made with such a material. It is evident however that this difficulty is also present with ordinary dense concrete. Aerated concrete is not now used for such structures but there is some evidence that it can be so used successfully.

The size of the precast units which can be used in practice is necessarily restricted by the practical limit to the size of the autoclaves that can be constructed and operated economically and effectively.

The use of aerated concrete for structural members of major importance such as building frames, columns or principal girders, would seem hardly appropriate or economical. Nor is aerated concrete likely to be used for bridge-decks, because exposed conditions favour the deterioration of the concrete. Nevertheless, where the reduction of weight is especially important, as in the case of movable or opening bridges, aerated concrete slabs might make a suitable light decking or might be used as filling provided that they are suitably protected against the weather.

The most important and useful application of aerated concrete in the form of reinforced units has been for enclosing elements, such as wall, floor and roof slabs in buildings. Loadbearing wall units are at present generally used only for buildings of limited height, up to four storeys, although taller buildings have been erected in Sweden with loadbearing aerated concrete walls. For tall buildings, aerated concrete wall slabs are not normally used as loadbearing elements but as partitions and—in the case of external walls—as non-loadbearing panels and cladding units, suitably protected by rendering.

In recent times, the development of large wall units has succeeded in the USSR.[1] These units are of single-storey height and dwelling-unit width and to produce them very large autoclaves, about 3·7 m in diameter, are needed. A very considerable initial investment is therefore required for a factory making such large units and this can only be justified if the number of identical units to be produced is very large. This condition appears to have been satisfied in the USSR where, because of the vast and urgent housing needs of a country devastated by war and because of the centrally controlled character of the economy, it has been possible to place very large orders for uniform components for multi-storey dwelling blocks. Nevertheless, these very large units are not now thought to be economical and it is generally agreed that adaptable slab units are to be preferred. An alternative and cheaper method of producing large single wall panels is to fasten standard small units together with adhesive layers and steel straps. Such slabs have been adopted in Western Europe, particularly in Germany.

In much of Western Europe, with the important exception of the areas much affected by war damage, the demand for new dwellings has been limited to the gradual replacement of wastage and the provision of housing for the natural increase of the population or for migrating population groups. The urgency, therefore, has been less pressing; there has been greater scope for developments on a small scale and there is a demand for greater variability. This has led to a greater variety of plans and materials. Moreover, the building industry in most Western European countries tends to be fragmented into many relatively small production units without central direction and control. In these areas of Western and Northern Europe and in some under-developed areas elsewhere, widely adaptable, standard components have been successfully developed, components that can be readily and speedily used for simple types of construction, with an infinite variety of plans and applications, without unnecessary restraint on the architect or builder.

Considerable experience has been gained with the production and use of such units in many countries. The materials and methods of construction have not been found to vary much and the structural properties and the performance of the manufactured products also tend to be similar. The reason for this uniformity may well be this: although the financial control and the policies of the aerated concrete industry appear to be in the hands of independent companies, technical direction and scientific research facilities are closely associated with the three major Swedish pioneering companies. Although the USSR, the USA and some countries in Eastern Europe and in Asia are not closely connected with these organisations, nevertheless their industries are themselves greatly dependent on the work that has been done since 1925 in Scandinavia.

During the last decades, however, the focus of large-scale production and development has shifted to the USSR and Germany for reinforced units and to the UK for blocks. Conditions of use vary considerably, not only because of a different emphasis on purpose, finish, workmanship and durability, and because of different building traditions, training, and design, in different countries, but also because of varying climatic conditions, frequently accentuated by man-made industrial environments. In applying the lessons learned in one country to the needs of another, the effects of these factors can rarely be accurately assessed without considerable experimental work and practical experience.

FLEXURAL RIGIDITY AND THE LOAD FACTOR AGAINST FAILURE AND AGAINST CRACKING

The behaviour under load of reinforced aerated concrete members is largely governed by the relatively low compressive strength and the low modulus of deformation (E-value) of the material. It is essential, therefore, in design, that the cross-sections of such members should be so dimensioned that the stresses in the compression zone are low; their low inherent stiffness must also be considered.

It appears that the manufacturers' design methods are generally based on the elastic theory, but some prefer load factor methods of design; according to Schäffler[2] both methods can form the basis of adequate design methods. In Sweden, neither of these approaches is considered to be entirely satisfactory by the Code of Practice Committee. In practice, acceptance tests are used to check the performance of flexural members,[3] by manufacturers and users alike; as with other types of precast product, the tests are apparently combined with empirical design rules, the main criteria being a minimum desirable load factor and permissible deflection requirements.

Numerous tests have been made on aerated concrete flexural members of different types, but, as with gravel concrete, there are still a number of problems on which reliable information is not available. For example, knowledge is still insufficient on the maximum strain of which aerated concrete is capable under different loading conditions, without crushing in compression or cracking in tension; on the stress–strain relationship at high stress and on the effect of sustained loading on this relationship; on the relationship between the cylinder strength, the cube strength and the actual bending strength of aerated concrete. Granholm estimated[4] that the ratio of the cylinder strength to the actual compressive strength of aerated concrete in a flexural member is about 1·25; the ratio of cube strength to actual strength in a beam or slab is[3] taken as 1·5. The relationship between cylinder strength and cube strength is therefore taken as 0·8–0·9. A parabolic stress–strain relationship appears to be reasonably well established.

As in the case of composite steel-concrete structures there is some doubt about the justification of assuming, as for conventional engineering design, that normal elastic conditions will prevail at working loads or that Bernoulli's classic theorem—that plane cross-sections remain plane under loading—necessarily applies. According to Granholm some slip of the reinforcing bars can take place, even where the bond and anchorage properties are seemingly satisfactory.[4, 5]

Tests at the Building Research Station[6] indicate that for short-duration loading the load factor against failure tends to vary according to the manner in which the beam or slab fails. The load factor against failure—i.e. the ratio of the failing load to the total design load—is not less than 2·5 where failure occurs as a result of yielding of the tension reinforcement. This is always followed by a series of secondary collapse phenomena in quick succession, viz. crushing of the concrete, buckling of the compression reinforcement and shear, or even anchorage failure at the crossbars. The load factor may be somewhat lower where primary failure is due to crushing of the concrete or where the beam collapses because of failure of the concrete in shearing. Flexural members should be so designed therefore that under excessive load they fail as a result of yielding of the tension steel, not as a result of shearing, or crushing of the concrete.

Where the units are exposed to severely polluted weather conditions without any protection while being under sustained loading, the load factor against failure may be reduced compared with short-duration loading to failure. This occurs as a result of chemical attack, possibly aggravated by high temperatures, followed by the development of longitudinal cracking along the reinforcing bars which weakens the member considerably. Failure then tends to occur as a result of shear. In practice, however, such conditions of use are exceptional.

Cracking of the concrete does not usually occur until considerable deformation has already taken place, corresponding to a steel strain varying between 800 and 1200×10^{-6}, at about 65–80 per cent of the failing load in bending. From load–deflection curves it appears however that in some cases, in fact, cracking occurred earlier, at about three-quarters of the load at which it became visible to the naked eye. Indeed, the open-pored texture of the surface of the material tends to conceal cracking.

With some types of aerated concrete the cracking load is higher in relation to the failing load than for similar members made of dense or lightweight aggregate concrete. High resistance against cracking seems to occur where the grain size of the aggregate is of the same order of magnitude as the grain size of the binder. The reasons for this are firstly, that the tensile strength of aerated concrete, in common with some other types of weak concrete can be high in comparison with their compressive strength. Secondly, cracking appears to be inhibited, at least in the initial stages, by a measure of thermal prestressing[6] which occurs as a result of the cooling down of each member immediately after extraction from the autoclave, from about 195 °C (365 °F) to normal air temperature, a temperature drop of 160 to 190 °C (288 to 340 °F). Since the coefficient of thermal expansion and contraction of the aerated concrete is about 8×10^{-6}—slightly less than that of ordinary concrete— whereas that of steel is about 12×10^{-6}, on the face of it the two materials would contract at a different rate, but for the effect of composite action between them. The resulting restraint, even if some allowances are made for creep and slip between the steel bars and the concrete, might introduce some prestress. However, moisture movement, creep of the concrete and variable restraint on the bars before autoclaving has taken place, make this initial prestress difficult to assess. Thirdly, higher cracking loads may result from the high extensibility of certain types of aerated concrete. This is supported by the observation that high crack resistance occurs in aerated concrete made with aggregates of fine grain size.

Whether designed with empirical methods or with conventional design methods. the maximum deflection of aerated concrete members is intended to vary between $1/250$ and $1/400$ of the span at working loads. Owing to the low modulus of deformation of aerated concrete the effect of the amount of reinforcement provided on stiffness is relatively greater than in ordinary reinforced concrete members. Both experimental work and theoretical considerations show[4] that the flexural stiffness does not increase in proportion with the increase of the tensile reinforcement or, indeed, of the modulus of deformation of the concrete. Imperfect transmission of the internal forces between the steel and the concrete may cause this, although there is evidence from manufacturers that this does not apply to cement-rubber-coated bars. The use of compressive steel is generally much more effective in increasing the stiffness of flexural members than in increasing the tension steel. Compressive reinforcement, which at first was only provided in aerated concrete elements as a safeguard against damage during transport or erection, should have at least the same concrete cover as the bars embedded in the tension zone. The compression bars themselves are normally much thinner than the tension bars, this led in some tests to failure as a result of buckling of the compression reinforcement. Fortunately, this type of failure is usually a secondary collapse phenomenon which occurs after yielding of the tension reinforcement, but it reduces the inherent reserve of safety of the structure, since collapse after the ultimate load is reached is immediate.

CODES OF PRACTICE AND THE GENERAL DESIGN OF FLEXURAL MEMBERS

It is worth recalling that methods of construction for which a broad and sufficient background of experience exists, generally come to be covered by standard specifications and Codes of Practice or by Agrément Certificates. These vary in different countries but represent a consensus of views. Though not always mandatory, they are often adopted by local authorities and other control authorities in their bylaws and building regulations and thus become binding in law; in most cases they are, in any case, binding by contract.

There is no code of practice to regulate the use of reinforced aerated concrete in the USA as yet, but in several countries codes of practice already operate or are being prepared. In Germany, for example, a definitive code of practice was issued in 1958;[8] in Finland a draft code has been issued, while in Sweden and Norway one was prepared by the appropriate code of practice committees acting in close collaboration.[3] Standard specifications are being prepared in the USA and some have been issued in the USSR. In the UK, provisions governing the use of autoclaved aerated concrete have been published in the codes of practice for concrete.[9,10] A draft international code is being published by CEB.[11]

The manufacture of autoclaved aerated concrete having a density of about 500 kg/m^3 (50 pcf) or less is limited in the UK at present to four companies working in co-operation for research and development with associated undertakings in Scandinavia where the manufacture and use of this material was first developed. In the absence of standard codes of practice it was natural therefore for their design practice to be guided in the main by the experience of their Scandinavian associates. Aerated concrete products and their application in construction must however, broadly comply in each country with its construction practices, specifications and codes, although these documents may not expressly include aerated concrete within their scope. For example, in the UK it was usual to take account of the general recommendations of CP 114:1957[10] for flexural members and reinforced wall slabs and of the recommendations of CP 111:1964[12] in the case of load-bearing masonry walls of aerated concrete before CP 116[9] and CP 110[10] made express provision. In the USA an interpretation of the standard is in progress for aerated concrete;[15] for flexural members the general recommendations of the ACI Building Code[14] are normally taken into account.

With regard to the general design of flexural members, these units are not usually a 'tailor-made' product; to warrant the substantial capital investment that is involved in erecting and equipping an aerated concrete factory, they must be mass-produced. The detailed design of the units is not, therefore, in the hands of individual consulting engineers but, at least in Western Europe, in the hands of the manufacturer. The consulting engineer merely sets out loading and user specifications and lays down conditions of acceptance.

Design calculations therefore were merely intended, first, to provide a starting point for the manufacturer's design procedure; the final form, dimensions, reinforcement, etc., emerge from the results of loading tests. Secondly, the design calculations should provide the theoretical foundation on which consultant, contractor, and local authority engineer can assess in the first instance the suitability of the manufacturer's design, in fact that function generally lapses. Although an agreed design method is considered desirable, until recently manufacturers have been somewhat reluctant to disclose details of the empirical design methods they use for their preliminary design.[4] There is no uniform and generally accepted convention which would govern the assessment of loadbearing capacity, stiffness and permissible stresses, such as exists, for example, in the case of ordinary reinforced concrete, although a start has in fact been made in some countries.

In Sweden, where experience with aerated concrete is greatest, both the elastic theory and the ultimate strength method have been rejected by the committee preparing the code of practice, because neither of these was found to comply with sufficient accuracy and consistency with the results of experiments, probably owing to variations in the protective coating used by the manufacturers. In Sweden, therefore, loading tests to destruction are preferred, with deflections also being recorded and this evidence is accepted by the supervising authority. A preliminary design is still used, however, apparently based on the elastic theory, using relatively high values for the effective modular ratio ($m = 150$–220) in the calculations.

This method has also been accepted in the UK. The use of high values for the modular ratio in the design of flexural members may result in rather shallow construction depths. In view of the known propensity of aerated concrete members to develop large deflections, care must be taken to provide adequately low span–depth ratios and sufficient compression reinforcement. With regard to acceptance tests, precedents for loading tests being admitted in the UK as proof of loadbearing capacity and stiffness for some types of structural component already exist, e.g. for loadbearing masonry walls in CP 111:1964[12] and for prestressed concrete members in CP 115:1958.[15]

In Germany, on the other hand,[8] a method of design based on the ultimate loadbearing capacity has been adopted similar to that in the British Code of Practice for reinforced concrete (CP 114:1957). For the purpose of the calculations this theory is based on the assumption that plane sections remain plane, i.e. that the composite action between steel and concrete is complete. Granholm[4] and Nilsson[7] have shown however that perfect compliance with this assumption can be expected even less than for normal reinforced concrete. This is presumably allowed for through the assumptions for the maximum strain for the steel and the concrete at failure.

The method of design is based on a theoretical load factor of 1·75 against yield failure of the tension reinforcement. The theoretical load factor against failure of the concrete in compression is taken at about 2·6, but this is based on the cube strength, which is known to be higher than the actual crushing strength of the concrete in bending.

The stress block in the compression zone is assumed to be in the form of a parabola, but the depth of the resultant compression obtained from experiments[2] is assumed to be $0·36 d_n$ as against $0·425 d_n$ in the British Code, d_n denoting the depth of the neutral axis.

The dimensions of the cross-section and the dimensions of the required reinforcement may be obtained with the aid of stress and deflection coefficients given in the German standard, DIN 4223. The Unified British Code for Concrete CP 110:197,[10] based on a limit state design approach, gives guidance for the structural use of autoclaved aerated concrete for the design, testing the erection of such units, as well as for the dimensional tolerances to be observed in production.

Where testing of prototype units is used to establish and control the strength of a unit, the design load should be derived from the characteristic load at the ultimate limit state established by the test, by dividing that load by a partial factor of safety of 1·5 and the partial factors of safety for loads given in the Code. If the deflections are deemed to be the governing factor then the total long-term deflection of a unit may be assumed to be twice the instantaneous elastic deflection under a test load. Special provisions must be applied, however, where units are exposed to high humidities or to an aggresssive environment. In the design calculations it is assumed that joints between adjacent ends of roof or floor slabs cannot resist bonding moments. In assessing the actual behaviour of such a system it should be taken into account, however, that bars embedded in the longitudinal joints between parallel slabs at the supports provide a measure of continuity.

BOND AND ANCHORAGE

The bond strength of aerated concrete tends to vary within wide limits, as shown previously, depending on the method adopted to protect the bars against corrosion, the strength of the concrete, the diameter of the bar and a number of other circumstances. In view of this uncertainty, anchorage attachments—usually welded crossbars—were found to be necessary even in favourable conditions to ensure sufficient interaction between the steel reinforcement and the concrete. Some manufacturers depend entirely on such welded crossbars for the transmission of the internal forces, others take account of the bond strength of the concrete in resisting internal forces.

Whether any account is taken of the bond strength of the concrete depends in practice on the type of corrosion protection used and on the purpose for which the members are used. With bitumen-coated bars the bond strength is generally neglected; where the reinforcement is covered with a cement–casein–rubber coating, manufacturers apparently rely on the inherent bond strength of the material if the bond stress does not exceed 0·25 M Pa (35 psi). If this stress is exceeded, then the residual internal force must be resisted by crossbars. In any case, however, at least two crossbars should be provided at each end of flexural members. The effective length of the crossbar, which is taken into account in the calculation of the force resisted by one weld, can be expressed by the following empirical formula:[16]

$$l_c = 29 \, d \, \frac{f_{YP}}{u}$$

where l_c is the effective length of crossbar which may be assumed to resist the anchorage force of one weld (mm); d is the diameter of the crossbar (mm); f_{YP} is the yield point stress of the steel (M Pa); and u is the cube strength of the concrete (M Pa).

The permissible pressure at the interface is generally assumed to be not more than two-thirds of the cube strength of the concrete. In fact, owing to triaxial stress conditions the safe stress at the interface might well be much higher.[16]

To determine the number of crossbars required, the strength of the weld between the latter and the main reinforcement must be taken into account. It has been recommended that the weld should be capable of resisting not less than one-half the load for which the main bars reach the yield point stress in the case of mild steel reinforcement and not less than 35 per cent of the load corresponding to the proof stress in the case of high-tensile steel bars.[8] In design, moreover, the permissible load resisted by each weld should not exceed one-third of its fracture load. According to the German code the maximum force resisted by each weld would not therefore be greater than that which corresponds to about one-sixth of the yield point stress of mild steel in the main longitudinal reinforcement. Detailed rules are given for the calculation of the number of crossbars needed.

According to the German code the crossbars placed within a distance equal to four times the thickness of the units from the ends of flexural members should be capable of transmitting at least one-half of the total force resisted by the longitudinal bars and the first crossbar should not be further than about 50 mm (2 in.) from the end. The distribution of the remaining bars should follow the shear force distribution, but at least one bar should be placed in the central section of the member.

In practice the requirement that the distance between adjacent crossbars should not exceed 0·5 m (1 ft 8 in.) has been found too restrictive. Two or three crossbars are usually provided at each end at not more than about 0·45 m (18 in.) centres and at least one bar is placed at the centre, to stabilise the reinforcing mat in the mould, as a manufacturing requirement. More are provided for very long beams.

RESISTANCE AGAINST SHEAR

The shear stresses in the concrete are generally calculated in accordance with conventional theory. For this purpose the permissible shear stress in the aerated concrete may be taken at about one-forty-fifth of the compressive strength, i.e. at about one-fifteenth of the permissible stress in bending. This stress is generally used in Germany[8] and Sweden and appears to be adequate. It also corresponds broadly to the practice laid down in the British Code of Practice for dense concrete CP 114:1965 where the permissible shear stress varies from one-tenth to about one-fifteenth; the corresponding stress in the ACI Building Code ACI 318–71 is one-fifteenth of the permissible bending stress in compression.

If the calculated shear stress in the aerated concrete exceeds this permissible stress in shear, then it has been the practice to increase the depth of the section rather than to include shear reinforcement. The provision of vertical or diagonal shear reinforcement is generally avoided in aerated concrete units because of manufacturing difficulties. Welded stirrups would be a considerable improvement,[4] however, where increased shear resistance is required.

For ordinary reinforced concrete the conventional methods of shear design are not always adequate, particularly for beams that do not contain shear reinforcement and in recent years there has been a tendency to insist on special shear reinforcement for all major beams, though not for slabs, since shear stresses are low in slabs.

In the case of aerated concrete, it seems doubtful whether the standard product of the industry—flexural units 0·45–0·60 m (18–24 in.) wide and up to 6 m (20 ft) long—can fairly be regarded as a slab or a beam for this purpose. Where several units are placed side by side and are interconnected along their edges lengthwise by grouting, and particularly where an additional mortar screed is placed on top of the slabs, a quasi-monolithic system is created. The risk of shearing failure in such a system would seem negligible and additional shear reinforcement in the individual units is unnecessary.

In some cases, however, aerated concrete members are used separately, without forming part of a slab system, for example as lintels or as trimmer beams, which may be subjected to severe loading conditions, particularly near the supports.

In general therefore such members should be designed with adequate shear reinforcement. In the case of trimmer beams or separate floor or roof members however the need for shear reinforcement is not always cogent. It seems that, where protection against the weather is adequate and exceptionally injurious industrial pollution of the atmosphere is not likely to occur, shear reinforcement may be safely omitted, provided that the shear stresses are not excessive. Where such unfavourable conditions are probable, however, special shear reinforcement should be added to resist all internal shear forces, particularly for lintels subjected to heavy loading.

DESIGN FOR FLEXURAL RIGIDITY

The initial elastic deflections of reinforced aerated concrete members due to selfweight and imposed loads can be controlled by suitable design, as in the case of ordinary dense reinforced concrete members. The permanent, time-dependent deformation of aerated concrete caused by the combined effects of shrinkage, creep, and thermal movements, in ordinary room temperature and normal humidity, however, is generally much lower than that of dense concrete. Its dimensional stability in use is derived from changes in the material introduced by the autoclaving process described previously, by which the essentially gel-like substance is transformed into a crystalline form of material, much more resistant to volumetric change.

Agreement has yet to be reached on the maximum deflection which might be deemed acceptable for flexural members of various kinds but in most countries the manufacturers comply with the deflection requirements of the relevant codes of practice for ordinary reinforced concrete construction. In general a deflection greater than 1/250 of the span would not appear to be tolerable under working load, while a deflection less than 1/400 of the span, on the other hand, would seem to be unnecessarily demanding for most ordinary uses.

For larger spans it is at times difficult to ensure sufficient stiffness, unless the slabs are specially designed, especially in roof slabs where a top screed which would give added stiffness is only rarely provided. To produce continuity over the supports of adjacent slabs, at least with respect to the imposed load, continuity bars are introduced near the supports (Fig. 20.1), thus reducing maximum deflections.

These continuity bars are placed in the grooves, between adjacent units, before grouting. Granholm suggested that an additional groove might be usefully provided at the top of roof slabs during manufacture, to allow the insertion and grouting-in of an additional continuity bar and thus further to reduce excessive deflections due to loading, moisture movement, and thermal deformations. Such continuity bars are not needed primarily, however, to reduce the maximum deflections that occur under normal conditions at mid-span, but rather to prevent the formation of an excessive

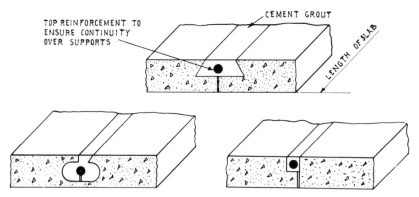

Fig. 20.1   Edge grooving along joints of reinforced aerated concrete floor and roof slabs.

slope at the ends of abutting slabs. Because of such a slope the waterproof roof covering membrane can be subjected to severe local stress which neither asphalt nor bituminous roofing felts can sustain indefinitely without cracking.

Empirical design methods are generally used to determine the deflections of flexural members. For example, the German code[8] limits the maximum deflection under working load to not more than 1/300 of the span and provides an empirical formula for design, intended to satisfy this condition.

To satisfy the corresponding requirements of the British Code of Practice for ordinary reinforced concrete (CP 114:1965), the *overall depth* of one-way slabs should not be less than one-thirtieth of the span. The effect of these regulations is similar, although the British rule is slightly more stringent for longer spans, particularly for roof slabs, while for shorter spans it allows shallower depths in the case of heavily loaded slabs.

To check the stiffness of manufactured units it is usual to make loading tests; the German code lays down a testing procedure for this purpose. The maximum deflection at mid-span obtained for the full load, including the selfweight and design imposed load acting at quarter-span points, must not exceed 1/300 part of the span; this corresponds to the limitation used for the design calculations. The load is imposed in two equal increments with an interval of 30 minutes. Deflection measurements are made immediately after loading and also after the load had been sustained for 30 minutes. Deflection measurements may also be required at the cracking load if the latter is found to be higher than the working load.

The span–depth ratio is not always a satisfactory criterion of stiffness. Where possible, deflections should be verified by calculations which in turn should be checked by loading tests.

Design is based on the assumption that the aerated concrete is air-dry, the loading tests being made in the laboratory on individual units. The loading test itself is of relatively short duration. These conditions impose certain limitations on the validity of the test results, for it is known that the loadbearing capacity of slabs exposed to humid conditions or to changes in atmospheric humidity is lower than that of slabs tested in the air-dry condition.

It is at times overlooked that in most practical cases there is a considerable additional margin of both stiffness and strength, compared with the individual slabs that are usually tested, for in practice aerated concrete units are seldom used singly in segregation. Normally several units are rigidly interconnected along their longitudinal edges and form a wide slab the behaviour of which is akin to that of the anisotropic plate. Both the stiffness and the loadbearing capacity of such a system are generally much higher than the sum of those of individual beams or of narrow slab, largely as a result of the lateral distribution of the bending moments; the shear stresses are also considerably lower. Reliable adhesion between adjacent slabs is ensured along their entire length by grouted grooves formed in the top corners of their cross-section (Fig. 20.1). These grooves, when filled with grout, are capable of resisting separation at the edges and prevent differential vertical movement of the slabs. Grooves of rectangular, swallow-tail, or even curved shapes, have been used and were found to behave satisfactorily. Swallow-tail shaped grooves are more likely to prevent differential vertical movement of the slabs, even after shrinkage had occurred in the grout. In general, however, shrinkage of the grout does not diminish the efficiency of the connection between adjacent slabs materially if the work of grouting is carefully carried out and the gauge is correct. The slabs must be laid with care, for aerated concrete is a friable material and is easily damaged during transport and erection.

In addition to the grouted grooves along the longitudinal edges, the cohesion of the units to form a slab can be further increased by a mortar screed which is sometimes placed on floors and more rarely on roofs. Owing to composite action between the aerated concrete members and the top screed, usually 25–50 mm (1–2 in.) thick, the loadbearing capacity of the system is enhanced considerably, its deflections are reduced and the sound insulation is improved. A mortar screed is not, however, necessarily placed for those purposes; it is in fact usually provided as a base for wood blocks or other forms of floor covering.

REFERENCES

1. Mironov, S. (1960). 'The Application of Large-size Cellular Concrete Units in the USSR', RILEM Symposium on Steam-Cured Lightweight Concrete, Gothenburg.

2. Schäffler, H. (1960). 'Über die Tragfähigkeit von bewehrten Platten aus dampfgehärtetem Gas- und Schaumbeton' ('Notes on the Loadbearing Capacity of Steam-Cured Reinforced Aerated Concrete Slabs'). RILEM Symposium on Steam-Cured Lightweight Concrete. Gothenburg.
3. Bergström, S. G., Essunger, G. and Warris, B. (1960). 'Preparation of Standards for Reinforced Lightweight Concrete in Sweden'. RILEM Symposium on Steam-Cured Lightweight Concrete. Gothenburg.
4. Granholm, H. (1960). 'Reinforced Lightweight Concrete', RILEM Symposium on Steam-Cured Lightweight Concrete, Gothenburg.
5. Cederwall, K. (1960). 'Tests on Reinforced Lightweight Concrete Beams', RILEM Symposium on Steam-Cured Lightweight Concrete, Gothenburg.
6. Short, A. and Kinniburgh, W. (1961). 'The Structural Use of Aerated Concrete', *The Struct. Engineer*, **39**(1) and (11).
7. Nilsson, S. (1960). 'Compressive Reinforcement of Lightweight Concrete', RILEM Symposium on Steam-Cured Lightweight Concrete, Gothenburg.
8. German Standard DIN 4223. 'Bewehrte Dach- und Deckenplatten aus dampfgehärtetem Gas- und Schaumbeton', ('Reinforced Roof and Floor Slabs of Steam-Cured Aerated Concrete'), Deutscher Ausschuss für Stahlbeton.
9. British Standard Code of Practice 116:1965. 'The Structural Use of Precast Concrete', British Standards Institution.
10. British Standard Code of Practice, CP 110:1972. 'The Structural Use of Concrete', British Standards Institution.
11. Draft International. Code for Aerated Concrete (1977), CEB, Paris.
12. British Standard Code of Practice 111:1961, 'Structural Recommendations for Loadbearing Walls', British Standards Institution.
13. Shideler, J. J. (1960). 'The Status of US Specifications for Cellular Concrete', RILEM Symposium on Steam-Cured Lightweight Concrete, Gothenburg.
14. American Concrete Institute Standard A.C.I. 318–71. 'Building Code Requirements for Reinforced Concrete', ACI, Detroit.
15. Walley, F. and Bate, S. C. C. (1959). 'A Guide to the British Standard Code of Practice for Prestressed Concrete' (115:1959),' British Standards Institution.
16. Phoenix, J. 'Tests on Siporex Floor and Roof Slabs', Private Communication.
17. Schäffler, H. (1960). 'Gas- und Schaumbeton; Verankerung der Bewehrung' ('Aerated Concrete; Bond Strength'), Bull. No. 136, Deutscher Ausschuss für Stahlbeton.

CHAPTER TWENTY-ONE

Aerated Concrete Roofs, Floors and Walls

SUMMARY

The design and use of various types of roof, floor and wall construction is considered, using reinforced aerated concrete precast panels.

GENERAL

For the construction of dwelling houses or other types of building up to two or three storeys in height, methods of construction using loadbearing aerated concrete units have proved in practice to be safe and economical. Loadbearing vertical wall slabs (Fig. 21.1) or masonry block walls (Fig. 21.2) are usually employed, supporting the roof and, in the case of several storeys, the floor loads as well. Reinforced aerated concrete units thus form the external and internal walls, lintels, floor slabs and roof slabs (Fig. 21.3).

In Sweden, Germany and most other countries where aerated concrete is manufactured, the module selected by the manufacturers is usually 50 cm (1ft 8 in.), but recent development tends towards standard widths of 60 cm (2ft) and even 75 cm (2ft 6in.). The module forming the basis of design should conform with the makers' stated dimensions. By suitable design and careful planning of the erection procedure, low-cost dwellings are being built with aerated concrete units to a large variety of architectural plans.

In the UK, the loading of roofs and floors and of the separate wall units for design must conform to Chapter V (Loading) of the British Standard Code of Practice CP 3[1] or the appropriate byelaw in force with the local authority concerned. The stability of the building as a whole must also be adequate in resisting safely lateral forces due to wind, earthquakes or other causes. The building and its foundations should be so designed that it is capable of resisting the combined effects as well as the separate effects of imposed loads and of the wind loads on the vertical surfaces, on the roof and on any part of the building above the general roof level, having full regard to the internal pressures caused by the wind.

The wind pressures to be used for the calculations are given in Codes of Practice and Regulations. On vertical surfaces these wind pressures should be considered as acting uniformly on the full height of the vertical walls. On sloping roofs the horizontal components of the wind forces acting half-way up the roof must be taken into account as an additional lateral force to be

FIG. 21.1 Reinforced aerated concrete vertical wall slabs in course of erection.

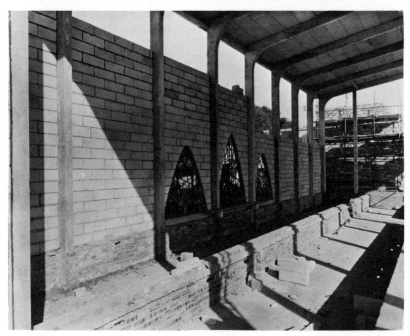

FIG. 21.2 Aerated concrete block wall during construction at Gracemount Church, Edinburgh.

FIG. 21.3   Reinforced aerated concrete factory roof in course of erection (Borg-
Warner Ltd., Letchworth).

resisted by the building. Wind loads acting on projections above the roof
should also be taken into account in calculating the stability of the building
as a whole.

Normally the resistance of a building against lateral forces must be
shown to be adequate by means of stability calculations. In some cases,
however, where it is obvious that walls, floors and roof are sufficiently rigid
and are sufficiently well interconnected to provide adequate stiffness for the
building as a whole, the effects of wind need not be checked by calculation
except for the foundations and for individual wall panels. These cases are
specified in the British Code of Practice CP 3, Ch. V, Pt 2.

ROOF SLABS

Thermal insulation

The thermal insulating capacity of some types of structural roof is
insufficient to satisfy even the modest requirements laid down by statute.[2]
For industrial buildings, as well as for office buildings and domestic
premises, a considerably higher insulation is often desirable and, in order to
achieve it, roof structures are provided with additional insulating elements.
On flat roofs the thermal insulating capacity can be increased by means of a

screed made of lightweight concrete or of similar insulating material which is placed between the loadbearing structure and the top waterproof membrane of asphalt or bituminous felt.

Where the roof is intended to be walked on or is used for other purposes which may involve wear and tear, an additional wearing surface is provided, usually in the form of precast concrete slabs.

To ensure that the thermal insulating capacity of the screed is sufficiently high, the material used for it must be very light and as a consequence it is usually also weak and brittle. It is, therefore, not a very suitable base for the waterproof membrane which is placed on top of it. It also has a tendency to trap moisture. The requirements of heat insulation may, therefore, conflict with the requirement for a waterproof membrane and a compromise to satisfy both is not easy to achieve. In recent years the number of failures of waterproof membranes owing to the weak and brittle base on which they are laid has increased and some manufacturers of such membranes have ceased to guarantee their product for any length of time for this reason.

With reinforced aerated concrete roofs, an additional screed for heat insulation can become redundant, since the thermal insulating capacity of a normal aerated concrete structural roof is usually adequate without additional insulation. Where a still greater degree of insulation is required, thicker roof slabs are used, rather than casting an additional screed. The aerated concrete also provides a hard and uniform surface to serve as a base for the waterproof layer. If care is taken to prevent excessive deflections leading to inadmissible slope at the supports and, subsequently, to cracking of the waterproof membrane, there is no need to fear premature failure of the asphalt or felt. In addition, the expensive and time-wasting additional operation of laying the screed is eliminated.

According to the requirements set by the humidity and temperature conditions on which the roof is based, aerated concrete roof structures may be of two main types, namely, solid roof slabs and ventilated cavity structures.

A solid roof must be thick enough to prevent condensation on the underside of the roof slab. For normal conditions in Great Britain, the minimum required structural thickness normally suffices to prevent condensation. Where high internal temperature and humidity are expected, however, a thicker roof, or—in extreme cases—a ventilated roof is necessary. Whereas with ventilated roofs the thickness of the roof slab will in practice depend solely on the degree of thermal insulation desired and on the loading standards that were adopted, for solid roofs the humidity and temperature will be additional criteria which must influence the dimensions of the roof slabs. A simple method is given in Table 21.1 for the calculation of the required minimum thickness for aerated concrete solid roofs made with aerated concrete with a density of $600 \, kg/m^3$ (37 pcf), to ensure that for given temperature and humidity conditions condensation cannot occur.

TABLE 21.1
MINIMUM THICKNESS OF ROOF UNITS IN mm TO AVOID CONDENSATION

Interior Temperature (°F)

	45	50	55	60	65	70	75	80	85	90
90	225	Above the heavy line ventilated roofs with a sealed soffit are necessary								
85	175	200								
80	100	125	175	200						
75	75	100	125	150	175	200	225			
70	75	75	100	100	125	150	175	200	225	225
65	75	75	75	100	100	125	125	150	175	200
60	75	75	75	75	100	100	100	125	150	150
55	75	75	75	75	75	75	100	100	125	125
50	75	75	75	75	75	75	75	100	100	125
45	75	75	75	75	75	75	75	75	75	100
40	75	75	75	75	75	75	75	75	75	75
35	75	75	75	75	75	75	75	75	75	75
	7	10	13	16	18	21	24	27	29	32

Interior Relative Humidity (%) *(vertical axis label)*

Interior Temperature (°C)

Structural design

The structural design of aerated concrete roof units is normally based on the assumption that each unit acts separately as a reinforced concrete beam (Chapter 20). The units are required to resist their own dead weight and the imposed load. For flat roofs and sloping roofs up to and including 10 degrees fall, where access is provided to the roof, allowance should be made in the UK for an imposed load of 1·4 MPa (30 psi) uniformly distributed over the plan surface of the roof, subject to certain minimum loads specified in the Code of Practice.[1] Where means of entry is only provided for cleaning, repairs and maintenance, an imposed load of 0·7 MPa (15 psi) is allowed for in design. For sloping roofs where no access is provided to the roof, no imposed loads need be allowed in design if the angle of slope is 75 degrees or more; intermediate values are allowed for slopes ranging between 10 degrees and 75 degrees. Roofs must also be capable of resisting the design wind forces and, for individual roof members, account must also be taken of local wind effects such as eddies and gusts which may increase the effective wind pressure.

Roof covering

The roof covering should comply with the relevant Codes of Practice.[3,4] A common roof covering to exclude rain-water consists of a double or treble layer of bituminous felt. The laying of the felt is generally undertaken by specialist firms.

Before laying the felt the aerated concrete surface must be coated with an asphalt solution or emulsion on which an asphalt compound is spread, followed by bituminous paper and finally the layers of felt (Fig. 21.4).

An adequate fall must be provided on flat roofs to ensure that rain-water can drain away. Since aerated concrete slabs are of uniform thickness, this fall must be provided in the structure itself to satisfy the design requirements of minimum slope. The desired fall will differ for different types of roof covering. For bituminous felt it should be not less than 1 in 20 or approximately 3 degrees. Metal sheeting, such as galvanised steel and copper or aluminium sheeting, is also being used. The slope required for such metal roof covering materials should be at least 7 degrees and

FIG. 21.4 Applying roofing felt to aerated concrete roof.

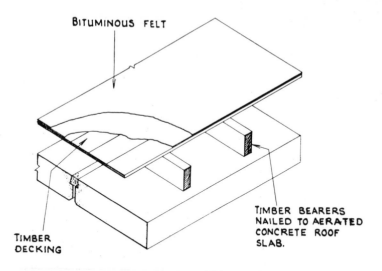

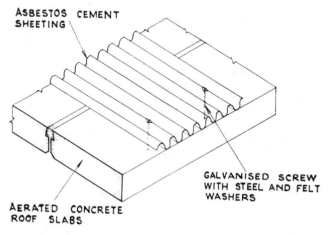

Fig. 21.5 Ventilated aerated concrete roof systems.

preferably not less than 10 degrees to ensure shedding of rain-water from the roof surface.

Concrete or clay tiles may also be used. For these it is usual to place first bituminous building paper on the roof surface over an asphalt compound; laths are then nailed to the slabs and the tiles are attached to the laths. The weight of tiles is greater than that of other types of roof covering and this must be taken into account in designing the roof structure.

Internal treatment

Treatment of the soffit is sometimes limited to finishing off the joints on the underside by chamfering the edges of the roof slabs at the factory. Alternatively, the soffit might be painted with a coat of limewash or with cement or silicate paint, but where the surface treatment is impermeable to vapour, the slabs should not be painted before the roof system has been given a chance to dry out. Additional protection to the underside of solid or ventilated roof systems in normal or fairly humid atmospheric conditions is not generally required, provided that the roof is not exposed to corrosive influences caused by acid atmospheric conditions. In the UK the normal finish is emulsion paint or a textural finish.

Where the internal conditions are excessively humid, however, for example in a laundry, or for the roof of a swimming pool, the top of the roof system may have to be ventilated (Fig. 21.5).

In addition to the ventilated roof space, it may also be advisable to protect the underside of the roof with an additional water-repellant coating, to prevent further penetration of moisture into the slabs from the interior of the building. Aluminium paint, oil paint or asphalt coating may be used. The asphalt can be covered for decoration with an emulsion aluminium paint, but oil paint should not be used. In some cases aluminium foil has been glued to the ceiling; this is easier to apply if backed by building paper.

Where, in addition, the atmosphere is heavily laden with corrosive impurities, such as sulphur in steelworks or foundries, the undersurface should be covered with a suitable coating of an anti-corrosive substance, such as asphalt. Chlorinated rubber paints or plastic paints are resistant against both alkalis and acids but cannot be painted on top of asphalt. Both these types of protective paint are sufficiently resistant against moisture penetration in themselves.

Construction details

Solid and ventilated roofs of various types made of aerated concrete are shown in Figs. 21.5–21.9. Ventilated roofs usually consist of a timber roof placed on top of the aerated concrete roof, the cavity between the top of the slabs and the timber roof being 50–75 mm (2–3 in.) deep; timber battens nailed to the aerated concrete are used to form the cavity which may be

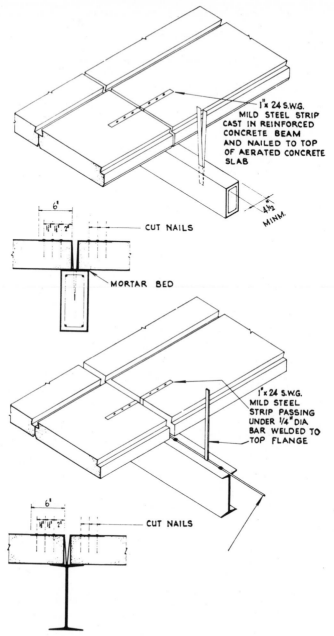

FIG. 21.6 Fixing aerated concrete slabs to supporting beams.

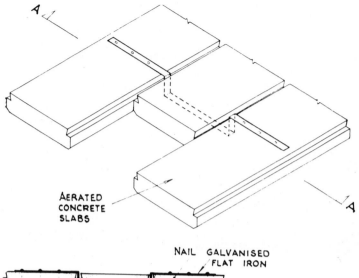

AERATED
CONCRETE
SLABS

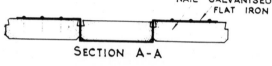

NAIL GALVANISED
FLAT IRON

SECTION A-A

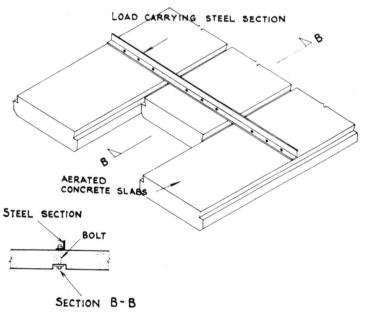

LOAD CARRYING STEEL SECTION

AERATED
CONCRETE SLABS

STEEL SECTION

BOLT

SECTION B-B

FIG. 21.7 Trimmer-beam support construction.

ventilated either through natural wind pressure or through mechanical
ventilation. Alternatively asbestos-cement sheeting may be used.

Where required for the structural design, aerated concrete slabs must be
adequately anchored to the supporting structure. Steel straps can be used
for this purpose. In the case of steep roofs or for heavy wind loading each
individual roof unit should be separately anchored to the supporting

FIG. 21.8   Aerated concrete slabs forming a flat roof supported on fabricated steel
girders.

structure (Fig. 21.6). The fixing required will depend on the height of the
building, on the slope of the roof, and on the thickness of the slab.

In long buildings, suitable expansion joints must be provided at not less
than 15-m (50-ft) centres, in accordance with good practice in reinforced
concrete work to correspond with joints in the main loadbearing structure.

For openings in roofs and floors, short units may be placed
intermediately, as required, their weight being supported by adjacent units
of normal length, provided that the latter are so designed that they are
capable of resisting the increased load safely. Alternatively, trimmer angles
might be included to transmit the loads to the supports (Fig. 21.7).

FIG. 21.9   Aerated concrete slabs forming the outer skin for an arched roof.

FLOOR SLABS

Aerated concrete flexural elements are used not only for flat roofs but also for floor slabs, although the use of such light units for party floors may be difficult to justify on functional grounds alone. For separating panels inside occupied buildings thermal insulation is generally of subordinate importance although it may be desirable at times to prevent the heating of unoccupied premises at the neighbours' expense. As for insulation against airborne sound, aerated concrete is not very effective, because of the very quality which makes it desirable in other respects, namely, its lightness. There is, however, some economic advantage in using the same material and type of construction throughout, for a large building contract; moreover, there is the saving in weight and the speed of erection must also count.

Reinforced aerated concrete floors have been used for industrial purposes under a loading of 4 MPa (80 psi) and more, over spans of up to 6 m (20 ft).

The structural design of aerated concrete floor slabs is based on the same principles as that of roof systems. In some cases a screed is added to serve as a base for the floor covering, but resulting also in greater stiffness and strength.

In some cases it may become necessary to increase the loadbearing

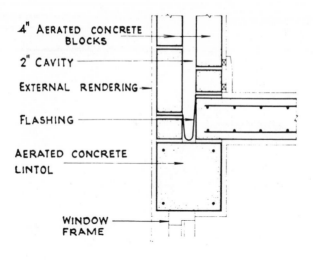

4" AERATED CONCRETE BLOCKS

2" CAVITY

EXTERNAL RENDERING

FLASHING

AERATED CONCRETE LINTOL

WINDOW FRAME

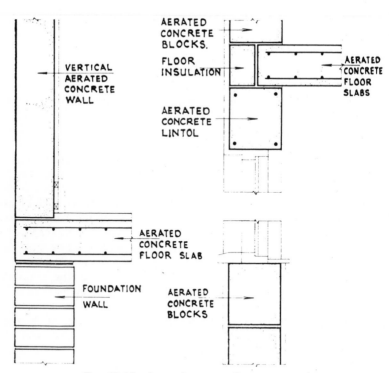

VERTICAL AERATED CONCRETE WALL

AERATED CONCRETE BLOCKS.

FLOOR INSULATION

AERATED CONCRETE FLOOR SLABS

AERATED CONCRETE LINTOL

AERATED CONCRETE FLOOR SLAB

FOUNDATION WALL

AERATED CONCRETE BLOCKS

FIG. 21.10   Aerated concrete floor construction.

capacity of some units within a system, owing to local increases in loading or sometimes the span may have to be increased. Since the thickness must usually remain the same throughout a floor system, it is by increasing the reinforcement percentage or the strength and density of the concrete that the loadbearing capacity of individual floor sections is enhanced or the span can be increased safely.

The design floor loading to be resisted by individual floor units is again laid down in the appropriate Code of Practice.[1] Where the main partitions are shown in the plan, their actual weight should be included in the dead load. Where they are not shown, an appropriate uniformly distributed load is assumed, being usually not less than 1 MPa (20 psi).

The imposed floor load comprises all floor loads other than dead loads. The design loads of basic floor space occupancies given in the Code of Practice provide for normal effects of impact and acceleration but not for any special concentrated load.

A number of floor constructions which have proved satisfactory in practice are shown in Fig. 21.10.

WALL SLABS

The design of walls is treated separately, but there are a number of special features which distinguish reinforced concrete wall panels.

Two main types of reinforced aerated concrete wall panel have found general application, namely, storey-high panels ('Vertical wall units'), varying in width 0·3–0·6 m (1–2 ft) and in thickness 75–250 mm (3–10 in.) and slabs placed on edge, on top of each other, fixed in various ways to columns placed at 2·4–6·0 m (8–20 ft) centres ('Horizontal wall slabs') (Fig. 21.11).

The latter system seems to derive from the traditional Swedish 'block' method of timber construction where rectangular baulks of timber of equal length are placed one on top of the other on their side. Though wasteful in the case of timber, this method of construction is very suitable for aerated concrete industrial buildings and even for dwelling houses.

With vertical wall slabs, (Fig. 21.12) the vertical joints between adjacent slabs or between slabs and columns are grouted through pre-formed grooves. 75 and 100 mm (3 and 4 in.) thick wall panels are butt-jointed with a thin layer of adhesive mortar. The horizontal joints of the horizontal wall slabs are sealed by means of jointing strips or mastic placed between the butting faces (Fig. 21.13).

Walls made of either horizontal or vertical slabs should not exceed 6·0 m (20 ft) in length without an intermediate stiffening crosswall or pier, unless additional stiffness is provided by other means, for example through a rigid connection to horizontal members. Where the wall is weakened by

FIG. 21.11   Horizontal cladding slabs for outside walls of multi-storey building in
Sweden.

substantial window openings this distance should be less, according to the
circumstances.

For non-loadbearing walls either horizontal or vertical units may be
used. Horizontal slabs are used where the vertical loads are transmitted to
the ground through a framed structure, incorporating columns to which the
slabs are attached. Where the walls are intended to be directly loadbearing,
i.e. where the floor or the roof is supported directly on top of the wall slabs,
vertical wall units would seem to be more economical, but they should not
be less than 150 mm (6 in.) thick for external walls. Normally loadbearing
walls should not be less than 100 mm (4 in.) thick. For a compression
strength (saturated) of about 3 MPa (400 psi) a basic permissible stress of

FIG. 21.12 Vertical wall slabs used as cladding.

about 0·6 MPa (80 psi) may be used in compression for vertical wall slabs. With increasing slenderness the stress reduction factors laid down in the Code of Practice CP 114:1965 have been used. For greater compressive strength the permissible stresses also become higher.

For walls made with vertical wall slabs, standard lintel units of aerated concrete are provided. The lintels usually bear along the width of one standard wall slab. On the Continent, the lintels are of standard depth, usually 250 mm (10 in.) or 500 mm (20 in.). In Britain, lintels are made in accordance with the standard block and slab sizes.

For horizontal wall slabs the lintels above doors and window openings are usually of the same height as that of the slabs so thay they may bond into the structure. All units are also designed to resist the wind loads prescribed by the Code CP 3.[1]

Where the floor and roof loads are transmitted directly to vertical wall slabs, care must be taken to ensure that the load is axial. Where eccentric loads occur, these must be taken into account in design, but accidental eccentricities will be taken care of by the normal reinforcement in the slabs. Slabs intended for external walls are reinforced symmetrically to resist wind forces in either direction, but partition slabs are generally only provided

FIG. 21.13 Preparation of dry joint between aerated concrete horizontal wall
slabs. Foamed plastic strips being nailed to the aerated concrete.

with reinforcement placed in the central plane of the slab. The main bars are
interlaced with welded crossbars.

In multi-storey buildings the wall units must transmit lateral forces to the
loadbearing frame or to the loadbearing membrane structure but for one-
or two-storey buildings it is safe to assume that the walls formed by the
aerated concrete wall slabs provide the necessary lateral stiffness without
any special provisions to resist wind forces. In such buildings and, indeed, in
frameless buildings up to three or four storeys in height, floor, roof and wall
panels act as an interconnected box frame, capable of transmitting external
loading, racking forces, and bending moments to the ground.

For buildings taller than three of four storeys frameless buildings are not generally made with aerated concrete loadbearing walls and flexural members. This method of construction would have advantages, however, if applied to aerated concrete, and considerable experience is already available with other types of material used in this way (for example, with brick walls and cast-*in-situ* concrete walls).

FIG. 21.14 'Large panel' wall united being assembled in Western Germany.

In some cases large panel construction has been used with aerated concrete. In the USSR the panels are high-pressure steam-cured in autoclaves of extra-large diameter. In Germany and Sweden each panel is assembled from a number of smaller aerated concrete units and glued and bolted together before being lifted into position on the site (Fig.21.14).

Where sanitary fittings or other appliances subjected to heavy wear are fitted to aerated concrete walls, the usual methods of attachment have not proved sufficiently durable and resistant because screws tend to pull out of the relatively soft material. It is therefore preferable to fix such appliances by tie-bars or bolts crossing through the supporting wall and to place a load distribution member—a large washer or a crossbar under a mat—at the end.

WORKMANSHIP AND ERECTION

The key to success in maintaining uniform material properties in large-scale factory production is the accurate control of all manufacturing processes. Effective control over the supply of the raw materials which must be of uniform quality, as well as over the processes of manufacture, is also essential. Without such control production of aerated concrete of uniform quality would not be possible on a large scale. An equally conscientious supervision of the erection processes on the construction site is of almost equal importance, but, owing to the often unpredictable sequence of events on the site, is in general much more difficult to achieve in practice.

Because of its relatively soft and friable nature, aerated concrete is easily damaged during manufacture, transit, storage and erection. After erection, moreover, unsound design of the supports and joints, for example inadequate bedding or differential movements at the supports, may lead to cracking at the corners. The ease with which aerated concrete can be nailed, cut, planed and chased, is also a strong temptation to damage these members on the site by placing service ducts and conduits without considering the harm that may be done in this way to structural safety. Reinforced aerated concrete flexural members and loadbearing wall slabs are generally designed for specific spans and must not be cut short if they are found to be too long for a particular job. If the ends are lopped off, vital transverse anchorage bars may go with them and the members are then weakened considerably. Design tolerances should be carefully laid down in

Fig. 21.15   Special trolley for placing aerated concrete floor and roof slabs.

FIG. 21.16   Aligning device for floor and roof slabs.

FIG. 21.17   Mobile crane for placing roof units.

FIG. 21.18   Placing non-loadbearing wall slabs.

advance and the appropriate members should be obtained for the job. Botching on the site can lead to trouble later.

Reinforced aerated concrete units are generally handled on the site with specially designed appliances often supplied by the makers. For roof and floor members, special mobile trolleys (Fig. 21.15), aligning tools (Fig. 21.16) and cranes (Figs. 21.3 and 21.17) have been designed with ingenious grappling devices to hold slabs firmly without risk of breakage. Wall slabs for loadbearing walls are usually reinforced symmetrically near both main faces and can be held in any lifting position without risk of damage. Wall slabs intended for partitions or for non-loadbearing walls usually only contain reinforcement placed in the central plane of the slab and should only be lifted on edge (Fig. 21.18). On the sites special trolleys (Fig. 21.1) are in general use. As an aid to contractors using this material, manufacturers of aerated concrete have evolved special drilling, perforating and cutting tools (Figs. 21.19 and 21.20).

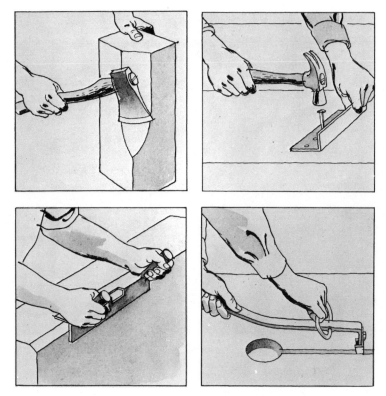

FIG. 21.19 Cutting, nailing and planning aerated concrete units on the site.

On a building site aerated concrete elements, like most other building materials and components should not be allowed to get wet or stand exposed to the weather for prolonged periods. There are at least two important reasons for avoiding this.

First, the main functional advantage of aerated concrete in a building, namely its high thermal insulation value, depends on its remaining dry: the thermal insulation capacity of wet aerated concrete is relatively low. Second, the strength of aerated concrete is higher when dry than when it is saturated. Repeated saturation and drying out may also lead to deterioration, particularly in an industrial environment.

The end supports of floor and roof slabs may be critical; if the ends are not adequately and evenly bedded, stress concentrations may develop near the corners and these could lead to breaking off of the corner pieces, exposing the reinforcement and damaging the protective coating which had been placed on it. Wide slabs are less vulnerable to this type of damage than

FIG. 21.20   Sawing aerated concrete on the site. Combined saw and file for cutting
the reinforcing bars.

individual members or narrow slabs. The remedy is simple; the slabs should
be bedded on fresh cement mortar, wall boarding, mineral wool or other
flexible material which yields under pressure and conforms to the shape of
the base of the slab at the supports. In this way the support reaction is
allowed to be distributed uniformly across the whole width of the slab.

Where the floor or roof loads are transmitted directly to loadbearing
vertical wall slabs, the vertical loads must not be allowed to cause excessive
load concentration at the edge of the slabs and thus lead to high local
stresses in the concrete. The permissible bearing stress must not be
exceeded.

Individual slabs are usually placed side by side and are combined to form
a slab system, by grouting the joints between adjacent slabs. It is obvious as
has been stressed earlier that grouting must be carried out conscientiously
to ensure the transverse distribution of the bending moments.

An interesting and important consequence of the increasing use of
aerated concrete in the form of reinforced units and as masonry blocks is
the revolutionary change this should bring not only to methods of building
and speed of building, but also the the attitude of mind required from site

FIG. 21.21   Erecting an aerated concrete dry jointed block wall, with nylon fixing discs.

workers, supervising engineers and designers alike, namely a development towards precision engineering in the building trades. The usual tolerance of 50–75 mm (2–3 in.) in building practice has, in fact, been often reduced in reinforced aerated concrete units to less than 3 mm ($\frac{1}{8}$ in.). With ground Ytong staves still greater precision is possible; by grinding, these staves are made with perfectly parallel sides to a dimensional accuracy of less than

0·125 mm (0·005 in.). With such units, and using dry or glued joints (Fig. 21.21), the deviation from the design dimensions even in very long or tall buildings is negligible. In a structure made to such a high accuracy, the manufacturer of building components and appliances can prefabricate with much greater confidence and it also allows the contractor and designer to work without costly 'making-good' operations.

REFERENCES

1. British Standard Code of Practice 3: Chapter V: 1952: 'Loading'. British Standards Institution.
2. Thermal Insulation (Industrial Buildings) Act, 1957, and the Thermal Insulation (Industrial Buildings) Regulations, 1958 (S.I. 1958, No. 1220).
3. British Standard Code of Practice 144.101:1961: 'Bitumen Felt Roof Coverings'. British Standards Institution.
4. British Standard Code of Practice 144.201:1952: 'Mastic Asphalt Roofing'. British Standards Institution.
5. British Standard Code of Practice 143: 'Sheet Roof Coverings'. British Standards Institution.
6. Building Research Station Digest No. 8 (Second Series): 'Built-up Felt Roofs', Building Research Station, Garston, Watford.

CHAPTER TWENTY-TWO

Use of Aerated Concrete

SUMMARY

A brief survey of the use of aerated concrete in practice is combined with a description of some notable structures or methods of construction.

In its practical application aerated concrete is more limited in scope than concrete made with lightweight aggregates. On the other hand, this is offset somewhat by the flexibility, approaching that of timber, with which aerated concrete elements can fit into a great variety of plans and structural systems, provided that its structural properties are properly taken into account. Although it is sometimes employed as a cast-*in-situ* insulating material for roofs, pipelines and cold stores, aerated concrete is primarily used as a precast material. Precasting large panels on the site without autoclaving has been successfully carried out on large, multi-storey buildings in Sweden ('Sund system') and in the USSR. More frequently, however, aerated concrete is used in the form of precast autoclaved units the size of which is

FIG. 22.1   House built with splashed Ytong blocks in Sweden.

mainly governed by the size of the autoclave. Large, room-sized units have been manufactured with the aid of large-diameter autoclaves in the USSR, but this appears to have been difficult and not always economical.

BLOCK MASONRY

Perhaps the most widespread use of aerated concrete is still in the form of masonry blocks for the construction of loadbearing or non-loadbearing walls (Fig. 22.1). The lightest of these blocks serve for insulation only, for

FIG. 22.2 Placing aerated concrete staves and blocks (Sweden).

example in conjunction with cast-*in-situ* loadbearing gravel concrete walls, where they are placed, usually without mortar bedding, inside the shuttering of the external walls, next to the outside shuttering panel, before casting. The concrete is then poured and compacted and allowed to harden. When the shuttering is removed, the wall is left with an external insulation of aerated concrete blocks which adhere to the gravel concrete. This is then

FIG. 22.3   Placing aerated concrete lintel in masonry block wall (Sweden).

rendered. The rendering must be carefully and evenly applied, since in humid climatic conditions renderings of uneven thickness may tend to separate from the wall owing to differential shrinkage and thermal stresses. This may lead to cracking and subsequent accumulation of moisture in the wall.

Aerated concrete masonry blocks and staves (Figs. 22.2 and 22.3) have found general application but not only because of the high thermal insulation and lightness of the material, but also because of the high degree of uniformity of their dimensions and physical properties. Nevertheless, for loadbearing walls aerated concrete masonry walls of less than 75 mm (3 in.) thickness should not be used.

Unrendered walls built with special facing blocks produced with a 10 mm ($\frac{3}{8}$ in.) thick outer decorative layer have been used with satisfactory results (Fig. 22.4).

FIG. 22.4   Separating walls made with Thermalite facing blocks in Holy Trinity Church, Smethwick, England.

Apart from blocks and staves, the principal structural forms of aerated concrete building elements used in practice are reinforced floor, roof and wall panels. These are standard articles capable of being used with different methods of construction, for a variety of purposes.

LOADBEARING VERTICAL WALL UNITS

For single-storey and two-storey dwelling houses, industrial buildings, schools and hospitals, reinforced aerated concrete units have been widely employed as loadbearing elements (Figs. 22.5–22.10). The spans used for flexural members are relatively small, up to 4·5 m (15 ft). Except for early examples containing unprotected reinforcement, external wall units in houses have shown no signs of deterioration. Loadbearing wall units are usually storey-high, narrow slabs, joined together along their vertical edges by mortar poured from the top, *in situ*. Loadbearing walls are not, in general, made with panels of less than 100 mm (4 in.) thickness, but internal partitions may be 75 mm (3 in.) thick and are butt-jointed with an adhesive mortar, the joint being about 3 mm ($\frac{1}{8}$ in.) thick. For the thicker panels the edges are usually grooved and the joints are made with ordinary 1:3 cement

FIG. 22.5   Siporex reinforced aerated concrete wall, floor and roof units in a two-storey house in Edinburgh, Scotland.

FIG. 22.6   'Hebel' house in West Germany using reinforced aerated concrete loadbearing wall, floor and roof units.

FIG. 22.7   Loadbearing aerated concrete vertical wall slabs and roof slabs in a school at Newport, Monmouth.

FIG. 22.8   Aerated concrete wall slabs in a single-storey house in Canada.

FIG. 22.9   Reinforced aerated concrete loadbearing wall and floor system in Sweden.

FIG. 22.10   Hospital in England built with loadbearing Durox aerated concrete wall and roof units.

mortar, about 25 mm (1 in.) thick. Suitable special trolleys are used to transport and place these panels on the site.

NON-LOADBEARING WALL CLADDING

Storey-high vertical wall units are also being used for the external non-loadbearing walls and in the partitions of multi-storey structures (Figs. 22.11–22.15). The loadbearing structure in these cases usually consists of a reinforced concrete frame or cast-*in-situ* loadbearing concrete walls. Where

Fig. 22.11   Reinforced Siporex aerated concrete wall slabs used as external cladding and partition walls in Sweden.

FIG. 22.12   Two-storey-high reinforced aerated concrete cladding system in Sweden.

FIG. 22.13   Vertical aerated concrete Durox cladding slabs at Coach Station, Heathrow Airport, England.

FIG. 22.14   Central pier at Gatwick Airport, England, using reinforced aerated
concrete wall and roof slabs.

the weather conditions are especially severe and thermal insulation of
exceptionally high standard is required, aerated concrete sandwich slabs
with an intermediate layer of foamed polystyrene resin are used for the
external walls. In a number of tall point blocks near Stockholm and
elsewhere in Sweden, the structural system is based on a reinforced concrete
tower which is first erected on the site with the aid of sliding shuttering. At
first the tower serves as a base for the tower crane; later it is used as a service
core during construction and also in the finished building (Fig. 22.16). The
tower is designed to carry a large part of the vertical loads and also acts as a
spine member in resisting horizontal wind loads. The remainder of the

FIG. 22.15   Cladding slabs being fixed to concrete frame at National Exhibition
Centre, Birmingham, England.

loadbearing structure consists of a reinforced concrete frame clad with
aerated concrete slabs. Since neither the latter nor the partitions are
designed to be loadbearing, this system of construction is flexible and
permits variations in floor plan.

Aerated concrete units are not used in the form of rigid frames because of
the difficulty of ensuring stiffness at the joints; in most cases this is also
difficult with ordinary reinforced concrete precast elements. Aerated
concrete elements, however, may be designed as hinged frames with cross-
walls.

FIG. 22.16   Siporex slabs used as cladding on 'Skarne' type multi-storey block in Sweden.

FIG. 22.17   Horizontal cladding slabs of reinforced aerated concrete used with a steel frame at Ninewells Hospital, Dundee, Scotland.

FIG. 22.18   Horizontal cladding slabs in a steel framed industrial building in Sweden.

Aerated concrete horizontal cladding slabs and panels fitting between columns are used for non-loadbearing external walls in domestic and industrial buildings, with an architecturally pleasing effect (Figs. 22.17–22.21). When used for multi-storey buildings however, the weight of the panels must be supported by the columns at least at every floor level (Fig. 22.22).

ROOFS

Aerated concrete flexural members are particularly suitable for industrial roofing (Figs. 22.23–22.25). In Sweden, for example, most industrial roofs are made with reinforced aerated concrete units: as a result of their high thermal insulating capacity these roofs allow a considerable saving in the cost of fuel and the capital cost of the building itself may be also reduced by more rapid erection than with other types of roofing. Surveys of existing aerated concrete roofs have shown them to be generally satisfactory and

FIG. 22.19   Horizontal cladding slabs of Siporex used with concrete framed
industrial building in Sweden.

FIG. 22.20   Horizontal cladding slabs of Siporex being attached to concrete frame
in Sweden.

durable. Where the surrounding conditions are particularly unfavourable, deterioration can be prevented by suitable surface treatments and by ventilation of the roof space. Aerated concrete roofing is also used to cover large halls (Figs. 22.26 and 22.27) and where the atmospheric conditions are not very severe, aerated concrete roof units have been used to cover large canopies.

For multi-storey buildings, aerated concrete roof slabs are frequently employed for the construction of flat roofs. As with other types of roofing, these are covered with a moisture-proof membrane of asphalt or bituminous felt. They are also used as floor slabs, where there is an

FIG. 22.21 Horizontal 'Hebel' cladding slabs on an industrial building in Switzerland.

FIG. 22.22 Aerated concrete large-panel units made by Hebel, used for a factory building in West Germany.

FIG. 22.23   North light roof with reinforced aerated concrete slab units for a factory in Denmark.

FIG. 22.24   Placing roof slabs on an industrial building in West Germany.

FIG. 22.25   Reinforced aerated concrete roof and wall construction at Heathrow Airport, England.

FIG. 22.26   Placing reinforced aerated concrete slabs on steel arches of hanger at Bromma Airport, Stockholm, Sweden.

FIG. 22.27   Reinforced aerated concrete roof system for Civic Centre at Reading, England, supported on concrete frame.

FIG. 22.28   Siporex reinforced aerated concrete slabs used for the flooring, roofing and partitions of a school at Seaham, Durham, England.

FIG. 22.29   Reinforced aerated concrete floor slabs being placed in Sweden.

economic advantage in using the same method of construction throughout. Floors are often covered with a mortar screed (Figs. 22.28 and 22.29).

Flexible though it is, reinforced aerated concrete cannot be successfully employed in a haphazard, inadequately prepared manner. It can be chased, drilled, sawn and nailed on the site, but units can be weakened seriously by being cut short on the site to fit into a position for which they have not been designed. It is essential for safety and also for speed of erection that the correct number of elements having the right dimensions should be available. Nevertheless, since the completed structure is not a loose construction of individual elements, but usually a nearly monolithic box, statically highly indeterminate and possessing considerable inherent stiffness, it has a large margin of safety against in-expert use of individual elements. The effects of local weakness caused by cutting, drilling or otherwise mutilating individual slabs will be distributed over much of the whole structure, but the damage caused must not be so severe as to endanger its functional usefulness.

Where aerated concrete is used in earthquake-prone areas the design must, of course, take account of the seismic forces involved. In Mexico, for example, Siporex units are employed in conjunction with a reinforced concrete frame, cast *in situ* between the slabs.

CHAPTER TWENTY-THREE

Lightweight Concrete in the Developing Countries

SUMMARY

Many of the lightweight concrete products developed over the years in Europe and North America are now being manufactured and employed in the developing countries. A list is given of these materials and the location of their use.

As mentioned in the foregoing chapters, lightweight concretes were initiated in different countries and at different times. Most of these are well-established building materials all over Europe and North America. In the past fifteen years or so a number have found their way to many of the developing countries, as well as to the older-established countries in the tropical and semi-tropical zones.

Pumice, being a lightweight rock found in many parts of the volcanic regions of Mediterranean, was used as a aggregate in classical times for the forms of concrete then in use. It was not until the mid-nineteenth century that its employment was resumed after the wide adoption of Portland cement and the use of the pumice deposits in the Rhine valley in Germany.

Pumice is found in several of the developing countries. In Kenya, it occurs in the Rift Valley and it is used at present mainly in thermal-resisting roof screeds. As the concrete block industry is well established in Kenya, it is expected that pumice will in future be widely used in concrete blocks.

Expanded-clay aggregate was made in the USA during the First World War for the concrete which was employed in building ships, a measure adopted to save steel. The experience thus gained was carried into the post-war period for use in housebuilding. Expanded-clay aggregate is being manufactured in Argentina and South Africa. Pilot plants for expanded clay have been installed in India and Pakistan. Although it is a capital-intensive industry it is likely that expanded-clay aggregate will be adopted in due course in the arid countries of the Middle East, since in these countries natural aggregates are either absent or are so contaminated with soluble salts as to be unsuitable for concrete, because of the high sulphate and chloride content. Moreover, many of the arid countries are oil-rich zones, better able to undertake high capital investment than many other countries in the developing world. In many cases urban or industrial expansion must rely in the long run on man-made aggregates if a conventional type of concrete is to be employed. Figure 23.1 shows the clay deposits at the Palta

Fɪɢ. 23.1   Clay deposits at Calcutta Water Works.

Water Works, Calcutta, one of the many sources of clay found in India. The Calcutta silt has been shown to be eminently suitable for expanded aggregate.

No-fines concrete was first used, in England, in the mid-nineteenth century. Its employment was brief and it was not until 1923 that it was re-introduced into Britain from Holland. At that time it was taken up in Scotland, mainly to meet the demand for post-war housing and to give employment to displaced unskilled and semi-skilled labour from the coal-mining industry during the industrial recession then being experienced. This technique of building is creating interest in some developing countries since, as already indicated, it lends itself to the employment of unskilled and semi-skilled labour.

Aerated concrete was first demonstrated as a feasible building material in the early days of the twentieth century but was not produced commercially until 1929. Although pioneered in Sweden and very widely used there, aerated concrete is produced today in many countries as far apart as the Arctic and the Equator. There are two forms currently in use, air-cured foamed concrete, and high-pressure steam-cured (autoclaved) aerated concrete.

Foamed concrete is by far the most widely used of the lightweight concretes in the emerging countries at the present time. This is as might be expected since it involves the minimum of capital investment, and the main ingredients, cement and sand, are available in many countries. Moreover, this product can be manufactured on a comparatively small scale, a factor which is of importance in countries made up of small communities. Indeed,

FIG. 23.2   Foamed concrete houses at Athi River, Kenya.

the production of air-cured, foamed concrete lends itself to manufacture on the building site, thereby obviating the need for transport of components. In the form of roof and wall panels, blocks, and solar tiles, foamed concrete is at present being used in Burma, Costa Rica, Ghana, Gibraltar, India, Kenya, Kuwait, Mexico, Nicaragua, Nigeria, Qatar, Saudi Arabia, Sri Lanka, South Africa, Trinidad, and Uganda.

Where financial means, population density, or other conditions favour the mass-production of a high quality product, autoclaved aerated concretes are to be found. In the developing countries today, autoclaved aerated concrete is being used in Cuba, India, Iran, Israel, Ivory Coast, Mexico, Venezuela and Zaire.

Foamed blast-furnace slag aggregate appears to have been developed originally in Germany. An improved modification was worked out and adopted for commercial production in England in 1935, and is still in use for this important aggregate.

FIG. 23.3   Pilot-scale plant for producing expanded clay, Lahore, Pakistan.

In countries where a flourishing iron and steel industry exists, foamed slag is a very cheap and particularly useful by-product. India is such a country and foamed blast-furnace slag has been produced there for a number of years.

Sintered pulverised-fuel ash (*fly ash*) as an aggregate was first produced commercially in England, in 1958. India produces large quantities of fly ash and much experimentation has already been carried out there in order to use it in its sintered form as a lightweight aggregate.

Perlite and vermiculite are minerals which when suitably expanded make extremely light aggregates and are found in a number of developing countries. Much attention is being directed to their exploitation as the basis of concrete with high thermal-insulation properties. Such concrete would be of great value in tropical countries in providing high resistance to solar heat gain.

Figure 23.2 shows foamed concrete houses at Athi River, Kenya, while Fig. 23.3 shows the pilot-scale plant for producing expanded-clay aggregate at Lahore, Pakistan.

CHAPTER TWENTY-FOUR

Concrete Blocks

SUMMARY

Types of blocks in common use are described and the principles and practice of blockmaking are outlined, as well as the machines employed. British and American specifications for blocks are given. The differences in practice and attitudes between American and British blockmakers are discussed.

GENERAL

Concrete building units simulating natural stone masonry in England goes back to 1850. It is not certain when lightweight blocks were first used, but the records show that blocks made from clinker and breeze were in use both in Britain and America as early as the latter part of the nineteenth century, although the production was probably small. The commercial production of aerated concrete blocks began in Sweden in 1929. In the interval blocks from various lightweight aggregates were introduced in several countries. At first the concrete block industry grew up in countries or districts which lacked stone or the clay necessary for burnt bricks, but in the course of time it became clear that the various types of concrete blocks had their own virtues apart from availability. Today about 80 per cent of all masonry work in America is carried out in concrete blocks; the corresponding figure in Britain, a country well supplied with brick clay, is about 35 per cent.

TYPES OF BLOCK

There are two basic types of concrete blocks, those composed of aggregate concrete and those produced from aerated concrete. The materials available for producing the former are described in Chapter 8, while the making of aerated concrete is the subject of Chapter 17. The aggregate blocks fall into two classes, those employing mineral aggregates and those made from organic aggregates, more specifically chemically stabilised sawdust or wood meal.

Aggregate concrete, because of the manner in which it is formed into blocks, lends itself to the production of a large number of shapes, both solid and hollow. On the other hand, aerated concrete blocks, because they are

FIG. 24.1 Types of aggregate concrete blocks.

wire-cut from a large slab, are limited to solid cuboid shapes. Some typical shapes of aggregate blocks are shown in Fig. 24.1.

MANUFACTURING PROCESS

The concrete in blocks differs from normal structural concrete in being only partially compacted and by requiring 'green' strength, that is the ability to be demoulded immediately after forming and being capable of being handled and transported immediately after demoulding. The principles of mix design for structural concrete are not valid therefore for concrete to be used in block-making. Crushed or vesicular aggregates are generally easier to use than more rounded particles, and the overall grading should be finer. The proportion of very fine particles is important in giving the cohesiveness essential to adequate green strength. Control of the overall grading as well as the control of the amount of water in the mix are both of vital importance.

Whether the blocks are made of lightweight or dense aggregate, the particles of aggregate should be bonded together by cement paste to form a relatively open structure by compacting the concrete only partially under the influence of vibration. While the concrete is being vibrated, the cement paste, being thixotropic, liquefies and flows to form menisci at the points of contact of the aggregate particles and so bonds them like a properly soldered joint between metals. When the vibration stops, the cement paste 'gels' or becomes virtually solid and the whole structure becomes firm enough to permit the block to be extruded from the mould and to be handled to the place where it will be cured. If the grading of the aggregate is unsuitable or the vibration ineffective, the required strength cannot be attained except by increasing the amount of compaction by pressure or tamping, so raising the density of the concrete. The difference between properly and improperly made blocks is illustrated in Fig. 24.2 due to M'Intosh.[1]

Because of the relatively low cement content of the mix and the need for a cohesive mix, it is important that the concrete be thoroughly mixed, either in a high efficiency mixer, which encourages the rapid production of cement hydrates, or for a longer period in a larger ordinary mixer, to give time for the hydrates to form.

A block machine, whether stationary or 'egg-laying', distributes the fresh concrete into a mould, compacts it, and ejects the moulded block; it then repeats the cycle. With a stationary machine the mould rests on a flat pallet on which the block produced remains until it has been transported to the curing area. As will be shown later, the mobile machine does not require pallets.

The methods used for feeding the concrete to the mould box do not always give an even distribution. Most machines make several blocks in one operation and there is a tendency for the outside blocks and those furthest from the supply point to receive less material than the other parts. As all blocks are compacted to the same final depth, those receiving less material must be of lower density than the rest, with consequent variation in other properties. The length and thickness of all blocks are controlled by the mould dimensions, but the height is determined by the pressure head and the level to which it is allowed to fall.

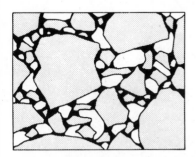 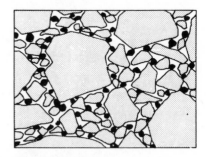

FIG. 24.2 Aggregate concrete blocks: (left) Ideal—particles of aggregate firmly bonded by cement paste at their points of contact; (right) Poor—particles inadequately bonded and strength achieved only with excessive density.

As mentioned above, the blocks after demoulding, must be matured. This means curing under moist conditions long enough for the completion of hydration, as explained in Chapter 4. However, once the necessary strength has developed, the blocks should be allowed to dry out and subsequently kept dry so as to minimise drying shrinkage (see Chapter 5). Drying before use also encourages carbonation shrinkage to take place. Blocks can be dried by artificial heating without damage, once they have been cured.

BLOCK MACHINES

Stationary machines vary from simple inexpensive manually-operated models to fully-automatic, high-speed, mass-production equipment. An example of the simplest machines is shown in Fig. 24.3 while one of the largest and most sophisticated is portrayed in Fig. 24.4.

The Lee Magnum Company, which makes a wide range of machines has designed their simple HBI machine to make plain solid blocks at the rate of 90 per hour; these blocks are nominal size 18 × 9 in. (458 × 229 mm) in thicknesses up to 9 in. The Besser machine is available as various models,

FIG. 24.3   Lee Magnum block machine.

but they all produce blocks in large quantity, commonly in excess of 1000 units per hour, 16 × 8 × 8 in. (406 × 203 × 203 mm) nominal dimensions. Although these latter machines are very expensive, the cost is not unduly high in relation to the overall expenditure for the whole installation, including buildings and services. Within this range of machines, there are numerous excellent block-producing units, both European and American.

In addition to stationary machines described above, there are a number of mobile or 'egg-laying' machines. These have one important advantage as mentioned earlier; they lay the blocks directly onto the smooth floor or concrete yard, thus avoiding the necessity for pallets. On the other hand, blocks so produced cannot conveniently be subsequently steamed-cured. A machine of this type is shown in Fig. 24.5, and can form more than 1000

FIG. 24.4 Besser block making machine.

FIG. 24.5 Multibloc mobile block making machine.

TYPICAL YARD LAYOUT

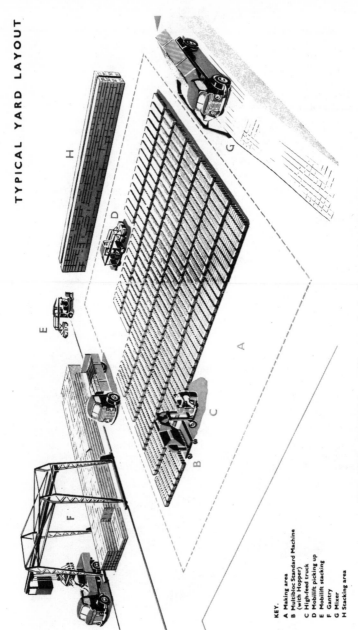

KEY.

A Making area
B Multibloc Standard Machine
  (with Hopper)
C High-feed truck
D Mobilift picking up
E Mobilift stacking
F Gantry
G Mixer
H Stacking area

FIG. 24.6   Typical layout for 'egg-laying' type of block making machine.

blocks, 18 × 9 × 9 in. (458 × 229 × 229 mm) per working hour. Figure 24.6 shows a typical layout for the mobile block-making machine.

SPECIFICATIONS

The dimensions and general properties of concrete blocks are regulated in Britain by the British Standard Specification, BS 2028:1968 (revised 1970).

This specification covers solid, hollow and cellular aggregate concrete blocks, as well as aerated concrete blocks. Such blocks are designated Types A, B or C, according to their properties, and are intended for use as follows:

Type A. For general use in building including use below the ground level damp-course.

Type B. For general use in building, including the use below the ground level dampproof course in internal walls and the inner leaf of external cavity walls. In other positions, such as below the ground level damp-proof course in the outer leaf of external walls, they should be solid, hollow, or cellular Type B blocks made with dense aggregate, or Type B blocks with an average compressive strength of not less than 7·0 MPa (1000 psi). Other Type B blocks may also be used below ground level damp-course in the outer leaf of external walls, even when they do not satisfy these requirements, if the manufacturer supplies authoritative evidence that the blocks are suitable for the purpose for which they are to be used. In the special case of leaves of external walls protected by tanking, any type of Type B blocks may be used.

Type C. Primarily for internal non-loadbearing walls, i.e. partitions and panels in framed structures.

The following definitions are as understood in British Standards:

Block. A walling unit (other than a half or other fractional unit) exceeding in length width or height the dimensions specified for bricks. The height should not exceed its length or six times its thickness, to avoid confusion with slabs or panels.

Solid block. A block is considered to be solid if the solid material is not less than 75 per cent of the total volume of the block calculated from the overall dimensions.

Hollow block. A block is considered to be hollow if it has one or more large cavities which pass through the block and the solid material is between 50 and 75 per cent of the total volume of the block as calculated from the overall dimensions.

Cellular block. A block is considered cellular if it has one or more large cavities which do not effectively pass through the block and the solid material is between 50 and 75 per cent of the total volume of the block calculated from the overall dimensions.

Aerated concrete block. A high-pressure steam-cured (autoclaved) block consisting essentially of an inorganic cementing agent, with or without the addition of fine inorganic aggregate, the aerated structure being formed either by generation of a gas, by chemical action within the mix prior to hardening, or by mechanical incorporation of air or other gas into the mix with the aid of chemical agents and mixing devices.

Block density. The density calculated by dividing the weight of a block by the overall volume, including holes and cavities.

Drying shrinkage. The difference between the length of a specimen which has been immersed in water, and the length when subsequently dried, all under specified conditions, expressed as a percentage of the length of the specimen.

Wetting expansion. The difference between the length of the specimen when dried and when subsequently immersed in water, all under specified conditions, expressed as a percentage of the length of the specimen.

The aggregates used in constructional lightweight concrete blocks are:

(1)   Foamed blast-furnace slag (expanded slag).
(2)   Furnace clinker (cinders).
(3)   Expanded clay, shale, or slate.
(4)   Natural pumice.
(5)   Sintered pulverised-fuel ash (fly ash).
(6)   Furnace bottom ash.

For very lightweight thermal insulating blocks, the aggregates used are:

(7)   Expanded perlite.
(8)   Exfoliated vermiculite.

Additives or admixtures. These are permitted in the mix where appropriate:

(1)   Pigments.
(2)   Substances to control set and hardening.
(3)   Substances to improve workability and reduce permeability.
(4)   Substances to cause foaming or gas generation.
(5)   Waterproofing or hydrophobic compounds.

TABLE 24.1
COMPRESSIVE STRENGTH OF TYPE B BLOCKS

Block type	Minimum compressive strength			
	Average of 10 blocks		*Lowest individual block*	
	(MPa)	*(psi)*	*(MPa)*	*(psi)*
B(2·8)	2·8	400	2·2	320
B(7)	7·0	1 000	5·6	800

Density limits. Type B and Type C shall be less than 1500 kg/m³ (93·6 pcf).

Wetting expansion. For blocks made with clinker aggregate the average value of the wetting expansion shall not exceed the approximate value for drying shrinkage, as given in Table 24.2.

TABLE 24.2
DRYING SHRINKAGE

Block type	Average compressive strength		Block density		Maximum drying shrinkage
	(*MPa*)	(*psi*)	(*kg/m³*)	(*pcf*)	(*per cent*)
B	less than 7·0	less than 1 000	Over 625	Over 39	0·07
			625 and less	39 and less	0·09
	7·0 and above	1 000 and above	All		0·08
C	all blocks		Over 625	Over 39	0·08
			625 and less	39 and less	0·09

The American ASTM Standard C145–71 defines the requirements for solid loadbearing concrete masonry, while C129–71 refers to hollow non-loadbearing concrete masonry units. These standards recognise two types of block, Type I, which carry a clause appertaining to moisture content in relation to drying shrinkage and Type II, which do not. Also there are two grades of block, Grade N, for general use such as exterior walls below and above ground level damp-course, which may or may not be exposed to moisture penetration or the weather, and for interior walls and back-up. Grade S blocks are limited in use to above damp course in external walls with weather protective coating, or walls not exposed to the weather.

TABLE 24.3
COMPRESSIVE STRENGTH

Block	Compressive strength			
	Average of 3 blocks		Lowest individual block	
	(*MPa*)	(*psi*)	(*MPa*)	(*psi*)
N I ⎫ N II ⎬	12·4	1 800	10·3	1 500
S I	8·3	1 200	7·0	1 000
S II	2·4	350	2·1	300

Like the British Standard, the ASTM Standard defines a solid block as a unit in which there is 75 per cent or more solid at any cross-sectional plane parallel to the bed plane. The hollow does not meet this requirement. Blocks having cavities must have a minimum shell thickness of 13 mm ($\frac{1}{2}$ in.). No block must deviate by more than 3·2 mm ($\frac{1}{8}$ in.) from the specification with respect to any one of its dimensions, length, thickness, or height.

TABLE 24.4
MOISTURE CONTENT FOR TYPE I LIMITS

Moisture content, maximum percentage of total absorption (average of 3 blocks)

Shrinkage (%)	Humidity conditions at job site or point of use		
	Humid	Intermediate	Arid
0·03 or less	45	40	35
0·03–0·045	40	35	30
0·045–0·065 max.	35	30	25

Blocks may be of lightweight aggregate or normal aggregate. They are classified as follows:

	Oven dried weight of concrete	
	(kg/m³)	(pcf)
Lightweight	1 680	105 max.
Medium weight	1 600–2 000	105–125
Normal weight	2 000	125 min.

DIFFERENCE IN ATTITUDE AND PRACTICE BETWEEN BRITISH AND AMERICAN BLOCK PRODUCERS

Differences between the British and American block industries are many, but they stem almost entirely from the fact that American industry is wedded to the idea that the concrete block should be considered, as indeed it is, a remarkably inexpensive substitute for dressed stone, and thus suitable as an exposed (facing) unit for exterior *and* interior use, yet efficiency of production has enabled manufacturers to sell at a price which is competitive with low-priced alternatives; British producers for the most part have as their objective the manufacture of an inexpensive alternative to common bricks, albeit a substitute with many advantages over the brick. So much do the Americans identify the concrete block with the normal use of dressed natural stone, that they call their wares, not concrete blocks, but 'concrete masonry units'.

The differences in aim naturally produce the differences in attitude and practice which manifest themselves at every point where comparisons are made between the industries in the respective countries. Such differences in commercial outlook and industrial practice do not in themselves imply vice or virtue on either side. The difference in aim has historical and social roots and is consolidated by economic and geographical considerations. However, some acceptance of the American philosophy in the British Isles is demonstrated by the investment by a few manufacturers in modern American or American-type equipment and the adoption, in some measure, of American production practice and standards of quality.

In the UK most firms make a standard block and in some cases a half block. On the other hand, American producers make a wide range of types and fractions of block. This divergence in production policy arises from the intended use of the block. At present, the British construction industry for the most part calls for blocks suitable only for subsequent plastering and rendering, so that it is of little consequence if a full-sized block has to be hacked down to some ill-fitting fractional block: it will not be visible in the finished work. In America, although some of the blocks produced might in fact be used in rendered or otherwise decorated walls, virtually all blocks are presumed to be destined for facing work, where every position in the wall must be furnished with an unblemished unit which fits exactly the space allotted to it. Thus the American block industry produces full blocks, halves, quarters, and other fractions, corner blocks (quoins), jamb blocks, both square and bull-nosed, lintel blocks, etc., these in several heights and thicknesses and several colours, solid and hollow, lightweight and heavy. The majority of producers in this way make at least 150 different blocks, but they make only one quality (i.e. with respect to appearance), fair-faced blocks, although they often produce a range of strengths and other physical properties. Manufacturers consider that having the equipment and organisation necessary to make 'premier' blocks, it is uneconomical to make 'commons'. The only 'seconds' they have available are blocks which have received blemishes in handling: these find their way into rendered work or cheap temporary buildings.

It almost goes without saying that in order to make blocks of satisfactory appearance much attention must be paid to detail in the production of the blocks: for example, great pains are usually taken to maintain uniform grading of the aggregates used, as well as the water content of the mix. Many aggregate manufacturers produce four or more graded fractions and dispense an agreed mixture to their various block-making customers: indeed some go so far as to send an engineer to a new customer's plant to ascertain the ideal mixture for his particular machines. Considerable care is taken to avoid segregation. All this is essential, not only for the good appearance of the blocks but also for consistency in other properties.

It seems that about 90 per cent of block producers in America use the three most sophisticated machines. The general view is that only the best machines will give an adequate output of top-quality blocks over long periods with the minimum of lost time and attention.

FIG. 24.7   Cubes ready for dispatch.

Not surprisingly, most manufacturers, having invested in a top-grade machine, have followed this up with block-handling equipment which gives rapid and safe transport for the blocks, as well as labour economy. Indeed, in America there is a high degree of mechanisation and automatic control. This is primarily for economic reasons, because instruments and machines cost less than men. But automatic control makes for uniformity of the product and mechanical handling reduces damage to the goods. Figure 24.7 shows blocks which have been automatically cubed. Figure 24.8 shows a fork-lift truck capable of lifting 4 cubes (432 blocks), enough to load one side of a normal truck, although in this instance it is carrying 3 cubes only. When blocks with cores are made, the bottom layer of blocks in each cube is sometimes automatically turned over so that the forks can penetrate the hollows, thus dispensing with wooden stillages.

This comparison of American and British block-making practice refers to mass-production and that mainly in the lightweight block field. Specialist firms in Britain engaged in making facing blocks produce units of excellent appearance and properties in many cases. These are mainly heavy concrete blocks.

It would appear that nearly all producers in America do some form of steam-curing: about 20–25 per cent do autoclaving, and this proportion is still rising: about 40 works employ one of the modifications of 'carbonation curing'. Autoclaving is regarded in most cases simply as an investment: some can see their way to make the investment, while others cannot. Those who do autoclaving feel that they are amply rewarded. They can, for example, charge a premium of a few cents and still have a large demand for

FIG. 24.8   Fork-lift trucks.

autoclaved blocks. Some manufacturers have sufficient saving from autoclaving to dispense with the premium charge.

Many block-makers in America offer the architect what is in effect a complete 'kit' to meet his requirements for the entire construction of the walls and floors, including windows and door frames of suitable module, lintels, reinforcing bars and of course blocks of every shape and size to carry out the design.

The new ASTM Standards specify maximum moisture content in the blocks in relation to the prevailing humidity in the various geographical regions, and to the potential drying shrinkage of the blocks. Consequently, blocks are kept as dry as possible and are frequently artificially dried by one means or another. For example, some firms draw dry air through the curing chambers at the end of the curing cycle in order to flush out the residual moisture from the blocks.

In the desert areas, blocks are stacked in the open (Fig. 24.9), but where rain is at all common the blocks are held in sheds (Fig. 24.10). Cubes are sometimes delivered wrapped in polythene sheet to keep them dry.

The compressive strength of blocks in America is generally higher than in the UK, and usually somewhat heavier. In general, this is not because such

FIG. 24.9   Blocks stacked in the open.

strength is required for structural reasons, but because blocks must withstand handling without damage to corners and faces. Blocks are seldom less than 7·0 MPa (1000 psi), even in the lightweight class, and are frequently 17·5–21·0 MPa (2500–3000 psi) in the heavy type.

Blocks are often made with a single vertical groove at the mid-point; when these are laid in half-bond with recessed joints they have the appearance of stack-bonding in square blocks, a very pleasing effect (Fig. 24.11). In some cases the vertical joints are recessed while the horizontal

FIG. 24.10   Blocks stacked in sheds.

FIG. 24.11   Grooved blocks giving appearance of stack-bonded square blocks.

joints are left flush, so giving the effect of vertical columns (Fig. 24.12). In other cases half-bonded blocks have the horizontal joints recessed and the vertical joints flushed; this gives a 'weatherboard' effect.

As it stands at present, about 80 per cent of the masonry work in America goes to concrete blocks; the corresponding figure in Britain is about 33 per cent. Some of the resistance to the wider use of concrete blocks in the British Isles is very deep-rooted, but much could be done to change this attitude by well-formulated promotional work.

FIG. 24.12   Half-bonded grooved blocks with raked-out vertical joints.

The annual output of concrete blocks in the USA (expressed as 16 × 8 × 8 in. or 406 × 203 × 203 mm) is believed to be at least 2800 million, which is about 9 times that of Britain (estimated at 300 million).

About half the concrete blocks made in America are lightweight. The lightweight aggregates, in order of importance, are as follows:

(1) Expanded clay, expanded shale, expanded slate.
(2) Expanded or foamed blast-furnace slag.
(3) Furnace clinker or cinders.
(4) Pumice and scoria.

REFERENCE

1. M'Intosh, J. D. (1973). Overseas Building Note, No. 150, Building Research Establishment, Watford.

CHAPTER TWENTY-FIVE

Lightweight Concrete Walls

SUMMARY

The differences in design methods used for materials and methods of construction which comply with established practice are compared with those used for materials and methods of construction which do not. Some important factors which influence the behaviour of walls are considered, viz. eccentricity and concentration of loading, and slenderness.

The design and performance of masonry block walls are described. The strength of such walls is governed by the strength of the units and of the mortar and by the workmanship employed. The design and performance of cast-in-situ unreinforced and reinforced lightweight concrete walls are discussed.

GENERAL

Walls only rarely have to be specially designed for strength in buildings of relatively low height because walls of such buildings are, in general, more than sufficiently strong and stiff if they are to satisfy other functional requirements, e.g. adequate thermal insulation and protection against the weather. In recent years, however, greater knowledge and experience of the actual behaviour and durability of materials used in structures has made it possible to employ these with greater boldness, under conditions that brought them somewhat nearer to their ultimate loadbearing capacity.

In the past, buildings more than five or six storeys high were not usually designed with loadbearing walls and the wall thicknesses employed were considerable. Recently, however, buildings of 20 storeys and even more have been safely erected, using cast-*in-situ*, no-fines concrete walls without reinforcement, having a uniform thickness not exceeding 260–290 mm (10–11 in.). In such cases walls must be purposely designed to possess adequate loadbearing capacity and structural safety.

Knowledge of the conditions of loading, the conditions of vertical and lateral support and a sound judgement of the permissible stresses or of the load factor or coefficients of safety that must be allowed for safety, are then necessary. Engineers must also be informed on the properties of the different types of wall—masonry, precast concrete panel walls or cast-*in-situ* concrete walls—made of a variety of materials. They must have a conception based on theory as well as on practical experience and research, of the effect of various important collateral factors, such as the presence of window and door openings, on the strength and stability of walls. Equal in its importance to structural considerations is the effect of durability.

The principles and the essential requirements relating to the strength and stability of walls have been set out with admirable conciseness in *Principles of Modern Building*,[1] together with an interpretation of the codes of practice.

LOADING

In accordance with the accepted conventions of engineering design every structure must be capable of resisting dead loading and imposed loading. Broadly, dead loading comprises the weight of the structure itself together with the weight of the remaining parts of the building supported by the structure. In the case of loadbearing walls, the dead load to be resisted at the base of the wall consists of the weight of the wall itself and of that part of the floors and roof and of the partitions above, which must be supported by it. The weight of these components and materials can be estimated according to BS 648:1964.[2]

Imposed loading comprises the loads that may vary with the occupation of the building, i.e. the weight of people, machines or materials, in addition to natural forces such as wind pressure and—in some cases—earthquake forces. It is common experience that the precise magnitude and nature of the imposed loading in a building cannot be determined accurately and, moreover, that the nature of the occupancy of most buildings, particularly of industrial buildings, may change during its useful life. It is, therefore, necessary to adopt a convention of imposed loading which is sufficiently broad to encompass a variety of loading possibilities having regard to the type of occupancy for which the building is suitable. At the same time this convention must not be so extravagant as to provide an unnecessarily high degree of safety against collapse or against excessive deformation.

The loading convention in general use in Great Britain is set out in the Code of Practice CP 3.[3] A statistical approach to the determination of imposed floor and roof loading was initiated by G. R. Mitchell.[4] The general treatment of the modern statistical theory of loads originates from the work of the CEB.[5,6]

NEW MATERIALS AND METHODS OF CONSTRUCTION: DESIGN CONSIDERATIONS

The design and construction of concrete walls of various types, i.e. masonry block walls, cast-*in-situ* reinforced or unreinforced concrete walls, or precast panel type walls should generally conform with Codes of Practice CP 111,[7] CP 114[8] or CP 110.[9] It is necessary, however, that materials and methods of construction that are not covered by the Codes of Practice should be given reasonable encouragement, otherwise building practice would obviously stagnate. Such materials and methods of construction are generally admitted, provided that the materials concerned conform with the appropriate British Standard Specifications or their equivalent and that the methods of construction are such as to ensure an adequate standard of strength and durability. In practice this rule is applied in a broad sense, for new materials can rarely have had the opportunity of being made the subject of a Standard Specification. Indeed, some lightweight aggregates suitable for structural use and most types of aerated concrete have not, in fact, been included in a British Standard until recently, but this has not prevented their use.

In such cases it is usual for contractors or manufacturers to apply to the appropriate local supervising authority for the granting of a waiver from the Building Regulations. The local authority is influenced by advice given by qualified expert opinion on the safety and durability of the particular material or method of construction. They have particular regard to certificates granted by the Agrément Authority. Such Agrément Certificates are granted in respect of new methods of construction and materials, usually on the basis of tests, for an initial period of three years and renewable for a further three years. They have been introduced to encourage innovations in the construction industries. After being used in practice for six years it is assumed that a useful and practical innovation can be incorporated in the appropriate British Standard or Code of Practice. In issuing such waivers, subject in some cases to approval by the appropriate Ministry, supervising authorities are guided above all by the statutory obligation imposed upon them to safeguard the safety of the inhabitants.

Where evidence is required of the safety of new materials or methods of construction not covered by a code of practice, it is necessary to submit the results of tests on completed structural components. In the case of masonry in the UK such tests are laid down in CP 111:1970 which specifies that tests should be representative of the materials, workmanship and details of the construction for which approval is desired. The test panels, at least two of which should be built for each wall construction, where it is intended to determine the strength under axial loading, should be 1·2–1·8 m (4–6 ft) in length and from 2·4–2·7 m (8–9 ft) in height. They should be built under conditions representative of the conditions in the actual building construction, and should be 28 days old at the time of testing. The load should be applied axially and uniformly along the top and bottom faces of the wall panel. Where the materials or methods of construction do, in fact, comply with the Code of Practice CP 111, permissible stresses obtained from wall tests may be used at the discretion of the designer, as an

TABLE 25.1

BASIC COMPRESSIVE STRESSES FOR BRICKWORK MEMBERS (AT AND AFTER THE STATED TIMES)

Description of mortar	Cement	Lime	Sand	Hardening time after completion of work[b] (days)	Basic stress in MPa corresponding to units whose crushing strength (in MPa)[c]								
					2·8	7·0	10·5	20·5	27·5	34·5	52·0	69·0	96·5 or greater
Cement	1	0–$\frac{1}{4}$[a]	3	7	0·28	0·70	1·05	1·65	2·05	2·50	3·50	4·55	5·85
	1	$\frac{1}{2}$	4$\frac{1}{2}$	14	0·28	0·70	0·95	1·45	1·70	2·05	2·80	3·60	4·50
Cement-lime	1	1	6	14	0·28	0·70	0·95	1·30	1·60	1·85	2·50	3·10	3·80
Cement with plasticiser[d]	1	—	6										
Masonry cement[e]	—	—	—										
Cement-lime	1	2	9	14	0·28	0·55	0·85	1·15	1·45	1·65	2·05	2·50	3·10
Cement with plasticiser[d]	1	—	8										
Masonry cement[e]	—	—	—										
Cement-lime	1	3	12	14	0·21	0·49	0·70	0·95	1·15	1·40	1·70	2·05	2·40
Hydraulic lime	—	1	2	14	0·21	0·49	0·70	0·95	1·15	1·40	1·70	2·05	2·40
Non-hydraulic	—	1	3	28[f]	0·21	0·42	0·55	0·70	0·75	0·85	1·05	1·15	1·40

[a] The inclusion of lime in cement mortars is optional.

[b] These periods should be increased by the full amount of any time during which the air temperature remains below 4·4 °C plus half the amount of any time during which the temperature is between 4·4 and 10 °C.

[c] Linear interpolation is permissible for units whose crushing strengths are intermediate between those given in the table.

[d] Plasticisers must be used according to manufacturers' instructions.

[e] Masonry cement mortars must be used according to manufacturers' instructions, and mix proportions of masonry cement to sand should be such as to give comparable mortar crushing strengths with the cement:lime:sand mix of the grade.

[f] A longer period should ensue where hardening conditions are not very favourable.

alternative to the permissible stresses laid down in the Code on the basis of Table 25.1.

Having obtained the failing loads of the walls, the lower of the two test results is used with a specified load-factor to give a permissible stress. The load-factors given in the Code normally vary from 5 where the slenderness ratio is 6 or less, to 10 for a slenderness ratio of 24, rising linearly with the slenderness ratio. If the compressive (wet) strength of the masonry units (bricks or blocks) lies between 2·1 and 2·8 MPa (300–400 psi)—some aerated concrete blocks fall under this heading—then the corresponding load-factors for slenderness ratios of 6 and 24 are increased to 7 and 12, respectively.

To obtain the permissible stress for a wall whose slenderness ratio differs from that of the test panel, the permissible stress obtained from the test should be multiplied by the ratio of the stress reduction factors appropriate to the actual wall and the test panel. The stress reduction factors for different slenderness ratios and methods of construction are given in CP 111. It appears that this rule was intended only to apply, however, where the actual wall and the design panel are of the same thickness and merely differ in height slightly.

Even with the increased load-factor in the Code it seems desirable to restrict the use of materials having a compressive strength less than 2·8 MPa (400 psi) to autoclaved aerated concrete blocks made under factory conditions, in which uniformity can be attained consistently. To admit lightweight or normal aggregate concrete blocks having an average compressive strength less than 2·8 MPa (400 psi) for the construction of walls would be in conflict with general practice in most countries.

PRINCIPAL FACTORS INFLUENCING THE BEHAVIOUR OF WALLS

The accepted principles of structural design appear to be readily applicable to walls made of concrete masonry or monolithic concrete. It is doubtful, however, whether in fact any other type of member is subject to such uncertainty and to so many discrepancies between the design assumptions and actual conditions. This may be the reason for reinforced concrete walls being the last type of structural member for which design rules have been established in codes of practice. Walls are subjected to direct compression and bending as are, indeed, columns and piers, but in general the degree of bending and the stresses induced by it are difficult to predict accurately. The effects of cross-walls and the forces occurring at the junction of walls with other walls and with floor and roof slabs are difficult to evaluate theoretically and the empirical conclusions derived from experiments sometimes lack conviction because of insufficient evidence.

A considerable amount of research has been carried out at the Building Research Station through the years on various types of wall construction and the results obtained have been largely incorporated in codes of practice. Advice on the interpretation and application of the codes as well as an explanation of their background is available from various sources.[1,10,11]

It has been established that in general the behaviour of loadbearing walls is greatly influenced by the conditions of support and loading, i.e. the degree of eccentricity of the imposed loads, by the slenderness of the wall, i.e. the ratio of its thickness and effective height, by the length of the wall in relation to its height, and by the material it is made of, i.e. whether or not it is capable of resisting tensile stresses.

Eccentricity of loading

In practice, loading imposed upon walls is rarely completely axial as the resultant of the external forces does not generally pass through the centre of gravity of the horizontal cross-section of the wall, which is usually in its middle line. The conditions of support of the wall itself and of the floor and roof members it has to support are such that while some eccentricity becomes often inevitable, particularly for external walls (Fig.25.1), it is not possible to determine its degree by theory alone.

Where eccentricity of loading is introduced, the even stress distribution across the cross-section, which characterises axial loading conditions, must change into an uneven stress distribution. Where, for a homogeneous cross-section, the distance of the resultant of the imposed loads from the centre line of the cross-section does not exceed one-sixth of the thickness of the wall, the stresses, though not uniformly distributed, will continue to be compressive throughout the cross-section. Where, however, this eccentricity is exceeded, some tension will occur in the material of the wall owing to bending that is induced. In reinforced concrete walls, these tensile stresses may be resisted by suitably placed reinforcing bars. In masonry walls and in plain concrete walls that do not contain shrinkage reinforcement, tensile stresses cannot in fact be resisted satisfactorily by the material of the wall itself, and its tensile strength is neglected for the purpose of the calculations. Where the eccentricity of loading reaches one-third of the wall thickness, a condition that may occur where the floor consists of flexible timber joists and boarding, this may affect the stability of the wall. To reduce the risks inherent in calculated or accidental eccentricity of loading on columns and walls, the permissible loads on compression members subjected to such loads must be reduced, compared with members subjected to purely axial loading.

Concentrated loading

Design calculations relating to walls are not restricted to loads that are uniformly distributed along the horizontal cross-section of the wall. In

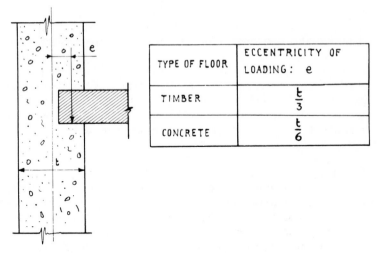

TYPE OF FLOOR	ECCENTRICITY OF LOADING: e
TIMBER	$\dfrac{t}{3}$
CONCRETE	$\dfrac{t}{6}$

ECCENTRIC LOADING ON EXTERNAL SOLID WALL

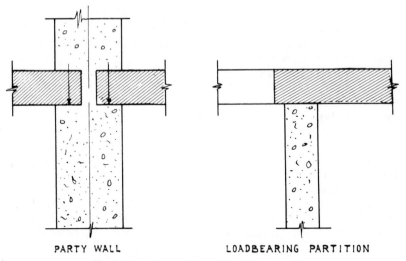

PARTY WALL   LOADBEARING PARTITION

FIG. 25.1   Eccentricity of loading on walls.

most structures, walls are also subjected to loads that are concentrated to a varying degree, arising from floor and roof beams, roof trusses, spine beams and lintels. In the case of concentrated wall loads, local failure due to crushing or splitting of the material beneath the load must be prevented. It was soon realised, however, that the theoretical bearing stresses for concentrated loads can safely exceed the stresses allowed for uniformly distributed loading, owing to the distribution of the load throughout the depth of the wall over a rapidly increasing area of concrete; in the immediate vicinity of the load there is a triaxial stress condition arising from the lateral restraint to which the material is subjected immediately beneath the load and the consequent increase in its resistance to crushing and splitting. In CP 111, therefore, the stresses allowed for concentrated loading only, are increased by 50 per cent compared with the usual permissible stress for uniformly distributed loading.

The effect of slenderness

With increasing height, compression members having the same cross-sectional dimensions tend to fail at a lower load. This cannot be entirely explained by elastic instability even in the case of compression members made of homogeneous materials, such as steel. Elastic instability may play some part but, essentially, the reduction of loadbearing capacity with increasing slenderness, particularly for struts of non-homogeneous material, such as masonry or concrete, is probably largely due to the greater sensitiveness of such members to bending induced by accidental eccentricities of loading. The performance of walls under loading is affected by their slenderness ratio, i.e. the ratio of the effective thickness to the effective height or length. This is reflected in the design of loadbearing walls as laid down in codes of practice.

The effective height which may be assumed for particular types of wall in design is deemed to depend on the conditions of support of the walls. For a wall that is effectively supported against horizontal displacement at both top and bottom, the effective height is taken to be three-quarters of the distance between these lateral supports. For a free-standing wall, i.e. one supported effectively at the bottom only, the effective height is taken to be $1\frac{1}{2}$ times the actual height. Generally the bottom of walls is assumed to be in a flat-ended condition. The effect of hinged supports which may occur in tests is not taken into account additionally.

Adequate lateral support is assumed to exist where the walls are restrained by concrete floor or roof slabs. For other type of construction, such as timber floors, suitable anchorage arrangements must be provided at the joints between floor and wall systems. Reinforced aerated concrete floor and wall slabs may be generally assumed to provide adequate lateral restraint for masonry walls and other types of walling on which they rest, without special anchorage arrangements.

Lateral forces such as wind loads must be eventually transferred to the ground through intersecting walls, gable-end walls, piers or buttresses; these must be adequately stiff to prevent excessive lateral movements. Where the lateral loads are transmitted to the cross-walls or piers through floor and roof slabs, these must be capable of transmitting the lateral loads acting as flat horizontal beams, and their joints to the walls and piers must be sufficiently strong.

In general the effective thickness which must be taken into account for the calculation of the slenderness ratio is the actual thickness of the wall. Where the wall is properly bonded into piers or to intersecting walls at suitable intervals, then the effective thickness to be assumed for the calculation may be increased (Fig. 25.2). The maximum increase is a two-fold one where the pier—including the wall—is at least three times as thick as the wall and the distance between adjacent piers is not more than six times the width of the pier. For the purpose of the calculations, intersecting walls are assumed to be equivalent to piers whose width is that of the intersecting wall and whose thickness is equal to three times the thickness of the stiffened wall. Piers may be intended to carry local loading or to stiffen a slender wall against lateral buckling or, alternatively, to prevent overturning under horizontal loading. Under imposed vertical loading account is taken of the increased resistance against buckling provided by the piers, by reducing the slenderness ratio and thus increasing the design load. The wall surfaces serve to transmit horizontal forces to the piers, but composite action between pier and wall does not generally appear to enhance the resistance of the piers against lateral forces considerably.

In the case of cavity walls the resistance of the loadbearing leaf against buckling or failure in bending owing to accidental eccentricities is increased by the other leaf. The latter must be securely attached, however, to the loadbearing leaf by means of metal ties or by other types of tie placed staggered at least 3 ft apart horizontally and 18 in. apart vertically. The ties must be durable and should be closer together near openings in the wall. The effective thickness of cavity walls may be calculated by one of two alternative methods, either of which may be used. Either two-thirds of the total thickness of the solid material in the wall or—where only one leaf carries the load—the thickness of that single loadbearing leaf is taken as the effective thickness. Usually the first method gives a more economical wall and a greater working load. Each leaf of a cavity wall must not, however, be less than 3 in. thick and the cavity must be not less than 2 in. nor more than 3 in. wide, where either of the leaves is less than 4 in. thick. With thicker leaves the cavity may be up to 6 in. wide, provided that an appropriate number of standard strip ties is used to connect the leaves of the wall securely.

The basic design working stresses are laid down in CP 111 for a theoretical slenderness ratio of six. Corrections are given in the code for higher slenderness ratios so as to reduce working stresses in accordance with the slenderness of the walls. The maximum slenderness ratio which may be permitted for walls differs with the method of construction and the materials used, but must nowhere exceed 24. The possibility of the

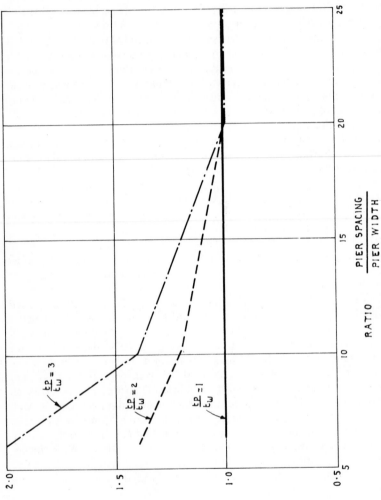

Fig. 25.2 The effective thickness of walls stiffened by piers, for the purpose of the calculation of the slenderness ratio for varying pier spacing and width, pier thickness (t_p) and wall thickness (t_w), as laid down in CP 111.

occurrence of secondary effects due to the lateral deformations of slender compression members should be kept in mind.

For reinforced concrete walls the permissible stresses are laid down in CP 114[8] and the reductions due to increasing slenderness are the same as those established for reinforced concrete columns (Fig. 14.2).

MASONRY WALLS

The most common use of lightweight concrete, as well as of aerated concrete, in the past has been in the form of precast building blocks. The advantages of lightweight concrete blocks compared with those made of dense concrete or with bricks are the greatly increased thermal insulation, and its lower weight, so that larger-sized units can be handled with ease on the site. With such lighter units, building can be speeded up considerably. The introduction of aerated concrete units not only increased the heat insulation which it was possible to obtain, still further, but also made a precision-made component available for the building industry.

The various properties masonry blocks are required to have are laid down in BS 2028.[12]

The use of concrete blocks in walls is dealt with by the following Codes of Practice:

CP 121.201 for ashlared masonry walls.[13]
CP 122 for block walls.[14]
CP 111.101 and CP 111.102 for structural recommendations for loadbearing walls.[7]

For the same height and for the same loading conditions the loadbearing capacity of masonry walls, including walls made with lightweight or aerated concrete block units, has been found to be governed mainly by the strength of the units, the strength of the mortar, the type of bond used, and the workmanship.

The strength of the units

It has become abundantly clear from the results of laboratory investigations that the strength obtained for different masonry block units depends very greatly on the method of test used. It was, therefore, necessary to lay down agreed methods of test for the determination of the unit strength before attempting to compare the latter with the strength of the wall. The standard test for masonry units for the UK has been laid down in CP 111.

The conditions of test for different specimens should always be the same or be easily comparable and should be within the capabilities of ordinary testing laboratories and precasting factories. These conditions tend to vary, however, in different countries. In Great Britain, for example, tests on blocks are made after immersion in water for at least 24 h, thus ensuring that at the time of testing the units are fully saturated with water. This rule was adopted because it is known that the crushing strength of a concrete unit is affected by its moisture content; to obtain comparable results from strength tests it is, therefore, necessary that the specimens tested should all have the same moisture content. A specified moisture content is difficult to attain, however, with any degree of accuracy. By testing the blocks in a saturated condition, i.e. at their maximum possible moisture content, uniformity is automatically ensured for all specimens tested. The same considerations apply to the requirement of curing works cubes of concrete in water.[5]

In some countries, e.g. in Scandinavia, testing in a standard condition has been rejected, because the actual percentage of moisture present may vary considerably at saturation for different types of concrete. In different concretes the effect of saturation on the compressive strength may, therefore, vary appreciably. With dense gravel aggregate concrete the effect of saturation on the strength is relatively small, with lightweight aggregate concrete it is usually somewhat greater, and for aerated concrete, as mentioned previously, it may induce a strength reduction of up to 30 per cent. Thus, in Great Britain, the makers of lightweight concrete units are placed in a somewhat unfavourable position from a commercial point of view because the recorded strength of their units is generally much below that which the units would resist under what are considered normal conditions of use and is also lower than that obtained for other competitive building materials.

On the other hand, compression tests are in essence no more than an index of performance. Testing in a saturated condition, in spite of some disadvantages provides a satisfactory safeguard for uniformity of test results for a material and variations in the effects of saturation might be taken into account by having different strength criteria of acceptance for different types of material. In practice this would admittedly raise some difficulties; it is not certain, moreover, that walls would not be subjected to loading in a saturated state. Where buildings are exposed to driving rain, water penetration through the rendering can occur. Rendering with a high cement content will crack readily and allow moisture to penetrate through the wall. The rendering may prevent the evaporation of the water, however, and the wall may remain wet for a prolonged period under load.

The strength of the mortar

Most of the available information on the effect of mortar strength on the strength of walls has been obtained from experimental work on brickwork.

The strength of mortar depends largely on the mix proportions and properties of the cement, lime and sand used. Lime is included to improve the workability of the mortar, but the addition of air-entraining or plasticising agents can ensure that plain 1:6 cement:sand mortars retain adequate workability for normal use without the addition of lime. Rich or strong mortars are not generally suitable for lightweight concrete block masonry work because they are too rigid.

The effect of the addition of lime on the strength of brickwork made with different mortar mixes is shown in relation to the strength of brickwork built with a 1:3 cement:sand mortar in Table 25.2.[1]

TABLE 25.2

EFFECT OF MORTAR MIX ON STRENGTH OF MASONRY

Proportions of lime and cement in the binder, by volume		Strength of brickwork built with the mortar mixes given				
		Strength of brickwork built with 1:3 cement mortar				
		For proportion of binder (cement and lime) to sand, by volume				
Lime	Cement	1:1	1:1½	1:2	1:3	1:4
0	100	—	—	0·96	1·00	—
50	50	0·72	0·87	0·94	0·96	0·92
60	40	0·70	0·84	0·90	0·92	0·87
70	30	0·66	0·77	0·84	0·87	0·81
80	20	0·58	0·68	0·74	0·79	0·71
90	10	0·47	0·56	0·60	0·65	0·59
100	0	—	—	—	0·48	—

An optimum mortar strength appears to exist for most types of masonry unit and the use of a richer and stronger mortar does not necessarily lead to greater wall strength. Within the limitations imposed by this rule, the strength of masonry walls generally increases if the binder contains a larger proportion of cement and less lime, i.e. if the strength of the binder increases. This is more pronounced for low strengths. For walls of higher strength, changes in the strength of the mortar used do not affect the strength of the wall very greatly. In the example mentioned earlier, the reduction of the mortar strength by about 40 per cent—as a result of using a mortar mix consisting of one part cement, one part lime and six parts sand instead of one part cement to three parts sand—only diminished the strength of the brickwork by about 4 per cent.

It is, therefore, a mistake to sacrifice workability in a mortar in order to attain a high mortar strength, for the strength of the wall is, in any case, very often considerably higher than the strength of the mortar. This is probably due to the triaxial stress conditions in the thin strip of mortar between courses, caused by the lateral restraint imposed on the mortar joint. The mortar strength may have to be increased, however, for work in cold weather; weak mortars may not set satisfactorily in cold weather and the mortar joint then may not have sufficient frost resistance.

In addition to being more workable, weaker cement–lime mixes have other advantages; for example, they are less likely to cause efflorescence and tend to improve resistance to cracking of the blocks. Cracking is generally caused by local movements of the foundations, shrinkage or stresses induced by thermal changes in the structure. Shrinkage movements are, in general, less with weaker mortars than with richer ones. Moreover, where cracking occurs in weak mortars it does not tend to spread into the blocks as in the case of walls built with stronger mortars where the stiff mortar joints exert a severe restraint upon the concrete blocks and frequently induce cracking in the blocks themselves.

THE RELATIONSHIP BETWEEN BLOCK STRENGTH AND WALL STRENGTH

Tests made at the Building Research Station indicate that the strength of masonry walls increases with the block strength, although not linearly, and

TABLE 25.3

REDUCTION FACTORS FOR SLENDERNESS RATIO FOR MASONRY WALLS

Slenderness ratio	Reduction factor			
	Axially loaded	Eccentricity of vertical loading as a proportion of the thickness of the member		
		$\frac{1}{6}$	$\frac{1}{3}$	$\frac{1}{2}$
6	1·00	1·00	0·98	0·97
8	0·92	0·92	0·87	0·85
10	0·84	0·82	0·76	0·73
12	0·76	0·72	0·65	0·60
14	0·67	0·62	0·54	0·48
16	0·58	0·52	0·42	0·35
18	0·50	0·42	0·30	0·23
21	0·47	0·38	0·25	0·17
24	0·44	0·34	0·19	0·11

Linear interpolation between values for the reduction factor is permissible.

that the wall strength is frequently higher than the cube strength of the mortar.

The permissible stresses given in CP 111 are for walls and piers having a slenderness ratio equal to unity, these stresses being related to the strength of the block and the mortar mix used. With increasing slenderness ratio and diminishing block strength the danger of failure of the wall due to buckling or unforeseen local eccentricities increases and the permissible stresses must, therefore, be diminished accordingly (Table 25.3).[7]

For average strengths and varying slenderness ratios the code of practice provides for load factors of about 6 to 18 against failure of a wall built with the richer mortar mixes. With decreasing unit strength, decreasing mortar strength and increasing slenderness ratio, the actual load factor increases considerably (Table 25.4).[1]

The permissible stresses established in the code are based on the assumption that the wall strength is about 40 per cent of the strength of the units when these are tested in accordance with the code. This relationship in general applies only to low and medium strength units. Experimental evidence indicates that with increasing unit strength the relationship between wall strength and unit strength is reduced to about 0·25. These conclusions were derived from numerous tests made on walls made both with brick and masonry block units where the ratio of block height to block thickness was about two-thirds. Where the height of the blocks is greater than two-thirds of its thickness, the ratio of wall strength to unit strength is increased considerably. Where the height/thickness ratio of the blocks is, therefore, greater than 2, the normal permissible stresses for walls laid down in CP 111 may be doubled, i.e. the ratio of wall strength to unit strength is taken as 0·8, a value that is close to the ratio of the strength of reinforced concrete walls to the cube strength. A multiplication factor intermediate between unity and 2 may be chosen by linear interpolation for walls built with blocks having height/thickness ratios intermediate between $\frac{2}{3}$ and 2.

The effect of this shape factor on the loadbearing capacity of masonry walls cannot be ascribed to a well-defined single cause. The experimental results indicate that the height/thickness ratio of individual blocks, the number of horizontal joints as well as the slenderness ratio of the wall itself, must have an important influence (Table 25.4). Since joints are a source of weakness, the greater the number of joints in a wall the greater the risk of premature failure.

Failure of masonry walls is rarely caused by a general crushing of the blocks; it usually occurs as a result of splitting of the wall or by a diagonal shear crack, accompanied by local crushing (Fig. 25.3). Frequently this is caused by failure of the mortar joints, for in such highly stressed material, where the mortar is restrained on all sides, a local fault in the material or a local variation of eccentricity of loading can lead to local failure and then to a general collapse.

TABLE 25.4
THE STRENGTH OF SOME STOREY-HEIGHT BLOCK WALLS UNDER AXIAL LOADING[1]

Type	Particulars of the blocks — Dimensions mm (in.)			Ratio: Height/Thickness	Mortar mix by volume (cement:lime:sand)	Strength — Block		Strength — Wall		Ratio: Strength of wall / Strength of block	Ratio: Strength of wall / Estimated permissible stress[a]	Estimated slenderness ratio
	l	*h*	*t*			(MPa)	(psi)	(MPa)	(psi)			
Foamed slag concrete blocks	254 (10)	203 (8)	203 (8)	1·0	1:2:9	2·5	370	2·1	310	0·83	(13)	9
	203 (8)	203 (8)	203 (8)	1·0	1:2:9	2·5	370	2·3	340	0·93	(14)	9
	457 (18)	228 (9)	228 (9)	1·0	1:4:9	3·9	560	2·5	370	0·66	10	8
Lightweight concrete blocks	457 (18)	228 (9)	228 (9)	1·0	1:4:9	2·8	410	3·0	440	1·08	15	8
	457 (18)	228 (9)	228 (9)	1·0	1:4:9	1·9	270	1·7	240	0·89	(13)	8
Hollow clay blocks	228 (9)	228 (9)	228 (9)	1·0	1:1:6	3·9	560	2·6	380	0·68	11	8
	304 (12)	228 (9)	157 (6)	1·5	1:0:3	3·0	430	2·5	370	0·86	17	12
	228 (9)	228 (9)	101 (4)	2·25	1:0:3	3·8	550	3·1	450	0·81	14	18
	304 (12)	228 (9)	76 (3)	3·0	1:0:3	5·6	810	6·0	870	1·06	27	24
Perforated clay block	228 (9)	228 (9)	108 (4¼)	2·1	1:4:3	29·6	4280	11·1	1610	0·38	20	17
Cored clinker block	457 (18)	228 (9)	228 (9)	1·0	1:2:9	3·2	460	2·4	350	0·76	11	8
	457 (18)	228 (9)	114 (4½)	2·0	1:1:6	3·5	500	3·0	440	0·88	13	16
Cellular clinker block	457 (18)	228 (9)	114 (4½)	2·0	1:1:6	4·1	590	3·2	460	0·78	12	16
	457 (18)	228 (9)	76 (3)	3·0	1:1:6	6·0	860	3·7	540	0·63	16	24

[a] For values in parenthesis strength is lower than that required by CP 111.

FIG. 25.3   Wall panel made with lightweight concrete masonry blocks, after testing to failure.

The lateral strength of masonry walls

The lateral strength of masonry walls has been examined using various support conditions, in numerous tests at the Building Research Station. The resistance of walls against lateral pressure is of considerable importance, for external walls are frequently subjected to horizontal wind pressures, and may be subjected to earth pressure, explosive effects, and accidental forces.

The test results show that failure under lateral loading is usually due to cracking caused by a breakdown of the bond between the masonry blocks and the mortar. As a rule, therefore, cracking is not due to tensile failure of the units themselves or of the mortar. Stronger mortar in itself need not have the effect of increasing the resistance of a masonry wall against lateral forces.[1]

It has been found also from many tests that the edge conditions of a wall have a very important influence on its lateral strength. Square wall panels simply supported along all four sides, for example, can resist lateral pressures that are seven times as high as the loadbearing capacity of identical walls supported at the top and at the bottom of the wall only. If the wall panels are built into rigid frames, the arching action which results in the wall acting as a flat dome enables the panel to sustain considerably higher forces even after cracking has occurred.

Simultaneous application of vertical and lateral loading also has the effect of increasing the resistance of a wall panel against lateral loading. Openings on the other hand are largely responsible for the liability of the walls to crack and they determine the direction of the cracks. They have a general weakening effect and reduce the lateral strength of walls.

Workmanship

The quality of the workmanship has an important effect on the strength of masonry walls. The wall strength may vary by 25–35 per cent as a consequence of variations in workmanship. The permissible stresses laid down in the various codes of practice were adopted having regard to the effect of indifferent workmanship. No allowance is made, however, for improved supervision and better workmanship in masonry walls by permitting an increase of the permissible stresses, as in the case of reinforced concrete walls.

Adequate bonding is required in masonry block walls in the ordinary way. Lintels should have a bedding equal to at least half the block length.

CAST-*IN-SITU* CONCRETE WALLS

In the UK cast-*in-situ* concrete walls including no-fines concrete walls should comply with CP 111.[7] The design stresses in concrete walls depend

TABLE 25.5
MAXIMUM PERMISSIBLE STRESSES FOR PLAIN LIGHTWEIGHT
CONCRETE WALLS

Maximum cube strength (works test) at 28 days		Maximum permissible stresses for a slenderness ratio of 15 or less	
(MPa)	(psi)	(MPa)	(psi)
14·0	2 000	2·6	380
11·0	1 600	2·1	310
8·3	1 200	1·6	230
5·5	800	1·1	160
2·8	400	0·5	80

Intermediate values may be found by interpolation

on the quality of the concrete. These stresses are given for example in Table
25.5 for ordinary grade concrete and in Table 25.6 for structural grade
concrete,[7] for a given slenderness ratio.

It should be noted that high-alumina cement concrete should not be used
in any structural members.

The uniformly distributed design stresses applicable to actual walls are
obtained by multiplying the basic stress given in Tables 25.5 and 25.6 by a
factor depending on slenderness, i.e. reducing linearly from 1·0 for a

TABLE 25.6
MAXIMUM PERMISSIBLE STRESSES FOR PLAIN CONCRETE WALLS OF STRUCTURAL
GRADE CONCRETE

Cement	Minimum cube strength at 28 days		Maximum permissible stresses for slenderness ratio of 15 or less
	Preliminary tests u_p	Works test u_w	
Portland cements	$1\frac{1}{3}$ times u_w	Not less than 15·8 MPa (2 250 psi) at 28 days	0·25u_w or a total of 10·5 MPa (1 500 psi) whichever is the less
High-alumina[a] cements	$1\frac{1}{3}$ times u_w	Not less than 35 MPa (5 000 psi) at one day	

[a] High-alumina cement concrete must not be used for structural members.

FIG. 25.4 Cast-*in-situ* loadbearing no-fines Lytag concrete wall construction.

slenderness ratio 15 to 0·70 for a slenderness ratio 24, as for reinforced concrete compression members according to CP 114:1957 (1965). Similarly, the design stresses are increased, as in CP 114:1957 (1965), for walls that are long in relation to their height. For example, where the length of a wall is greater than twice its height, the increase may be 20 per cent.

The normal permissible stresses may be exceeded by 25 per cent for the purpose of resisting eccentric or lateral loading, and by 50 per cent for concentrated loads.

Cast-*in-situ* loadbearing wall construction is generally associated in many parts of Western Europe with various mixes of no-fines concrete (Schüttbeton). In Germany and France foamed slag has been used widely with an additional fines content of about 10 per cent, using sand, crushed granulated slag or crushed air-cooled slag. Schüttbeton derives its German name from the method used for its placement: it is a 'poured concrete', placed without compacting (Fig. 25.4). In Great Britain, gravel aggregate has been used for this type of wall construction (Fig. 7.2).

For no-fines concrete mixes and, indeed, for porous types of concrete of any kind that are made with a minimum of compaction, it is difficult to make control specimens that would have a convincing similarity to the properties of the concrete which is actually poured in the structure on the site. Compaction by vibration is generally undesirable during the casting of the walls because it would reduce thermal insulating properties and the same degree of compaction cannot be obtained with the cubes as in the structure itself. In France, vibration is often adopted to obtain greater strength in walls, but this is not generally practised elsewhere. Compaction, however, critically influences the strength of no-fines concrete and, indeed, all its other properties.

Nevertheless, numerous experiments carried out mainly in Germany and at the Building Research Station in England give some indication of the relationship which may be assumed to exist between the strength of walls made of no-fines concrete and that obtained with 15 cm (6 in.) cubes. In general the ratio of wall strength to cube strength is lower than for ordinary graded concrete, and it seems to depend on the type of aggregate used. For gravel aggregate a ratio of 0·45–0·50 would appear to be adequate. In the light of tests a ratio of 0·40 would be more appropriate for lightweight aggregates; CP 111 applies to lightweight aggregate concrete and also to no-fines concrete (Chapter 7).

Where no-fines concrete is used, the eccentricity of loading must be kept low because, in general, reinforcement cannot be satisfactorily used with this type of material in industrial areas, except with special corrosion protection and no-fines or gap-graded concrete is itself weak in tension. For this same reason it is important to eliminate or to reduce to a minimum any movements due to differential settlements of the foundations or those due to thermal changes or shrinkage. A very stiff foundation system is, therefore, essential for cast-*in-situ* loadbearing no-fines concrete structures.

Since the walls do not generally contain reinforcement, for multi-storey structures the floor and roof slabs are relied upon to ensure stability (Fig. 25.5). In addition, however, it is usual on the Continent to place a wall beam under each successive floor slab, containing at least two 10 mm ($\frac{3}{8}$ in.)

FIG. 25.5 Cast-*in-situ* no-fines foamed slag concrete building in course of construction in Düsseldorf, Germany.

diameter mild steel bars suitably protected against corrosion by cement slurry, or by casting the wall beam of graded dense concrete (Fig. 25.6). The forces that occur at corners and edges are not accurately known, however.

The window and door openings are a source of weakness not only because of the stress concentration which occurs at the corners in this type of construction, but also because of the difficulty of ensuring that the concrete placed at the window sills is strong enough. Reinforcement is, therefore, frequently placed at wall openings, particularly in external walls; at window sills the concrete is often specially cast with graded material containing reinforcement (Fig. 25.7). Increase in strength due to ageing

FIG. 25.6   Placing no-fines lightweight concrete on a site.

FIG. 25.7   Cast-*in-situ* no-fines foamed slag concrete wall construction. Space left for reinforced dense concrete window sill.

should not be assumed to take place in no-fines concrete for design. The modulus of elasticity is likely to diminish somewhat with time.

CAST-*IN-SITU* REINFORCED CONCRETE WALLS

The design of such walls is based in the UK on CP 114[8] or CP 110,[9] the Codes of Practice for reinforced concrete in building. It is more flexible than the design of plain concrete walls based on CP 111 can be.

Plain concrete walls may, and indeed usually do, contain reinforcement to distribute cracking and shrinkage stresses and the minimum shrinkage reinforcement recommended by CP 111.201, or even less than that amount, would qualify such members to be regarded as reinforced concrete walls. Such reinforcement for reinforced concrete walls would be 0·4 per cent by volume. The thickness of the walls must not be less than 10 cm (4 in.) and the lateral reinforcement may be reduced to 0·1 per cent where the latter is not required to prevent buckling of the vertical bars, i.e. where the vertical bars are not loadbearing.

Reinforced concrete loadbearing walls must be designed as columns and bending should be taken into account. In fact, only rarely would reinforcing bars be needed to resist direct compressive stresses. More usually, reinforcement is required to resist shrinkage, cracking and bending stresses. CP 114 recommends that the reinforcement should be equally divided between vertical and horizontal bars but, where the vertical bars are not loaded in compression, the lateral reinforcement may be half of that provided in the vertical bars. It would seem, however, that failure of walls in compression usually takes place by splitting or by a vertical or inclined crack which would best be resisted by the provision of an adequate measure of horizontal reinforcement. It would, therefore, be preferable to distribute the total amount of reinforcement provided for reinforced concrete walls in such a way that twice as much horizontal reinforcement is present as vertical, as in the case of plain walls containing shrinkage reinforcement.

In general, two layers of reinforcement will be placed and it is essential to ensure that these are tied together adequately with transverse bars. Transverse bars may only be omitted to facilitate compaction of the concrete where the walls are not heavily loaded and where the vertical reinforcement is not required to resist compression. In thin walls a single layer of reinforcement may be used.

Permissible stresses in the concrete, including walls, are laid down in CP 114 for nominal mixes and for mixes designed for strength. The strength obtained from control tests may vary from those specified by plus or minus 25 per cent, and the permissible stresses in that case may also be different from those given in the Code by the same proportion.

The strength of axially loaded reinforced concrete walls is greatly affected by the ratio of wall height and length and the Code of Practice therefore, allows an increase in permissible stresses for walls with a height/length ratio less than 1·5 (Table 25.7).[8] The maximum stress increase is 20 per cent; where the effective height of the wall exceeds 15 times its thickness, however, the permissible stresses in the walls must be reduced in accordance with the rules for slender columns.

TABLE 25.7
STRESS INCREASE FOR LONG WALLS

Ratio of storey height to length	1·5 or more	1·0	0·5 or less
Percentage increase in permissible stress	0	10·0	20·0

For intermediate values the increase in stress may be interpolated.

LIMIT STATE DESIGN OF WALLS

For plain and reinforced concrete walls CP 110[9] is the appropriate guidance document in the UK. It distinguishes between short and slender, braced and unbraced concrete walls. A wall is considered slender when its ratio of effective height to thickness exceeds 12. A wall is considered as braced where its lateral stability is safeguarded by stiffening arrangements, e.g. cross-walls, designed to resist all lateral forces perpendicular to the face of the wall. Except for single-storey buildings, the layout and detailing of the structure should be such that the walls are effectively braced.

The effective height of reinforced walls is generally obtained in the same way as for columns but where the ends are assumed to be simply supported then the effective height for reinforced walls is obtained as for plain concrete walls. In both cases the effective height varies between three-quarters of the distance between lateral supports, for properly braced walls, to twice the actual height where the walls are held at one end only.

The limiting slenderness ratio, i.e. the ratio of effective height to thickness which should not be exceeded, is 40 for reinforced braced or 20 for plain or reinforced unbraced concrete walls. For columns the limiting slenderness ratio is somewhat higher because walls are generally thinner than columns and the disposition of the reinforcement can be less effective.

With regard to the incidence of loading, both the British Code, CP 110, and the ACI Code, ACI 318[15] provide that the portion of the wall near the edge should be treated as a compression member subject to bending and compression, as appropriate, while the middle sections can be assumed to resist axial loading.

To take account of slenderness, walls may be designed on the basis of an additional moment, thus taking account of the effect of deformations caused by loading, on the internal forces in the member and its behaviour both at ultimate and service conditions. For lightweight concrete walls due allowance must be made for the increased deformations due to the lower deformation modulus of lightweight aggregate concrete, by a somewhat higher additional moment in the case of slender walls. Other methods of approach for the design of slender members are set out in the CEB Code [16] and the CEB *Design Manual for Buckling*[17] to take account of secondary effects on slender compression members, the model column method being preferred.

For plain concrete walls similar considerations apply but particular attention must be given to the general concept of the structure to ensure that the walls are properly braced and that it is adequately safe with respect to accidental loading as well as normal load events and combinations.[18]

Following the partial collapse of a multi-storey large panel structure in London in 1968 after a gas explosion,[19] it has been generally accepted that measures are necessary to ensure that collapse of a section or part of a structure does not lead to disproportionate damage to the entire building. For low-rise buildings special precautions do not seem necessary and cast-*in-situ* reinforced concrete structures are considered to be adequately safe against accidental loading ('progressive collapse') in any case. For tall plain concrete or precast concrete structures the bracing of the walls must be checked, peripheral as well as transverse horizontal tying arrangements must be introduced and the vertical reinforcement must be such that the possibility of accidental loading is taken into account.

For masonry walls the latest 1977 Draft CP 111,[20] has accepted limit state methods of design, primarily to ensure an adequate margin of safety against the ultimate limit state being reached. The design strength therefore must not be less than the design load. Equally, safety against reaching the serviceability limit state is warranted by suitable detailing, complying with the instructions of materials makers and keeping account of advice from experienced engineers. In general, excessive cracking and deformations are avoided if the partial safety coefficients against ultimate failure are observed. Emphasis is also placed on attention to general layout and robustness of design. To counteract with reasonable economy and effectiveness the risk of progressive collapse due to accidental loadings, in addition to robust design and attention to the layout of the walls, the draft code recommends that buildings should be designed for a uniformly distributed horizontal load equal to 1·5 per cent of the total characteristic dead load above any level; that protection bollards or walls should be provided to protect important structural elements against impact loading by vehicles; and that the connections at floors and roofs should be such as to ensure adequate anchorage and tying to the walls.

The principal characteristic loads should be obtained from CP 3, Chapter V Part I, and are defined as G_K, the characteristic dead load, which is the weight of the structure including finishes, fixtures and partitions; Q_K, the characteristic imposed load; and W_K, the characteristic wind load. The partial safety factors r_f to be used for given load combinations, to ensure the least favourable effect, are:

Dead and imposed loads: $1 \cdot 0 \, G_K$ or $1 \cdot 4 \, G_K$; $1 \cdot 6 \, Q_K$.

Dead, and wind loads: $0 \cdot 9 \, G_K$ or $1 \cdot 4 \, G_K$; $1 \cdot 4 \, W_K$ or $0 \cdot 015 \, G_K$ whichever is the largest.

Dead, imposed and wind loads: $1 \cdot 2 \, G_K$; $1 \cdot 2 \, Q_K$; $1 \cdot 2 \, W_K$ or $0 \cdot 015 \, G_K$, whichever is largest.

To reduce risk of accidental damage: $1 \cdot 05 \, G_K$; $0 \cdot 35 \, Q_K$, (when the imposed load is quasi-permanent in character): $1 \cdot 05 \, Q_K$); $0 \cdot 35 \, W_K$.

All these four load combinations should be checked and the most severe should be used for design. Increased γ_f values should be used for exceptionally severe conditions.

The characteristic compressive strength of masonry made with units of varying dimensions and compressive strengths is given in the code for bricks, hollow blocks and solid blocks, for different mortar strengths. These data are modified to take account of varying conditions, e.g. of the thickness of the wall, the type of material, the shape of the blocks or bricks.

The partial safety factors γ_m appropriate for normal loads and for different production control and construction control levels vary from $2 \cdot 5$ to $3 \cdot 5$ being one-half of these values to account only for the probable effects of misuse or accidental loading.

For the calculation of the loadbearing capacity of walls, taking account of slenderness and eccentricity of loading, the concept of the capacity reduction factor β is accepted.

Design rules are given for walls of various support and loading conditions, including accidental loading, with special regard to tying requirements.

As an alternative design method, wall tests may be used and detailed testing requirements are given for these. From the tests the characteristic strength of masonry may be deduced.

REFERENCES

1. Building Research Station (1959). *Principles of Modern Building*, Vol. 1, HMSO.
2. British Standard 648:1964. 'Schedule of Weights of Building Materials', British Standards Institution.
3. British Standard Code of Practice 3, Chapter V, 'Loading', British Standards Institution.
4. Mitchell, G. R. (1969). 'Loadings on Buildings—a Review Paper', Symposium on concepts of Safety of Structures and methods of design, IABSE, London.

5. Ferry Borges, J. (1972). 'Dynamic Loads—in Particular Wind and Earthquake Loads', Civil Memoria No. 407, Laboratorio Nacional de Engenharia, Lisbon.
6. Mathieu, H. (1974). 'Manual on Structural Safety', Bulletin No. 102, CEB, Paris.
7. British Standard Code of Practice 111:1970. 'Structural Recommendations for Loadbearing Walls', British Standards Institution.
8. British Standard Code of Practice 114:1969. 'The Structural Use of Reinforced Concrete in Buildings', British Standards Institution.
9. British Standard Code of Practice 110:1972. 'The Structural Use of Concrete', British Standards Institution.
10. Scott, W. L., Glanville, W. H. and Thomas, F. G. (1965). *'Explanatory Handbook on the British Standard Code of Practice for Reinforced Concrete* 114:1957 (*as amended in* 1965), Concrete Publications, London.
11. Bate, S. C. C., Cranston, W. B., Rowe, R. E. *et al. Handbook on the Unified Code for Structural Concrete* (*CP* 110:1972), Cement and Concrete Association, London.
12. British Standard 2028: 1968. 'Precast Concrete Blocks', British Standards Institution.
13. British Standard Code of Practice 121.201:1951. 'Masonry Walls Ashlared with Natural Stone or with Cast Stone', British Standards Institution.
14. British Standard Code of Practice 122; 'Walls and Partitions of Blocks and Slabs', British Standards Institution.
15. Building Code Requirements for Reinforced concrete (ACI 318-71), American Concrete Institute, Detroit.
16. International System of Standard Codes of Practice, Vol. 2, 'Model Code for Concrete Construction', Draft (1977), CEB, Paris.
17. Design Manual for Buckling, (1977). CEB, Paris.
18. Addendum No. 1 (1970). 'Large Panel Structures and Structural Connections in Precast Concrete' to British Standard Code of Practice, CP 116:1965 and CP 116: Part 2: 1969, 'The Structural Use of Precast Concrete', British Standards Institution.
19. Ministry of Housing and Local Government (1968). 'Report of the Inquiry into the Collapse of Flats at Ronan Point', HMSO.
20. Draft Code of Practice for the Structural Use of Masonry Part 1: (1976) 'Unreinforced Masonry', British Standards Institution.

Conversion Tables

LINEAR MEASURE

in	ft	cm	m
1	0·083 3	2·54	0·025
12	1	30·48	0·305
0·394	0·032 8	1	0·01
39·37	3·281	100	1

SQUARE MEASURE

in^2	ft^2	yd^2	cm^2	m^2
1	0·006 94	0·000 772	6·452	0·000 645
144	1	0·111	929·03	0·092 9
1 296	9	1	8 361·3	0·836
0·155	0·001 076	0·000 12	1	0·000 1
1 550	10·764	1·196	10 000	1

CUBIC MEASURE

ft^3	yd^3	Imperial gal	US gal	dm^3 ($\sim$ 1)	m^3
1	0·037 1	6·229	7·480	28·317	0·028 3
27	1	168·18	201·98	764·55	0·765
0·160 5	0·005 95	1	1·201	4·546	0·004 55
0·134	0·004 95	0·833	1	3·785	0·003 79
0·035 3	0·001 31	0·22	0·264	1	|1·001
35·315	1·308	219·97	264	1 000	1

WEIGHTS

lb	ton	short ton	kg	tonne
1	0·000 446	0·000 5	0·453 6	0·000 454
2 240	1	1·12	1 016·05	1·016
2 000	0·893	1	907·18	0·907
2·204 6	0·000 984	0·001 02	1	0·001
2 204·62	0·984 2	1·102 3	1 000	1

STRESSES		PRESSURES		DENSITY	
lb/in^2	kg/cm^2	lb/ft^2	kg/m^2	lb/ft^3	kg/m^3
1	0·070 31	1	4·882 4	1	16·018
14·223	1	0·204 8	1	0·062 43	1

THERMAL CONDUCTIVITY		THERMAL CONDUCTANCE	
Btu in/ft^2 h °F	kcal/m h °C	Btu/ft^2 h °F	kcal/m^2 h °C
1	0·124 0	1	4·882 4
8·063 6	1	0·204 8	1

Bibliography

BARANOV, A. T., BAKHTIYAROV, K. I. and BOBROV, O. D. (1962). The strength and durability of aerated concrete, *Beton i Zhelezobeton*, **8**(9), 397–402.
PIETRUSINSKI, M. (1962). Autoclaved aerated concrete, *Przeglad Budowlany* (3), 166–7.
ROBERTS, N. P. (1962). Bond and crack control behaviour of a cold-worked deformed bar in structural lightweight concrete, *Struct. Concr.*, **1**(6), 273–84.
SKUPIN, L. and WEISS, V. (1962). Buckling strength of lightweight concrete, *Pozemni stavby* (3), 131.
SOKOLOVICH, V. E. (1962). Protecting reinforcement against corrosion in aerated concretes, *Stroit. i Arkh.* (6), 112.
WIJLER, L. (1962). Reinforced lightweight concrete, Bulletin 98, Israel Institute of Technology, Haifa.

BENIAMINOVICH, I. M. and BEREZIN, N. N. (1963). Application of non-autoclaved aerated slag concrete in building, *Beton i Zhelezobeton*, **9**(7), 303–7.
BOLDT, G. (1963). Porous concretes in theory and practice, *Betonsteinzeitung*, **29**(2), 65–73.
BÖCKL, W. (1963). Lightweight concrete products, *Betonsteinzeitung*, **29**(1), 31–7; (2), 54–64.
BUTT, YU. M. and KAUTBAEV, K. (1963). Methods of improving the durability of autoclaved silicate materials. *Stroit, Mat.* **9**(9), 10–12.
FALK, H. and SAHLIN, S. (1963). Full-scale tests on walls of disc-locked Ytong units interacting with *in-situ* floor slab, *Meddelande* No. 6, Kungl. Tekniska Högskola, Inst. för byggnads-statik, Stockholm.
KHUTORYANSKII, M. and TSATSKINA, F. (1963). Deformation of perlite concrete products during steam curing, *Budiv. Mat Konst.* (Kiev), **5**(4), 25–8.
LEVIN, N. I. (1963). Strength and deformation properties of autoclaved aerated silicate concrete, *Stroit. Mat.*, **9**(1), 16–20.
LEVIN, N. I., *et al.* (1963). Adhesives for joining cellular concrete wall panels, *Stroit. Mat.*, **9**(9), 16–17.
RUDNAI, G. (1963). Könnyübeton (Lightweight concrete), Akademiai Kiado, Budapest.
SILAENKOV, E. S. and ZARIN, R. A. (1963). The state of steel reinforcement in walls made of aerated concrete, *Beton i Zhelezobeton*, **9**(7), 307–10.
SPIVAK, N. YA, *et al.* (1963). Lightweight concrete panels for floating floors of large-panel buildings, *Beton i Zhelezobeton*, **9**(7), 298–303.
TISCHER, K-H. (1963). Shrinkage and swelling of various lightweight concretes, *Betonsteinzeitung*, **29**(2), 74–8.

BALÁZS, G. (1964). Effect of calcium chloride on the strength of autoclaved concretes, RILEM Internat. Conf. on Accelerated Hardening of Concrete, Moscow.

BLONDIAU, L. (1964). Solubilisation of quartitic fines during autoclaving and the behaviour of reinforcement in autoclaved lightweight concrete, *Rev. Mat.* (584), 138–50.

YEREMENKO, YU. M., *et al.* (1964). Lightweight structural concrete, *Stroit. Mat.* **10**(11), 32–3.

EVANS, R. H. and ORANGUN, C. O. (1964). Behaviour in flexure of reinforced lightweight aggregate (Lytag) concrete beams, *Civ. Eng. & Pub. Wks. Rev.*, **59**(694), 597–601.

FELDMAN, YA. G. (1964). Accelerated curing by infra-red radiation, *Beton i Zhelezobeton*, **10**(6), 256–60.

GRANT, R. M. and LAYTON, W. (1964). Further analysis of possible mechanisms for production of foamed blastfurnace slags, *Aust. J. appl. Sci.*, **15**(1), 10–12.

HANSON, J. A. (1964). Replacement of lightweight aggregate fines with natural sand in structural concrete, *J. Amer. Concr. Inst.*, **61**(7), 779–92.

HILLERBORG, A. (1964). Forces in joints between lightweight concrete slabs, *Nordisk Betong*, **8**(3), 367–78.

HOBBS, C. (1964). Physical properties of lightweight aggregates and concretes, *Chem. Ind.*, (15), 594–600.

HOGNESTAD, E., ELSTNER, R. C. and HANSON, J. A. (1964). Shear strength of reinforced structural lightweight aggregate concrete slabs, *J. Amer. Concr. Inst.*, **61**(6), 643–56.

KINNIBURGH, W., *et al.* (1964). Symposium on lightweight aggregates, *Constr. Concrete*, **2**(5), 234–46.

KRIVITSKII, M. YA. and SCHASNYI, A. N. (1964). Linear deformations and humidity of aerated concrete, *Stroit. Mat.*, **10**(6), 40–1.

KRUML, F. (1964). Long term deformation characteristics of lightweight concrete, *Stavebnicky Casopis*, **12**(7), 402–13.

LLEWELLIN, J. D. (1964). Lightweight aggregates in blocks, screeds and panels, *Chem. Ind.* (15), 601–9.

LOMUNOV, K. F. and MUCHALOV, A. I. (1964). Methods of preventing defects on exposed surfaces of silicate products (during autoclaving), *Stroit. Mat.*, **10**(3), 21–3.

NURSE, R. W. and WHITAKER, T. (1964). Strength tests of steam-cured concrete, RILEM Internat. Conf. on Accelerated Hardening of Concrete, Moscow.

REICHARD, T. W. (1964). Creep and drying shrinkage of lightweight and normal weight concretes, *Monograph 74*, Nat. Bur. Stand, Washington, D.C.

SELVAGGIO, S. L. and CARLSON, C. C. (1964). Fire resistance of prestressed concrete beams. Influence of aggregate and load intensity, *I. Port.-Cement Ass. Res. Dev. Lab.*, **6**(2), 10–25.

SZCZUHOV, A. F. (1964). Investigating aerated concrete during autoclave curing, *Izvest. Stroit. Arkhit.*, Novosibirsk, **7**(10), 68–73.

WASHA, G. W. and FEDELL, R. L. (1964). Carbonation and shrinkage studies of non-plastic expanded slag concrete containing fly ash, *J. Amer. Concr. Inst.*, **61**(9), 1109–24.

WELCH, G. B. and PATTEN, B. J. F. (1964). Structural lightweight aggregate concrete, *Constr. Rev.*, **37**(2), 22–8.

BRZAKOVIC, P. (1965). Lightweight aggregate from expanded clay, *Naše Grad.*, **15**(5), 856–66.

CEB. (1965). Lightweight concrete structures, Bulletin d'Information No. 51, Paris.

CZAJEWSKI, H. (1965). Lightweight concrete based on keramzit, *Biul. Inst. Tech. Bud.*, **18**, 12–15.

DANILOV, B. P. and PRIEZZNEV, B. A. (1965). Non-autoclaved aerated slag concrete in large panel construction, *Beton i Zhelezobeton*, **11**(2), 9–12.

DIAMANT, M. I., *et al.* (1965). Industrially manufactured aerated concrete wall panels based on ash and Portland blastfurnace slag cement, *Beton i Zhelezobeton*, **11**(2), 12–16.

DUNHAM, H. (1965). Ceramic processes used in the manufacture of lightweight aggregates from clay minerals, *Chem. Ind.* (29), 1274–6.

ELMROTH, A. and HÖGLUND, I. (1965). Influence of moisture on the thermal resistance of external walls of aerated concrete, *Proc. RILEM/CIB Symposium on Moisture Problems in Buildings*, Helsinki. Vol. 2, Section 4, Paper 10.

GLADKI, J. (1965). Properties of gypsum-fly ash-cement lightweight concrete, *Czasopismo techniczne*, **87**(11), 33–5.

GRIMER, F. J. (1965). Tests on lightweight concrete columns, *Struct-Concr.*, **2**(12), 503–20.

HANSON, J. A. (1965). Optimum steam-curing procedures for structural lightweight concrete, *J. Amer. Concr. Inst.*, **62**(6), (Part 1), 661–72.

KINNIBURGH, W. (1965). 'Moisture content and moisture migration in aerated concrete'. Symposium on Calcium Silicate Products, London.

KOMLOS, K. (1965). Investigations of the workability of expanded-clay concrete. *Beton und Stahlbetonbau*, **60**(1), 15–19.

KRUML, F. (1965). Long term deformation of lightweight concrete (creep). *Stavebnicky Casopis*, **13**(3), 137–44.

LANDGREN, R., HANSON, J. A. and PFEIFER, D. W. (1965). An improved procedure for proportioning mixes of structural lightweight concrete, *J. Port. Cement Ass. Res. Devel. Lab.*, **7**(2), 47–65.

LEHMAN, H. O., *et al.* (1965). Fatigue strength of $\frac{3}{4}$ in studs in lightweight concrete (push-out tests). Centre for Highway Research, The University of Texas, Austin.

LEWIS, R. K. and BLAKEY, F. A. (1965). Moisture conditions influencing the tensile splitting strength of lightweight concrete, *Constr. Rev.*, **38**(8), 17–22.

MALINOWSKI, A. D. R. (1965). Volume changes of lightweight (aerated) concrete during repeated wetting and drying, *Proc. of RILEM/CIB Symposium on Moisture Problems in Buildings*, Helsinki. Vol. 1, Section 2, Paper 35.

PORTMANN, H. J. (1965). Lava aggregate for structural lightweight concrete, *Betonsteinzeitung*, **31**(11), 650–4.

REINSDORF, S. and KUEHNE, G. (1965). High-strength structural lightweight concretes, *Baustoffind*, **8**(8), 228–34.

ROESSER, K. (1965). Structural lightweight concrete in the USA, *Archit. Build. News*, **227**(25), 1181–4.

SCHULZ, B. (1965). Constructional lightweight concrete of Leca expanded clay. *Beton*, **15**(3), 93–9.

SCHULZ, B. (1965). Principles of the manufacture of lightweight structural concrete from expanded aggregates, *Betonsteinzeitung*, **31**(11), 638–43, (12), 695–700.

SCOTT, J. (1965). Granite surface on aerated concrete in Siberian wall panels, *Cement Lime & Gravel*, **41**(1), 20.

SPIVAK, N. YA., BOWLIN, D. K. and BADJAGLAN, V. C. (1965). Influence of the structure of keramzit concrete on the properties of wall panels, *Beton i Zhelezobeton*, (11).

WALZ, K., BONZEL, J. and BAUM, G. (1965). Tests on high strength lightweight concrete, *Beton*, **15**(2), 59–65; (3), 107–14.

WEIGLER, H. and REISSMANN, K. (1965). Investigations on structural lightweight concrete, *Betonsteinzeitung*, **31**(11), 615–29.

ZHELEZNYI, V. I. (1965). Ice formation in waterproofed aerated concrete, *Beton i Zhelezobeton*, **11**(12), 30–3.

EVANS, R. H. and ARRAND, C. O. D. (1966). Ultimate strength of axially loaded reinforced lightweight aggregate (Aglite) concrete columns, *Civ. Eng. & Pub. Wks. Rev.*, **61**(722), 1125–8.

HARMATHY, T. Z. and BERNDT, J. E. (1966). Hydrated Portland cement and lightweight concrete at elevated temperatures, *J. Amer. Concr. Inst.*, **63**(1), 93–112.

HAUBERT, H. (1966). Statistical quality control of the production of lightweight concrete external wall elements, *Baustoffind*, **9**(11), 328–32.

HENNIG, N. (1966). Studies of the production of aerated concrete with vibration during expansion, *Baustoffind*, **9**(10), 300–3.

HOLLINGTON, M. W. (1966). Lightweight concrete finishes, *Struct. Concr.*, **3**(5), 269–72.

HOLM, T. A. and PISTRANG, J. (1966). Time-dependent load transfer in reinforced lightweight concrete columns, *J. Amer. Concr. Inst.*, **63**(11), 1231–46.

JANOWSKI, Z. (1966). Loadbearing concrete of Keramzit, *Czasopismo techniczne*, **71**(10), 15–19.

JANOWSKI, Z. (1966). Determining physical properties of Keramzit aggregate. *Czasopismo techniczne*, **8**(71), 24–7.

JINDAL, B. K. (1966). Design and testing of precast reinforced lightweight concrete slabs, *Indian Concr. J.*, **10**(5), 199–203.

KARASUDA, S., et al. (1966). Behaviour of lightweight aggregate concrete, *J. Soc. Mat. Science Japan*, **15**(157), 724–32.

KAUFMAN, S. and MAMES, J. (1966). Investigation of prestressed lightweight concrete of sintered shale aggregate, *Arch. Inzyn. Ladowej*, **12**(4), 428–37.

KIMURA, S. and SUZUKI, N. (1966). Effect of the quality of artificial lightweight aggregates on the compressive strength of the concrete, *J. Soc. Mat. Science Japan*, **15**(157), 699–706.

KOZAK, R. (1966). Reinforcing lightweight concrete with prestressed concrete elements, *Arch. Inzyn Ladowej*, **12**(2), 217–19.

MALHOTRA, H. L. (1966). Fire resistance of lightweight concrete structures, *Struct. Concr*, **3**(2), 49–57.

MIZURO, T., et al., (1966). Fatigue properties of reinforced artificial lightweight-aggregate concrete beams, *J. Soc. Mat. Science Japan*, **15**(157), 707–15.

OKADA, K. and KOYANAGI, W. (1966). Flexural strength of lightweight aggregate concrete slabs, *J. Soc. Mat. Science Japan*, **15**(157), 716–23.

OKUSHIMA, M. and KOSAKA, Y. (1966). Mechanical properties of lightweight aggregate concrete for structural use, *J. Soc. Mat. Science Japan*, **15**(157), 691–8.

OMSTED, H. (1966). Creep of prestressed lightweight concrete, *J. Prestressed Concr. Inst.*, **11**(6), 40–5.

ORANGUN, C. O. (1966). Axial loading tests on short reinforced lightweight aggregate (Lytag) concrete columns, *Struct. Eng.*, **44**(9), 291–4.

RUTLEDGE, S. E. and NEVILLE, A. M. (1966). The influence of cement paste content on the creep of lightweight aggregate concrete, *Mag. Concr. Res.*, **18**(55), 69–74.

SCHNEIDER-ARNOLDI, A. C. (1966). Possible applications of improved granulated slag in concrete, *Beton*, **16**(11), 458–60.

SCHULZE, W., REICHEL, W. and GUNZLER, J. (1966). Lightweight structural concrete with Agloporit, *Baustoffind.*, **9**(1), 14–18.

TUROWITZ, S. (1966). Agloporite aggregate for lightweight concrete, *Czasopismo techniczne*, **8**(71), 1–9.

DIKERMAN, N. I., *et al.* (1967). Lightweight high-strength Agloporite concretes, *Stroit. Mekh*, (6), 10–11.

EVANS, R. H. and PATERSON, W. S. (1967). Long-term deformation characteristics of Lytag lightweight aggregate concrete, *Struct. Eng.*, (1), 13–21.

GOTTSCHALK, J. (1967). Experiments on non-destructive testing of pumice concrete, *Mat.-Pruef*, **9**(4), 131–9.

GRIMER, F. J. (1967). The durability of steel embedded in lightweight concrete, *Concrete*. **1**(4), 125–30.

HÁJEK, J. (1967). Steam cured aerated concrete in wall and roof panels in Czechoslovakia, *Tech. Dip. SNTL*, **9**(1), 29–33.

McCORMICK, F. C. (1967). Rational proportioning of preformed foam cellular concrete. *J. Amer. Concr. Inst.*, **64**(2), 104–10.

NESBIT, J. K. (1967). *Structural Lightweight Aggregate Concrete*, Concrete Publications Ltd. London.

PILNY, F. and HIESE, W. (1967). Heavy and light concrete made from burnt refuse, *Bautech*, **44**(7), 230–8.

TEYCHENNÉ, D. C. (1967). Structural concrete made with lightweight aggregates. *Concrete*, **1**(4), 111–22.

VIRONNAUD, J. and MALDAGUE, J. C. (1967). Expanded shale concretes. *Ann. Inst. Bâtim.*, **20**(231–2), 455–91; 492–9.

ABRAMS, M. S. and GUSTAFENE, A. H. (1968). Fire endurance of concrete slabs as influenced by thickness, aggregate type, and moisture, *J. Port. Cement Ass. Devel. Lab.*, **10**(4), 9–24.

ANON. (1968). Constructional lightweight concrete—research results and examples of application from the Institute for Reinforced Concrete, Dresden, *Beton*, **18**(11), 431–8. (In German with English summary.)

ANON. (1968). Recommended practice for selecting properties for structural lightweight concrete. *J. Amer. Concr. Inst.*, **65**(1), 1–19.

ARNOLD, P. J. (1968). Thermal conductivity of masonry materials, *J. Inst. Heat & Vent. Engnr.*, **37/8**, 101–8.

448　　　Bibliography

BESSEY, G. E. (1968). 'The world development and economic significance of the aerated concrete industry', International Congress on Lightweight Concrete, London.

BUDNIKOV, P. P., ELINZON, M. P. and YAKUB, I. A. (1968). 'The structure, composition, and some properties of lightweight aggregates used for concrete in the USSR', International Congress on Lightweight Concrete, London.

ELIND, O. (1968). 'Some properties and practical aspects of hardened aerated concrete: Swedish experiences', International Congress on Lightweight Concrete, London.

HOHWILLIER, F. and KÖHLING, K. (1968). Styropor lightweight concrete, Betonsteinzeitung, 34(2), 81–7. (In German.)

KORNEV, N. A., et al. (1968). Widening use of lightweight concrete in building construction, Beton i Zhelezobon, 14(5), 1–3. (In Russian.)

MALHOTRA, H. L. (1968). Fire Resistance of lightweight concrete, First International Congress on Lightweight Concrete, London.

OTT, K. (1968). The technology of structural lightweight concrete made from vitreous fine aggregate, International Congress on Lightweight Concrete, London.

SCHULZE, W. and GÜNZLER, J. (1968). Corrosion protection of reinforcement in structural lightweight concrete, Betonstein Ztg. 34(5), 252–7. (In German.)

SCHUMACHER, J. and DELALIER, P. (1968). Lightweight concrete, Centre Scientifique & Technique du Batiment, Cahiers, (780), 35 pp., Paris.

SØRLI, I., RUSHOLT, J. and ELISSON, L. (1968). Structural application of Leca concrete in Norway, Denmark, and Sweden, Betonsteinzeitung, 34(5), 245–51. (In German.)

STEINDL, A. (1968). Tests on structural lightweight concrete in Austria, Betonsteinzeitung, 34(5), 241–4. (In German.)

WEIGLER, H. and KARL, S. (1968). Frost- and de-icing salt resistance and abrasion resistance of structural lightweight concrete, Betonsteinzeitung, 34(5), 225–40; (11) 581–3.

WENNSTRÖM, I. (1968). The use of aerated concrete units for low-rise housing: planning and design, architectural properties and some experience with completed houses, International Congress on Lightweight Concrete, London.

ZELGER, C. (1968). Damping measurements on a prestressed lightweight concrete structure, Beton, 18(5), 175–6.

BONROVSKI, J. and BARDHAN-ROY, B. K. (1969). A method of calculating the ultimate strength of reinforced and prestressed concrete in combined flexure and shear, The Structural Engineer, May 1969 and Jan. 1970.

BUZHEVICH, G. A., DOVZHIC, V. G., et al. (1969). Lightweight Aerated Keramzite Concrete, Stroyizdat, Moscow.

GRIMER, E. T. and HEWITT, R. E. (1969). 'The force of the stress–strain curve of concrete, interpreted with a diaphase concept of material behaviour', International Conference on Civil Engineering Materials, Southampton.

KONKEL, E. V. (1969). Building costs for lightweight concrete, gravel concrete, steel, Civil Engineering ASCE, 65–9.

PAPROCKI, A. (1969). Manufacturing large-scale concrete components, Centre Scientifique & Technique du Bâtiment. Cahiers, (102), No. 892, Paris. (In French.)

WEIGLER, H. and KARL, S. (1969). Creep of lightweight concrete on early loading, *Betonsteinzeitung*, **35**, 299–328.

ANON. (1970). *An Introduction to Lightweight Concrete*, Fourth edition, Cem. & Concr. Assoc. Tech. Advis. Series, London.

BUZHEVICH, G. A. (1970). *Lightweight Concretes made with Porous Aggregates*, Stroyizdat, Moscow.

CEB-FIP. (1970). International recommendations for the design and construction of concrete structures, CaCA London.

DENNIS, R. H. (1970). Admixtures for reducing the water absorption rate of autoclaved building materials, *Chem. & Indust.*, **12**, 377–80.

HAEGERNANN, H. (1970). Lightweight concrete made with expanded clay strength and functional questions, *Betonsteinzeitung* **36**.

HEUFERS, H. (1970). Long-term shrinkage and creep investigations on high strength lightweight concrete and on comparable ordinary concretes, *Technisch-Wissenschaftliche Mitteilungen Dickerhoff Zement*, Wiesbaden, Heft 5.

KRAMPF, L. (1970). Fundamental research into the behaviour of lightweight concrete under fire loading, *Kurz Cerichte aus der Bauforschung*, **11**, 3–5.

MACIAG, T. (1970). The prestressed lightweight concrete roof for Doncaster racecourse grandstand, FIP Congress Prague, *Concrete*, June, p. 14.

MINNICK, L. J. (1970). Lightweight concrete aggregate from sintered fly-ash, *US Highways Research Record*, **307**, 21–32.

NEVILLE, A. M. (1970). *Creep of Concrete, Plain Reinforced and Prestressed*, North Holland Publishing Co., Amsterdam.

PATRY, H. (1970). Investigation of the economics of reinforced lightweight (Leca) and ordinary concrete beams of rectangular cross-section. *Betonsteinzeitung*, **10**, 612–13.

THE SCIENTIFIC RESEARCH INSTITUTE OF BUILDING ECONOMY. (1970). Economic efficiency and rational fields of application in building of new building materials and structures, Moscow.

VIRONNAUD, L. (1970). Physical Properties of lightweight concrete, *Rev. d. Mat. de Constr. et d. Trav.*, Publ. No. 662, 338–42.

ZELGER, C. (1970). Is weight the only difference between lightweight and ordinary concrete, *Beton*, **20**(3), 90–5.

ACI BUILDING CODE 318–71. Commentary on Building Code Requirements for Reinforced Concrete, Detroit.

BOBROWSKI, J. and BARDHAN-ROY, B. K. (1971). Structural assessment of lightweight aggregate concrete, *Concrete*, July 1971.

BUZHEVICH, G. A. (1971). *Technology and Properties of new Types of Lightweight Concretes made with Porous Aggregates*, NnZhB, Stroyizdat, Moscow.

CVR-Report (1971). 'Lightweight concrete (lichtbeton)', Commissic voor Vitvoering Research Soetermeer.

JENNY, D. P. and LITVIN, A. (1971). Lightweight concrete: a symposium of 13 papers under the title, 'Structural lightweight—an accepted constructural material, Amer. Concr. Inst., 321 pp.

KRAUSS, R. and BACHMANN, H. (1971). Bending and shear tests of partially prestressed lightweight concrete beams, ETH Zurich.

LUSCHE, M. (1971). Contribution to the collapse mechanism of ordinary and lightweight concretes in a compact structure subjected to compression, Dissertation Bochum.

ONATZKU, S. P. (1971). *The Production of Keramzite Aggregate*, Stroyizdat, Moscow.

SASSE, R. (1971). A definition of the compressive strength of concrete by means of a structural model concept, *Betonsteinzeitung*, 35(3), 151–5.

SCHUTZ, F. R. (1971). The influence of the elasticity of the aggregate on the crushing strength of the concrete, Dissertation TU Aachen.

SERAPIN, I. G. (1971). *Technology of Large Concrete Structures for Dwellings and Public Buildings*, Stroyizdat, Moscow.

STORK, J. (1971). Functional classification of lightweight concrete, RILEM CEB-FIP Colloquium, Copenhagen.

WALZ, K. (1971). The production of concrete in accordance with the German Standard DIN 1045, *Betonverlag*, Dusseldorf.

WEIGLER, H. and KARL, S. (1971). The properties of presently available lightweight aggregates and their importance for the manufacture and properties of reinforced lightweight concrete, *Betrusteinzeitung*, 37(9), 27–38.

CEB (1972). *Model Code for concrete structures*, 2nd draft, Bulletin. d'Information No. 111, Paris.

COOK, D. J. (1972). Polystyrene aggregates; lightweight concrete using expanded polystyrene beads, *Constructional Review*, 3, 52–3. New South Wales.

ONET, T. (1972). Study of the deformations of lightweight concrete beams subjected to short duration bending tests, The Polytechnic Cluj.

SHORT, A. (1972). Notes on the CEB draft practice manual on lightweight concrete, *Concrete*, 6.

SHULE, W., *et al.* Thermal conductivity of building materials. Normal and lightweight concrete, cork panels, and foamed plastics. Effect of temperature and humidity, *Bauforshung*, 42, Berlin.

THE CONCRETE SOCIETY (1972). 'A comparative study of the economics of lightweight concrete'. Report of the Cost-Price Comparison Working Party, London.

WEIGLER, H. and KARL, S. (1972). *Reinforced Lightweight Concrete, Manufacture, Properties and Design*, Bakeverlag, Wiesbaden and Berlin.

WEIGLER, H., KARL, S. and LIESEO, P. (1972). The bending load capacity of reinforced lightweight concrete, *Betonwerk und Fertigtedl Technik*, 38(5), 324–34, 38(6), 445–9.

ANON. (1973). Lightweight aggregate from cerials, *Building materials*, 300–7.

ATAN, Y. and SLATE, F. O. (1973). Structural lightweight concrete under biaxial compression, *ACI J Proc.* 70(3), 182–6.

AURICH, H. (1973). Ultra lightweight concrete, *Beton*, 25 (5), 213–16. (In German.)

BOMHARD, H. and SPARBER, J. (1973). The rock-prestressed lightweight concrete cantilever arm of the ski-jumping platform at Oberstdorf and considerations on the applicability and strength of structural lightweight concrete, *Beton und Stahlbetonbau*, 68(5), 107–17.

BRUCKNER, H. (1973). Prefabricated wide span beam in prestressed lightweight concrete, *Beton und Stahlbetonbau*, 68(1), 1–8.

BRYNDUM, M. (1973). Literature review on lightweight structural concrete, The University, Copenhagen.

BUZHEVICH, G. A. (1973). *Structure, Stability and Deformation of Lightweight Concrete*, Materials Coordinating Council, Stroyizdat, Moscow.

CORMON, P. (1973). *Betons Legers d'Aujourd'hui (Present-day lightweight concrete)*, Editions Eyrolles, Paris.

FREITAG, W. (1973). The behaviour of structural lightweight concrete at constant and variable fatigue loading, Dissertation TH, Darmstadt.

HARMATHY, T. Z. and ALLEN, L. W. (1973). Thermal properties of selected masonry unit concrete, *J. Amer. Concr. Inst.*, 132–42.

HEIMAN, J. L. (1973). Long-term deformations in the tower building, Australia Square, Sydney, *ACI J Proc.*, **70**(47), 279–84.

ITBTP (1973). Experiences et realisations de structures en betons de granulats legers aux Pays-Bas, *Annales de l'ITBTP, série Beton*, No. 133, Paris.

KOCH, K. and SPITZNER, J. (1973). The strength scatter in well compacted lightweight concrete, *Betonwerk and Fertigteiltechnik*, **3**, March 1973.

KONG, F. K. and SHARP, G. R. (1973). Shear strength of lightweight reinforced concrete deep beams with web openings, *Structural Engineer*, **51**(8), 267–84.

KORNEV, N. A. (1973). Lightweight concrete with porous fillers, *Na Stroikakh Rossü*, No. 2, Moscow.

KRUML, F. (1973). Influence of constant rate of loading on ultimate strain of lightweight concrete, *Cement & Concrete Research*, **34**, 429–32.

LEWICKI, B. and GAJOVNIK, R. (1973). Rheological properties of lightweight concrete, CEB Symposium Technological University Cracow, Special Publ. No. 3, 92–110.

LISIECKI, K. H. and BURZIK, C. Protection of the reinforcement in gas concrete and lightweight aggregate concrete against corrosion, *Baustoffind.* **16**(6), 7–11. (In German.)

LYDON, F. D. (1973). Some criteria for the choice and use of lightweight concrete, *Build International*, **6**(3), 34–8.

MIRONOV, A. A. and USKOVA, V. G. (1973). Economic efficiency of structures of high strength lightweight concrete. *Beton i Zhelezobeton*, No. 11, Moscow.

OLESKIEWICZ, S. (1973). The analysis of the deformation of lightweight concrete, CEB Symposium Technological University Cracow, Special Publ. No. 3, 60–70.

ORCHARD, D. F. (1973). *Concrete Technology, Vol. 1, Properties of Materials*, Third Edition, Applied Science Publishers Ltd, Barking, England.

PALJAKI, I. (1973). Thermal conductivity in damp building materials measured by a stationary method, *Byggmasteren*, **52**(6), 20–2. (In Swedish.)

PETROVA, K. V. (1973). Crack width in elements of lightweight concrete with porous fillers, *Beton i Zhelezobeton*, No. 12.

PILTZ, G. and HESSE, E. (1973). Investigation of the suitability of colliery waste for the production of expanded clay aggregate, *Ziegelindustrie*, **9**, 316–24.

PIRADOV, A. B. (1973). *Structural Properties of Plain and Reinforced Lightweight Concrete*, Stroyizdat, Moscow.

PLOUSKI, W. (1973). Thermal conductivity and moisture content of lightweight aggregate concrete, CEB Symposium, Technological University, Cracow, Special Publ. No. 3, 137–46.

452   *Bibliography*

SHORT, A. (1973). Lightweight concrete, CEB course on Structural Concrete, Lisbon.

SKARENDAHL, A. (1973). Lightweight aggregate and lightweight aggregate concrete, *Svenska Forskings Institutet for Cement och Beton Handlinger* No. 47, Stockholm.

SWAMY, R. N. and IBRAHIM, A. B. (1973). Shrinkage and creep properties of high early strength of structural lightweight concrete, *Inst. of Civ. Engrs. Proc. Pt 2, Research and Theory*, **55** (Sept.), 635–46.

TANAKOV, M. M. and EMELYANOV, V. G. (1973). The load bearing capacity of slag–pumice concrete columns under eccentric compression, *Beton i Zhelezobeton*, No. 8.

URMSTON, C. W. B. and BESSEY, G. E. (1973). Structural lightweight concrete using lightweight aggregate with aeration, *Chem. & Indust.* **7**, 300–7.

ZOLDNERS, N. G. and PAINTER, K. E. (1973). Pelletized expanded slag aggregate for structural lightweight concrete, *Canada Dept. of Energy, Mines & Resources, Mines Branch, Report No. IR* 75–13, Ottawa, 18 pp.

ACI. (1974). 'Proportioning concrete mixes', Symposium, Special Publ. 46, Detroit.

ADAMEK, J. and JANECKY, J. (1974). Light loadbearing concrete of Agloporite, *Stavivo*, **52**(1), 26–30. (In Czech.)

ANON. (1974). Some aspects of flat roof design in the UK, *Development and Materials Bulletin*, **71**, 1–5.

ANTONENKOV, N. E., *et al.* (1974). *Agloporite Gravel Concrete from Power Station Ash*, Informenergo, Moscow.

BACHMANN, H. (1974). Tests on partially prestressed lightweight concrete beams subjected to sustained loading, *Zement und Beton*, **76** (Sept & Oct) ETH Zurich.

BHISE, *et al.* (1974). Use of lightweight concrete in precast construction, *Indian Concrete J.*, **48**(8), 248–50.

BOBROWSKI, J. (1974). Specifications and Codes of Practice for Lightweight Aggregate Concrete, Cembureau, Paris.

BOLOGNA, G. (1974). Lightweight aggregate concrete: technology and world application, Cembureau, Paris, 312 pp.

CORMON, P., VIRINNAUD, L., CHABREL, L., *et al.* (1974). Artificial lightweight aggregate concretes, *Inst. Technique du Batiment et des Travaux Publics, Annales*, **321**, 1–103. (In French.)

GUNASEKARAN, M. (1974). Alkali-resistant glass 'cane' reinforced for structural lightweight concrete, *Indian Concrete J.*, **48**(10), 314–15.

HAWKINS, N. M. and CORLEY, W. G. (1974). Moment transfer to columns in slabs with shearhead reinforcement, Portland Cement Assoc., R & D Bulletin RD 37 OID, Skokie, Ill., USA.

HAWKINS, N. M., CRISWELL, M. E. and ROLL, F. (1974). Shear strength of slabs without shear reinforcement and Shear in reinforced concrete, ACI Special Publ. 42, Detroit.

JINDAL, B. K., BHISE, N. N., Kishan Lal Sharma, K. N. (1974). Use of lightweight concrete in precast construction, *Indian Concrete J.*, Aug., 248–50.

KARNI, J. and CARMEL, D. (1974). Lightweight concrete made with artificial lime, *Build International*, **7**(4), 349–54.

KITA-BADAK, M., MALOLEPSKY, J. and STOK, A. (1974). Lightweight aggregate produced by expansion of shales from the Carpathian region, *Cement-Wapno-Gips*, **29/41**(1), 14–17. (In Polish.)

KONG, F. K. and SINGH, A. (1974). Shear strength of lightweight concrete deep beams subjected to repeated loads and Shear in reinforced concrete, ACI Special Publ. 42. Detroit.

KUDRYAVTSEV, A. A. (1974). Loadbearing capacity and deformations of flexible Keramzite concrete columns under long-term loading, *Beton i Zhelezobeton*, No. 10, Moscow.

KUDRYAVTSEV, A. A. (1974). *Prestressed Keramzite Concrete*, Stroyizdat, Moscow.

KUNZE, W. (1974). Sintered fly-ash pellets as aggregate for structural lightweight concrete, *Betonwerk und Ferteil Technik*, **40**(1), 50–5. (In German.)

KUNZE W. (1974). Tests on lightweight aggregate made of sintered coal-washery refuse, *Beton*, **24**(6), 217–22, (In German.)

Lightweight Aggregate Concrete—Technology and World Applications (1974). Cembureau, Paris.

LOVEWELL, C. E. (1974). A method for proportioning structural concrete mixes with fly ash and other pozzolanas, ACI Special Publ. 46, Detroit.

MAJDIC, A., BRAUN, M., GELSDORF, G., *et al.* (1974). Preparation of lightweight concrete test specimens for reproducible properties, *Ton Industrie-zeitung*, **98**(11), 279–86.

MIGLIACCI, A., MOSCA, A. and SCIROCCO, F. (1974). Mechanical and elastic characteristics of lightweight concretes made with 'Leca' of Italian production, Milan Polytechnic, Milan.

MUHAMMAD, A. and QASIM, M. (1974). Bloating characteristics of some Pakistani soils, *Build International*, **7**(5), 399–425.

NORTHWOOD, T. D. and MONK, D. W. (1974). Sound transmission loss of masonry walls: 12 inch lightweight concrete blocks comparison of latex and plaster sealers, National Research Council of Canada, Division of Building Research, Building Research Note No. 93, Ottawa.

ORANGUN, C. O. (1974). The suitability of periwinkle shells as coarse aggregate for structural concrete, *Materiaux et Constructions* **7**(41), 341–6.

RAMM, W. (1974). Interaction diagrams for structural components of rectangular cross-section made with unreinforced normal and lightweight concretes, *Beton und Stahlbetonbau*, **69**(8), 187–90.

SELL, R. and SCHMIDT-HURTIENNE, K. D. (1974). *The Particle Strength of Artificial Aggregates and its Effect on Concrete Strength* and *The Compressive Strength of Lightweight Concrete*, Ernst, Berlin.

SHORT, A. (1974). Lightweight aggregate concrete, *Concrete*, **8**(7), 47–8.

SOROKA, I. and JAEGERMANN, C. H. (1974). Steam curing of lightweight aggregate concrete under atmospheric pressure, Bulletin No. 218, Israel Institute of Technology in the Field of Building, Haifa, 10 pp.

SPIVAK, N. Ya., BAULIN, D. K. and STRONGINETAL, N. S. (1974). Lightweight concrete large-panel dwelling structures, *Zhilishnoe Stroitelstro* No. 12.

SPRATT, B. H. (1974). The structural use of lightweight aggregate concrete, *Cement & Concrete Association*, Wexham Springs.

SWAMY, R. N. and IBRAHIM, A. B. (1974). Flexure characteristics of structural lightweight reinforced and prestressed concrete beams ACI Special Publ. 43, Detroit.

454   *Bibliography*

TOUBEAU, G. (1974). Manufacture of lightweight aggregate from washery screen discard, *Chemical Abstracts*, **81**(04).

VAQUIER, A., MORIN, D. and THENOZ, B. (1974). Water movements in lightweight concrete and their influence upon shrinkage and compressive strengths, *Review des Materiaux de Construction*, **690**, 291–9.

VENUAT, M. and TAN-THANH-PHAT, M. (1974). A new construction material— lightweight coloidal concrete, *Review des Materiaux de Construction*, **687**, 88– 99.

VIEST, I. M. (1974). Composite steel-concrete construction, *ASCE Proc. J. Structural Division*, **100**(SD5), 1085–139, New York.

ZUANCA, ASSOC, RSFSK SEMINAR (1974). 'New trends in the design of reinforced concrete structures', House of Scient. and Techn. Information, Moscow.

ARSENTSEV, V. A. and ELINZON, M. P. (1975). Synthetic porous aggregate from industrial waste for lightweight high strength concretes, *Stroitel'nye Materialy* **21**(8). (In Russian.)

BALÁZS, G., KOVAKS, K. and PAPP, A. (1975). Polystyrene-bead aggregate lightweight concrete, *Kozlekedesi Dokumentacios Vallalat*, Bucharest, 112 pp.

BERGMANN, K. (1975). Production of lightweight concrete elements using expanded clay, and their surface treatment using the Keraflamm process, *Ziegelindustrie*, **9**, 330–5. (In Swedish.)

BRUSKOVA, L. N. and KUDRYAVTSEV, A. A. (1975). The stability and crack resistance of prestressed Keramizite concrete elements of oblique cross-section. *Beton i Zhelezobeton*, No. 6.

CUVELLIEZ, G. (1975). Calculation of the deformations of lightweight structural concrete, *Tech. Trav.*, **352**, 89–92.

FIP (1975). Guides to Good Practice: *CEB-FIP recommendation for the design of concrete structural members for fire resistance*. CaCA, London.

GRASSER, E. and PROBST, P. (1975). Flexural measurements in lightweight reinforced concrete, Munich.

GUNASEKARAN, M. (1975). The strength and behaviour of lightweight concrete reinforced with metallic fibres of mixed aspect ratios, *Indian Concrete J.*, **49**(2), 48, 49, 55.

GUNASEKARAN, M. (1975). The strength and behaviour of lightweight concrete beams made with sintered fly-ash aggregates and fibre reinforced partially, *Indian Concrete J.*, **49**(11), 332–4.

KORNEV, N. A. and PETROVA, K. B. (1975). *Design and Construction of Reinforced Concrete Elements of Lightweight Concrete*, NIIzhB, Stroyizdat, Moscow.

KOZITSKII, YU. A. and KORNEV, N. A. (1975). Creep and shrinkage of high strength Keramzite concrete, *Beton i Zhelezobeton*, No. 4.

KRAUSE, H. and PICHOCKI, E. (1975). Enriched fly ash for lightweight concretes, *Cement Wapno Gips*, **29/41** (8–9), 264–8.

OSTUND, P. O. (1975). The behaviour of materials at high temperatures, *Byggmastaren*, **54**(6), 14–16, 19–20.

PAVLOV, S. P. (1975). Mathematical model of the cost of manufacturing Keramzite aggregate, *Stroilstelstvo i Arkhitektura*, Series 1, Issue 2, Moscow.

PAVLOV, S. P. and ZHITKEVICH, R. K. (1975). Selection of high-stability lightweight concrete taking the strength factor into account, *Beton i Zhelezobeton*, No. 4.

ROSTASY, F. S., ALDA, W. and TEICHEN, K. T. (1975). Creep and pulsating creep of lightweight concrete, *Bauingenieur*, **50**(12), 455–9.
ROSTASY, F. S. and KOCH, R. (1975). 'Design for crack control of reinforced lightweight concrete walls', Behaviour in service of concrete structures, Inter-Association Colloquium, Preliminary Report, Vol. 2, 835–46, Stuttgart.
SKARENDAHL, A. (1975). Lightweight aggregates, *Nordisk Beton* **6**, 21–5. (In Swedish.)
SUSSMAN, V. (1975). Lightweight plastic concrete, *Proc.* **72**(7), 321–3.
VENUAT, M. and TRAN-THANH-PHAT, M. (1975). New research on lightweight colloidal, *Review des Materiaux de Construction*, **693**, 99–106.
WALZ, K. (1975). *Beton Technische Berichte 1974*, Research Institute for the Cement Industry, Dusseldorf.
WEIGLER, H. and NICOLAY, J. (1975). Structural lightweight concrete: temperature and cracking tendency during hardening, *Betonwerk und Fertighteiltechnik*, **41**(5), 226–32; (6), 295–8.
WESTHOFF, W., NOLDE, H. and KRAMPF, L. (1975). The behaviour of the compression zone in reinforced lightweight concrete beams under fire load, *Berichte aus der Bauforschung*, **97**, Ernst, Berlin.

DARTSCH, B. (1976). Preventive measures against cracking in concrete, *Beton*, **26**(4), 130–4.
HALSTED, P. E. (1976). Corrosion of reinforcement and prestressing tendons, a state of the art report, *Materiaux et Constructions*, **9**(51), 187–206.
KRYLOV, B. A. and KHAKHUTASHVILI, G. N. (1976). Electro-thermal treatment of lightweight concretes in monolithic construction, *Beton i Zhelezobeton*, **22**(3), 30–2.
LAL, K. SINGH, R. and UPADHYAYA, V. G. (1976). Bloated clay: an unconventional artificial lightweight aggregate, *Indian Concrete J.* **50**(6), 174–80, 186.
LILES, K. J. and TYRRELL, M. E. (1976). 'Waste glass as a raw material for lightweight aggregate', US Bureau of Mines, Dept. of Investigation R.I. 8104: Washington. 8 pp.
LYDON, F. D. (1976). Research on lightweight concrete in the United Kingdom 1967–76, *Magazine of Concrete Research*, **28**(95), 101–4.
MATTOCK, A. M., LI, W. K. and WANG, T. C. (1976). Shear transfer in lightweight reinforced concrete, *J. Prestressed Concr. Inst.*, **21**(1), 20–39.
SCHULE, W., JENISCH, R. and GREULICH, H. (1976). Measurements of the heat insulation of moist building components, *Gesundheits Ingenieur*, **1/2**, 17–18, 23–6.
VENUAT, T. M. (1976). Problems arising from taking lightweight colloidal concrete from the laboratory to the construction site, *Review des Materiaux de Construction* **699**, 91–4.

CEB-FIP Manual of Aerated Concrete (1977). The Construction Press, London.
CEB-FIP Manual of Lightweight Aggregate Concrete (1977). The Construction, Press, London.
CEB-FIP (1977). *Model Code for Concrete Design and Construction*, 3rd Draft, Bulletin, d'Information No. 117, Paris.

Index

Accelerators, 21
Acid-soluble sulphate, 130
Acoustic properties, 72–7
Aerated concrete, 39–40, 291–309
  applications, 332, 371–91
  binder, 22
  bond strength, 322–31, 339
  construction methods, 332
  damage susceptibility, 364
  definition, 291
  density, 39, 291, 301, 320
  design, 332–45
  development, 6, 10, 393, 396
  dry process, 297
  foam methods, 295, 299–301
  gasification, 294
  grinding, 296
  handling on site, 366
  in situ, 292, 299
  loadbearing units, 346
  manufacture, 293–301
  precast concrete in conjunction
    with, 317
  precast units, 292
  preformed foam method, 301
  properties, 3, 88, 301–7
  protection against deterioration,
    310–21
  structural forms, 374
  structural members, 332
  wet process, 296
Aglite, 120, 157, 272
Agrément Certificates, 337, 415
Air-cooled slag, 113
Air-entraining agents, 22, 122
Aluminium powder process, 295
Autoclaving, 39, 47, 52–3, 54, 57,
    292, 297, 304, 314, 326, 372,
    409

Barges, 271
Beams, lightweight concrete, 208–11,
    235
Bernoulli theorem, 335
Bitumen
  binder, 136
  coatings, 315, 316, 327
Blast-furnace slag, 113, 394–5
Bloating, 118
Block machines, 398–403
Block walls, 262, 346
  cracking, 58–63
  joints, 370
  strength effects, 426–30
BMW Central Administration
    building, 272
Bond
  concept, 243
  development, 236–7
  performance of reinforced concrete,
    189, 198
  strength, 146, 252
    aerated concrete, 322–31, 339
    factors affecting, 323
    reinforced lightweight aggregate
      concrete, 189–204
  stresses, 241–3
  tests, 191–5
Brazilian test, 153
Bridges, 267–9
British Standards
  aggregates, 142
  concrete blocks, 403
  masonry blocks, 423
  see also Codes of Practice
British thermal unit, 65
Building, 74
Building blocks, 6, 134
Building Regulations, 98, 142, 415

Building Research Station, 145, 193, 195, 207, 209, 211, 252, 311, 312, 316, 317, 335, 418, 426, 430, 433

Calcareous aggregates, 144
Calcium
  chloride, 21, 134, 174
  silicate hydrates, 43
  sulphate, 48
Calorie, 65
Carbon dioxide, 19, 52, 180–1, 305, 310
Carbonation, 18–19, 52, 177–81, 185, 187
Cast-*in-situ* concrete walls, 430–6
Cast-*in-situ* construction, 144
Cast-*in-situ* wall construction, 279–83
Caulking, 62
Cavity walls, 77, 88
CEB–FIP International Recommendations, 186, 188, 203
Cement
  content, 173, 186, 187
  setting, 17–18, 42
  slurry coating, 316
  sulphate-resisting, 20
  types and nature of, 16
  see also Portland cement
Cement–casein–rubber coating, 328
Cement–sand mortars, 48
Ceramic cladding, 283
Ceramic surface treatments, 315
Characteristic values, 228–9
Chemical reactions, 15–23, 42, 44, 81
Clay-based aggregates, 202, 209
  see also Expanded clay
Clinker, 141
  aggregate, 3, 109–18, 184, 262, 405
  chemical composition, 109
  cleaning, 112
  combustible matter, 110, 112
  re-burning, 112
  supplies, 8
  unsoundness, 111
Coarse aggregate, 116

Codes of Practice
  ACI, 203–4, 206, 215, 239, 240–1, 243, 250, 271, 337, 341, 437
  CP-3, 348, 361, 414
  CP-110, 14, 35, 185, 187, 191, 203, 213, 214, 216, 219, 220, 225, 235, 243, 245, 246, 248, 252, 337, 339, 415, 436, 437
  CP-111, 337, 338, 415, 417, 420, 421, 423, 427, 430, 433, 436
  CP-114, 141, 185, 191, 205, 214, 215, 217, 221, 232, 233, 234, 240, 242, 243, 245, 337, 338, 341, 343, 423, 432, 436
  CP-115, 252, 254, 338, 361, 415
  CP-116, 141, 214, 216, 217, 219, 221, 232, 233, 234, 240, 337
  CP-121, 201, 423
  CP-122, 423
  NTU-3-49, 206
Colliery waste, 8
Colloidal adhesion, 189
Columns, 237–9
Composite members, 269–71
Compressive strength, 44, 150, 302
  concrete blocks, 409
  no-fines concrete, 95, 102
Compressive stresses, 238–40
Concrete
  blocks, 31, 396–412
    aerated concrete, 396–8
    aggregate concrete, 396–8
    British and American practice, 406–12
    compressive strength, 405, 409
    definitions, 403
    density, 405
    drying shrinkage, 405
    'green' strength, 398
    manufacturing process, 398
    mass-production, 408
    moisture content, 406, 409
    output statistics, 412
    production policy, 407
    shape factor, 427
    specifications, 403–6
    stack-bonding appearance, 410
    strength considerations, 423–4

Concrete—*contd.*
  blocks—*contd.*
    types of, 396, 403
    wall strength factors, 426
    walls, 423–6
    weatherboard effect, 411
    masonry units, 407
Conduction, 65
Control measures, 364
Convection, 65
Conversion tables, 441–2
Corrosion, 173–81, 310–11
  prevention, 312–17
  protection, 340
Costs, 8, 140–1
Cracking, 58–63, 111, 207, 209–11,
    216, 249–50, 304, 318, 335,
    336, 364, 373, 426
Creep, 165–70, 254, 255, 304
Crossbars
  number of, 340
  welded, 329, 340
Crushing strength, 24, 29, 33, 35, 40
Curing, 42–54, 186, 399, 409
  air, 48, 57
  autoclave, *see* Autoclaving
  chemistry of, 42–3
  high-pressure steam, 45, 48, 52, 56,
    292, 295, 304, 326
  intermittent steam, 49–50
  kilns, 50
  low-pressure steam, 46, 47, 49
  methods, 48–54
  temperature effects, 44
Cylinder splitting test, 153

Damage effects, 391
Deflection
  measurements, 343
  requirements, 334, 342
  span ratio, 247
Deflections of flexural members, 343
Deformation, 335
  limit states, 227
  under load, 224
Density, 35, 40, 320
  aerated concrete, 39, 291, 301, 320

Density—*contd.*
  bulk dry, 68
  concrete blocks, 130, 405
  lightweight concrete, 1, 150, 155
  limit state, 437–9
  no-fines concrete, 101
  screeds, 136
Design
  considerations, 213–56, 332–45
  loads, 231
  methods, 13, 220–32, 338
  strengths, 231
Deterioration, protection against,
    310–21
Developing countries, 392–5
Diatomite, 132
  concrete, 133
Dowel-action, 205
Drying, 56, 58, 60, 88, 96, 304, 399
Durability, 81–8, 146
Durisol, 135
Durox cladding slabs, 379

EEC, 143
Elastic design method, 220, 221, 223,
    338
Elastic instability, 420
Environmental conditions, 317
Environmental protection, 7
Epoxy resins, 315
E-values, 221, 223, 244, 253, 255, 283,
    303, 317, 334
Exfoliated vermiculite, 257–9
Expanded clay
  aggregate, 4, 10, 118–23, 150, 263,
    269, 271, 392
  concrete, 122–3, 184, 266
Expanded perlite, 259–60
Expanded shale, 118–23
Expanded slag, 114
Expanded slate, 123–6
  concrete, 125
Expansion joints, 356

Facing work, 62
Fine aggregate, 116

Fire
  protection, 78–81
  resistance, 307
  tests, 81
Flakiness Index, 99
Flexural members, design of, 337–9
Flexural rigidity, design for, 342–4
Floating dock, 279
Floor
  constructions, 359
  screed, 290
  slabs, 266, 272, 357–9
Foamed concrete, 394
Foamed slag, 10, 12, 114–18, 144, 174
  concrete, 152–3, 163, 167–9, 174,
    182–4, 261, 265
France, 10, 142
Frost action, 81
Furnace bottom ash, 130

Galvanising, 314
Gascon, 307–9
Germany, 9, 10, 12, 143, 146, 182,
    185, 338, 363
Gothenburg, 12
Grading, 32
Grandstand, Doncaster, 277
Grouted grooves, 344
Guy's Hospital, 272

Hair-cracking, 99
Haydite, 118
Heat bridging, 67
Hebel cladding slabs, 386
Hydration, 17, 42–4
Hydrolysis, 17, 42, 44

International Recommendations, 13

Kensington Maintenance Depot, 279
Keramzite, 263
Kieselguhr, 132
Kinney–Osborne Process, 114
k-values, 305, 306

Lagging slabs, 182–3
Leca, 119, 120, 144, 289
  aggregate concrete, 286, 287
Lightweight aggregate concrete
  applications, 261–90
  loadbearing uses, 107–38
  structural use of, 139–49
Lightweight aggregates, 1, 4, 25, 32,
    35, 88, 99, 107–38, 141, 412
  availability, 8
  development, 8
  output of, 7
  production of, 11
  structural reinforced concrete, for,
    144
  unused resources of, 9
Lightweight concrete
  characteristic properties, 1
  definition, 1
  functional properties, 64–90
  physical properties, 29
  structural, 32, 150–72
  types of, 3
  uses, 1–2, 5
Lignacite, 134–5
Lime, 15, 22
Limit state design, 225–8
Load–deflection curves, 335
Load–deformation relationship, 224
Load design method, 221–2
Load factor, 334, 335, 339, 417, 427
Local damage limit states, 227–8
Lytag, 145, 276, 288

Magnesium sulphate, 48
Marina City Towers, Chicago, 273
Masonry blocks, 372–4
Mastic compound, 62
Mexico, 391
Mix additives or admixtures, 21, 317,
    404
Mix design, 24–41, 216–20
Mixes, 398
  designed, 219, 220
  nominal, 217
  prescribed, 219, 220
  standard, 217

Modulus of deformation, 93, 158-61, 221, 283, 334
Modulus of elasticity, 303
Modulus of rupture, 153-8
Moisture
  accumulation, 320
  content, 305, 319, 327, 406, 409
  effects, 137, 306
  movement, 170-1
  penetration, 90, 98
Mortar, 62
  screed, 344
  strength, 424-6
Mulberry Harbour, 271, 279
Multi-storey buildings, 140, 265, 271-6, 286, 287, 385
Multi-storey structures, 93, 378, 433

No-fines concrete, 3, 29-30, 91-106, 393, 433
  compressive strength, 95, 102
  definition, 91
  density, 101
  design, 102-4
  fixing of heavy appliances to, 104
  history and development, 92
  loadbearing walls, 104
  making, 99-102
  mixing, 100
  modulus of deformation, 93
  moisture penetration, 98
  shrinkage, 96
  shuttering, 102
  strength, 93
  testing, 104-6
  thermal conductivity, 92, 97
  uses, 91
Noise
  levels, 75
  nuisance, 72
Nuclear physics research laboratory, Oxford, 279

One Shell Plaza, Houston, Texas, 273
Organic aggregates, 133, 141

Pantheon, 4
Partial safety coefficient, 229, 232
Partially compacted lightweight aggregate concrete, 31
Party walls, 74, 92
Perlite, 259-61, 395
Permeability, 186, 187
Permissible load, 233
Permissible stresses, 215, 219-22, 224, 233, 238-46, 255, 417, 423, 427, 430, 431, 436
Phosphate treatments, 314
Plasticisers, 22
Porosity, 88, 90, 173, 310
Porous aggregate, 3
Portland cement, 15-17, 20, 42, 295
Post-tensioning, 253, 267
Potassium nitrite, 317
Pozzolanas, 18
Pozzolanic properties, 130, 140, 165
Precast aerated concrete, 292
Precast box units, 266
Precast concrete
  in conjunction with aerated concrete, 317
  panels, 263-7
Precast prestressed beams, 267
Precast units, 332
Precasting, 371
Prestressed lightweight concrete, 225, 251-5
Prestressed 'pencils', 317
Proof stress, 221
Pulverised-fuel ash
  raw, 130
  sintered, 126-9, 140, 145, 150, 169, 202, 209, 272, 276, 395
Pumice, 9, 12, 131, 144, 174, 183, 184, 261, 265, 392

Quality control factors, 173, 187, 364

Radiation, 65
Rain penetration, 88-90

Raw materials, 9
Reinforced concrete, 140, 141, 144, 173, 322, 436, 437
  bond performance, 189, 198
  research, 145–6
  resistance against deterioration, 182–8
Reinforcement, 100–4, 112, 141, 189, 249, 298, 322, 433–4, 436
  anti-corrosive surface coating, 327
  bare bars, 322–3
  bituminous coating, 327, 328, 340
  cement–casein–rubber coating, 328, 340
  continuity bars, 342
  corrosion of, 173–81, 310–11
  corrosion prevention, 312
  corrosion protection, 340
  deformed bars, 191, 195, 199–203, 242–3, 245, 328
  effect of bar diameter and position and embedment length, 323–6
  effect of length of embedment, 198
  end anchorages, 329
  high-tensile steel bars, 200, 245
  high-tensile steel strand, 267
  longitudinal, 232
  mild-steel bars, 191, 195, 244
  permissible stresses, 243–6
  plain round bars, 195, 198, 242–4
  position of bars, 197
  prevention of deterioration, 318–20
  protective coating, 313
  ribbed bars, 200
  rusting, 327
  shadow effect, 325–6
  slip resistance, 200–1, 203
  strength of, 246
  transverse, 205, 250–1
  welded crossbars, 329
Research, 11, 12
Retarders, 21
RILEM classification, 3
Road surfaces, 283
Roof
  covering, 351
  screed, 289
  slabs, 144, 266, 272, 348–56

Roofs, 319, 320, 346, 383–91
  aerated concrete flexural members, 383
  construction details, 353–6
  internal treatment, 353
  structural design, 350
  ventilated, 353
Rubber
  coatings, 315
  latex, 316

Safety
  factor, 6, 238, 439
  levels, 230
  standards, 228–32
  tests, 415
Sand addition, 150, 153, 163, 199
Sawdust, 133
  cement, 134
Schüttbeton, 433
Scoria, 131
Screeds, 135–7, 289–90, 344, 349
Screen wall, 288
Seismic forces, 391
Self-curing, 45
Serviceability limit states, 227
Shadow effect, 325–6
Shale concrete, 184
Shales, 8, 118
Shear, 232–8
  design, 232
  failure, 205, 206, 211, 233, 234
  performance, 211
    design equations, 206, 207
  reinforcement, 205, 211, 233–6, 241, 342
  resistance, 205–12, 234, 341–2
  strain, 241
  strength, 146, 208
  stress, 205, 211, 232–6, 240, 341–2
Ships, 271
Shrinkage, 19, 47, 48, 55, 58–60, 81, 88, 96, 110, 170–1, 251, 253, 255, 304, 305, 399, 404
Shuttering, no-fines concrete, 102
Siporex, 378, 382, 389, 391

Skarne type multi-storey block, 382
Ski-jump platform, 277
Slate, 123–6, 145
Slender beams, 248
Slenderness ratio, 417, 420, 421, 427, 432, 437
Sodium
  chloride, 21
  nitrite, 317
  sulphate, 48
Soffit treatment, 353
Sound
  absorption, 73, 307
  insulation, 73, 75, 77, 92
  properties, 72–7
  reduction factor, 73
  transmission grades, 74, 75
Spalling, 88, 112
Span–depth ratio, 246
Splitting strength, 155, 157
Stability, 346, 348, 433
Steel, *see* Reinforcement
Steel/concrete bond, 189–91
Stiffness, 224, 246, 255, 336, 342–4, 391
Stockholm, 12
Strain, 224
Strength, 43, 44
  no-fines concrete, 93
Stress
  concentrations, 367
  distribution, 222, 418
  reduction coefficients, 248–9, 361, 417
Stress–strain relationship, 223
Sulphate resistance, 20, 187–8
Sulphur and sulphur compounds, 112, 130, 141, 184, 311, 318, 320
Sund system, 371
Surface deterioration, 181
Sweden, 338, 363, 371, 380, 383, 393, 396

Temperature stresses, 81
Tensile strength, 153–8, 210
Tensile stresses, 207
Tension failure, 210

Testing
  no-fines concrete, 104–6
  prototype units, 339
Thermal conductance, 66, 98
Thermal conductivity, 3, 64–6, 68–72, 92, 97, 293, 305–7
Thermal insulation, 3, 31, 64, 98, 165, 257–61, 265, 289, 348, 367, 380
Thermal resistivity, 66
Thermal transmittance, 66, 67, 69
Thermocrete, 282
Tobermorite, 22
Transport costs, 8

Ultimate limit states, 226
Ultimate strength
  design method, 222, 223
  formula, 232
  method, 338
Uniform stress distribution, 222
United States of America, 10, 140, 142, 146, 191, 215, 252, 406–12
USSR, 11, 12, 143, 146, 333, 363, 371
U-values, 67, 69, 98, 305

Vermiculite, 257–9, 261, 395
Vibration limit state, 228

Wall
  slabs, 346, 359–63
    joints, 359
    loadbearing, 364
    non-loadbearing, 366
  units, 333
Walls, 262
  block, *see* Block walls
  cast-*in-situ* concrete, 430–6
  cast-*in-situ* construction, 279–83
  cast-*in-situ* reinforced concrete, 436
  cavity, 421
  concentrated loading, 418
  concrete blocks, 423–6
  design and construction, 414–17
  eccentricity of loading, 418, 433

Walls—*contd.*
  factors influencing behaviour,
    417–23
  failure of, 427, 430
  lateral strength, 430
  lightweight concrete, 413–40
  limit state design, 437–9
  loadbearing, 360, 374, 414, 433, 436
  mortar strength, 424–6
  non-loadbearing, 360
  non-loadbearing cladding, 378–83
  permissible stresses, 431
  slenderness effects, 420–3
Waste
  material, 140
  utilisation, 3
Water
  absorption, 88

Water—*contd.*
  content, 33
Water/cement ratio, 25, 33, 35, 94,
    161–3, 187, 220
Water-reducing agents, 22
Water Tower Plaza, Chicago, 273
Wetting expansion, 404, 405
Wind
  forces, 351
  loads, 348, 356, 420
  pressures, 346
Wood particles, 134
Workability, 22, 24, 33, 35, 140, 163,
    164, 186
Workmanship quality effects, 430

Yield point stress, 221